Contents

Holt Algebra 1

Contents continued

Holt Algebra 1

Holt California
Algebra 1

Ready to Go On?
Intervention and Enrichment
with Answers

HOLT, RINEHART AND WINSTON

A Harcourt Education Company

Orlando • **Austin** • New York • San Diego • London

Contents continued

Holt Algebra 1

Contents continued

Holt Algebra 1

Assessment

Use the *Section Quizzes* to assess the student's proficiency after you have provided Intervention, or use the *Section Quizzes* to assess the student's retention on the new concepts taught in the lessons.

Enrichment

For those students who show proficiency on the *Ready to Go On? Section Quizzes*, provide them with the appropriate *Enrichment* worksheets. The worksheets extend the concepts taught in the lessons.

Other Materials Available for Ready to Go On? Intervention and Enrichment

- *Ready to Go On? Intervention and Enrichment* is available in different formats:

Ready to Go On? Intervention and Enrichment [CD-ROM]—allows teachers to assign the *Ready to Go On? Pre- and Post-Tests* to whole classes or individual students. The Reports show which students are having difficulty on particular lesson skills. Teachers can choose to have Intervention materials automatically assigned to students requiring help.

Ready to Go On? Intervention and Enrichment Online—provides diagnostic assessment and Intervention. The *Ready to Go On? Pre-Test Reports* show which students are having difficulty on particular lesson skills. Teachers can choose to have the Intervention materials automatically assigned to students requiring help. Once students have completed the Intervention, the system automatically assigns the appropriate *Ready to Go On? Post-Tests*. The *Ready to Go On? Post-Test Reports* show which students are proficient and which students need more help.

Holt Algebra 1

Using the Ready to Go On? Intervention and Enrichment in Your Class

The Ready to Go On? Intervention helps students to perform successfully by providing opportunities for you to address students' weaknesses before the students are given summative assessments. *The Ready to Go On? Intervention* provides skills and problem-solving intervention for students having difficulty mastering concepts taught in the lessons.

Ready to Go On? Intervention

After teaching each section of lessons, have students complete the *Ready to Go On?* page in the student book. This page targets the lesson skills necessary for success in the chapter. For students requiring help, use the appropriate *Skills Intervention* or *Problem Solving Intervention* worksheets. Each worksheet provides step-by-step scaffolding prompts to help students understand the lesson concepts and skills.

A chart at the end of each section correlates the lessons with the appropriate intervention and enrichment materials. The chart appears in the Teacher Edition. A sample is shown below.

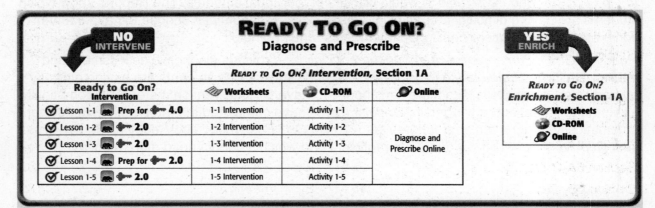

Holt Algebra 1

Student's Name _____

Individual Lesson Skills Checklist

Chapter	Lesson	Prescription	Skill Mastered

Holt Algebra 1

SECTION 1A Ready to Go On? Problem Solving Intervention
1-1 Variables and Expressions

An algebraic expression contains variables, constants, and operations. A variable is a letter or symbol used in an expression to represent a value that can change, like *x*, and a constant is a value that does not change, like 3.

A swimmer is competing in a 50-lap race. Write an expression for the number of laps left after the swimmer has completed *c* laps.

Understand the Problem

1. How many laps is the race? _____

2. What variable represents the number of laps? _____

3. What are you being asked to do?

   _____

Make a Plan

4. The phrase *number of laps left* corresponds to which operation symbol? _____

5. Identify the constant in the problem. _____

6. Identify the variable in the problem. _____

Solve

7. What value should be written first in the expression, the constant or the variable? Why?

   _____

8. Write an expression for the number of laps left after the swimmer has

   completed *c* laps. _____ − *c*

Look Back

9. Think of a simpler problem: The race is 50 laps. If you swim 20 laps, how

   many laps will be left? _____

10. Now use your expression to determine the following: If the swimmer has

    completed 20 laps, how many laps left does he have left to swim? _____ − 20 = _____

    Is the number of laps left to swim more or less than 50 laps? _____

11. Does your expression represent the situation? Explain.

    _____

Holt Algebra 1

Name _____ Date _____ Class _____

1-1 Variables and Expressions

Find these vocabulary words in Lesson 1-1 and the Multilingual Glossary.

Vocabulary		
variable	constant	numerical expression
algebraic expression		evaluate

Translating from Algebra to Words
Give two ways to write each algebraic expression in words.

A. $8 + k$

Identify the constant in the expression. _____

Identify the variable in the expression. _____

Name two words that mean the same thing as the + symbol. _____ _____

Write the expression $8 + k$ in words: the _____ of 8 and k OR k added to _____.

B. $\frac{c}{4}$

What operation does the fraction bar indicate? _____

Identify the divisor in the expression. _____   Identify the dividend. _____

When you find the answer to a division problem you find the _____.

Write the expression $\frac{c}{4}$ in words: c _____ by 4 OR the quotient of _____ and _____.

Evaluating Algebraic Expressions
Evaluate each expression for $x = 6$, $y = 5$, and $z = 2$.

A. xy

What operation is indicated by the expression? _____

What value should you substitute for x? _____ for y? _____

Rewrite the expression using the substituted values. (___)(___) Simplify. _____

B. $x - z$

What operation is indicated by the − symbol? _____

What value should you substitute for x? _____ for z? _____

Rewrite the expression using the substituted values. ___ − ___ Simplify. _____

1

Holt Algebra 1

SECTION 1A · Ready to Go On? Skills Intervention
1-2 Adding and Subtracting Real Numbers

Find these vocabulary words in Lesson 1-2 and the Multilingual Glossary.

Vocabulary		
absolute value	opposites	additive inverse

Adding Real Numbers
Add.

A. $52 + (-13)$

When you add two numbers with different signs, find the difference of their

_____ and use the sign of the number with the _____ absolute value.

What is the absolute value of 52? _____   What is the absolute value of -13? _____

Find the difference of the absolute values of 52 and 13. _____

What is the sign on the number that has the greatest absolute value? _____

What is $52 + (-13)$? _____

B. $x + (-10)$ for $x = -12$

When you add two numbers with the same sign, _____ their absolute values and

use the _____ of the numbers.

What value should you substitute for x? _____

Rewrite the expression using the substituted value. _____

What is the absolute value of -12? _____   What is the absolute value of -10? _____

Find the sum of the absolute values of -12 and -10. _____

What is the sign on the numbers? _____   What is $-12 + (-10)$? _____

Subtracting Real Numbers
Subtract 40 − 57.

To subtract a number, _____ its opposite. What is the opposite of -57? _____

Rewrite the expression using the opposite, or additive inverse, of -57. _____

When the signs of the numbers are different, find the _____ of their absolute values.

What is $57 - 40$? _____

What is the sign on the number that has the greatest absolute value? _____

So, what is $40 - 57$? _____

Holt Algebra 1

Ready to Go On? Problem Solving Intervention
1-2 Adding and Subtracting Real Numbers

To add or subtract numbers with the same sign, add the numbers and use the sign of the numbers. To add or subtract numbers with different signs, subtract the smaller number from the larger and use the sign of the larger number.

The outdoor temperature is currently −6°F. By midnight the temperature is predicted to increase 14°F. If the prediction is accurate, what will be the outdoor temperature at midnight?

Understand the Problem

1. What is the current temperature? _____

2. What is the predicted temperature increase? _____

3. Should the predicted midnight temperature be less than or more than −6°F? _____

Make a Plan

4. Plot −6°F and 14°F on a number line.

$$-8°\ -6°\ -4°\ -2°\ \ 0°\ \ 2°\ \ 4°\ \ 6°\ \ 8°\ 10°12°14°16°$$

5. What number is larger, −6 or 14? _____

6. What is the sign of the larger number? _____

7. Since the current temperature is predicted to increase, do you need to add or subtract the two temperatures to find the midnight temperature? _____

Solve

8. Find the sum. −6°F + 14°F = ? Remember: to add numbers with different signs, subtract the smaller number from the larger and use the sign of the larger number.

    _____ − 6 = _____; So −6°F + 14°F = _____.

9. Is the sum positive or negative? How do you know?

    _____

Look Back

10. Use the number line in Exercise 4 to help you check your answer. Plot your answer from Exercise 8 on the number line in Exercise 4.

11. How many degrees does the temperature have to increase to go from

    −6°F to 0°F? _____   How many degrees does the temperature have to increase

    to go from 0°F to the point you just plotted? _____

    Add these two values ____ + ____ = ____; If the sum is 14, your answer checks.

Holt Algebra 1

SECTION 1A Ready to Go On? Skills Intervention
1-3 Multiplying and Dividing Real Numbers

Find these vocabulary words in Lesson 1-3 and the Multilingual Glossary.

Vocabulary	
reciprocal	multiplicative inverse

Multiplying and Dividing Signed Numbers
Find the value of the expression 5(−8).

If two numbers have the same sign, their product or quotient is _____.

If two numbers have different signs, their product or quotient is _____.

Are the signs in the expression 5(−8) the same or different? _____

So, what is the product of 5(−8)? _____

If the expression were changed to −5(−8), is the product positive or negative? _____

Dividing by Fractions
Divide −14 ÷ $\frac{7}{9}$.

Two numbers are reciprocals if their product is _____.

If you switch the numerator and the _____ of a fraction, you

get the reciprocal of that number. What is the reciprocal of $\frac{7}{9}$?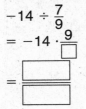

$-14 \div \frac{7}{9}$

$= -14 \cdot \dfrac{9}{\boxed{}}$ Multiply by the reciprocal.

$= \dfrac{\boxed{}}{\boxed{}}$ Multiply the numerator. Multiply the denominator.

$= \underline{}$ Simplify. The signs are different, so the quotient is _____.

Multiplying and Dividing with Zero
Divide 80.2 ÷ 0.

The product of any number and 0 is _____.

The quotient of 0 and any nonzero number is _____.

Can you divide a number by zero? _____

80.2 ÷ 0 is the same as $\frac{80.2}{0}$.

So division by zero is _____.

Holt Algebra 1

Name _____ Date _____ Class _____

The product or quotient of two numbers with the same sign is positive.
The product or quotient of two numbers with different signs is negative.

The airplane Paul is traveling on averages 520 miles per hour. If the plane has been in the air for $3\frac{1}{2}$ hours, how far has the plane traveled?

Understand the Problem

1. What is the average rate of the plane? _____

2. How long has the plane been in the air? _____

3. What are you trying to determine? _____

4. What should be the units of your final answer? _____

5. Should your answer be more than or less than 520? How do you know?

_____

Make a Plan

6. To find distance, do you multiply or divide the rate and time? _____

7. Write the decimal equivalent of $3\frac{1}{2}$ hours. _____

8. Let *d* represent the distance traveled. Write an equation to represent the situation.

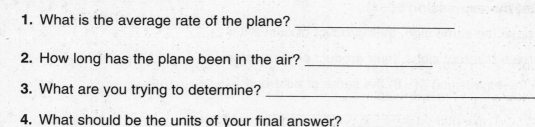

| Rate of the plane | · | Time the plane has been in the air | = | Distance Traveled |

_____ · _____ = *d*

Solve

9. Multiply. $520 \cdot$ _____ $= d$ How far has the plane traveled? _____
   _____ $= d$

10. Is the product positive or negative? _____ How do you know? _____

Look Back

11. To check a multiplication problem, you can divide the _____ by either of the two factors.

12. Use division to check your answer. Substitute the value for *d* from Exercise 9.

$\dfrac{d}{520} = \dfrac{\boxed{}}{520} =$ _____; If the quotient is 3.5, your answer checks.

Holt Algebra 1

Name _____ Date _____ Class _____

Ready to Go On? Skills Intervention
1-4 Powers and Exponents

Find these vocabulary words in Lesson 1-4 and the Multilingual Glossary.

Vocabulary		
power	base	exponent

Evaluating Powers
Simplify each expression.

A. $(-4)^4$

What is the base in the expression? ____

What is the exponent in the expression? ____

The exponent tells how many times the base is used as a factor.

Rewrite the expression using -4 as a factor _____ times.

_____ × _____ × _____ × _____

Is the product positive or negative? _____

_____ × _____ × _____ × _____ = _____   So, $(-4)^4 = $ _____.

B. -6^2

What is the exponent in the expression? _____

Keeping in mind that the negative sign is *not* in parenthesis, what is the base in the expression? _____

Rewrite the expression as $-1 \times 6 \times$ ____. Is the product positive or negative? _____

$-1 \times 6 \times$ ____ = _____ Simplify.

C. $\left(-\dfrac{1}{3}\right)^3$

What is the base in the expression? ____

What is the exponent in the expression? _____

Is the negative sign part of the base? _____ Why? _____

Use $\left(-\dfrac{1}{3}\right)$ as a factor _____ times. $\left(-\dfrac{1}{3}\right) \cdot \left(-\dfrac{1}{3}\right) \cdot \left(-\dfrac{1}{3}\right) = $ _____

Writing Powers
Write 125 as a power given the base of 5.

Check to see how many factors of 5's it takes to get a product of 125.

$5 \times 5 = $ _____; Does this equal 125? _____

$5 \times 5 \times 5 = $ _____; Does this equal 125? _____ Write the power: $5^{\square}$

Holt Algebra 1

SECTION 1A Ready To Go On? Skills Intervention
1-5 Roots and Irrational Numbers

Find these vocabulary words in Lesson 1-5 and the Multilingual Glossary.

Vocabulary			
square root	perfect square	cube roots	natural numbers
whole numbers	integers	rational numbers	
terminating decimal	repeating decimal	irrational numbers	

Find Roots
Find each root.

A. $\sqrt{64}$

A number multiplied by _____ to form a product is called a square root of that product.

What symbol is used to represent positive square roots? _____

What number multiplied by itself equals 64? $8 \cdot$ ___ $= 64$

Complete: $\sqrt{64} = \sqrt{8 \cdot \underline{\quad}} = \underline{\quad}$

B. $-\sqrt{625}$

What symbol is used to represent negative square roots? _____

What number multiplied by itself equals 625? $25 \cdot$ ___ $= 625$

What is the opposite of this value? _____

Complete: $-\sqrt{625} = -\sqrt{25 \cdot \underline{\quad}} = \underline{\quad}$

C. $\sqrt{\dfrac{49}{81}}$

Complete: $\sqrt{49} = \sqrt{7 \cdot \underline{\quad}} = \underline{\quad}$ Complete: $\sqrt{81} = \sqrt{9 \cdot \underline{\quad}} = \underline{\quad}$

You can rewrite $\sqrt{\dfrac{49}{81}}$ as $\dfrac{\sqrt{49}}{\sqrt{81}}$. So, $\dfrac{\sqrt{49}}{\sqrt{81}} = \dfrac{\sqrt{7 \cdot \underline{\quad}}}{\sqrt{9 \cdot \underline{\quad}}} = \dfrac{\square}{\square}$.

Classifying Real Numbers

A. $\sqrt{18}$

$\sqrt{18} = 4.242640687$

Since this number is not a perfect square, it is _____.

B. $\dfrac{9}{11}$

$\dfrac{9}{11} = 0.8181\overline{81}$

Since this number can be written as a repeating decimal it is a _____.

Holt Algebra 1

Name _____ Date _____ Class _____

You can use square roots of perfect squares to help estimate the square roots of other numbers.

Angie is installing a window in the shape of a square. The window will cover 150 square feet. Find the length of a side of the square window to the nearest tenth of a foot.

Understand the Problem

1. What is the area of the window? _____

2. What is the shape of the window? _____

3. What are you trying to determine? _____

Make a Plan

4. What do you know to be true about the side lengths of a square? _____

5. If you know the area of the square how can you determine the length of the side of a square? $A = s^2$
   $\sqrt{A} =$ _____

6. Is the area of the window a perfect square? _____ So, estimate to find the side length.

7. Find the two perfect squares that surround 150.

144		169
$\sqrt{144} =$ ___ $12^2 =$ ____	150	$\sqrt{169} = 13$ $13^2 = 169$

Solve

8. Find $\sqrt{144}$. _____ Find $\sqrt{169}$. _____

9. So the square root of 150 is between _____ and _____.

10. Guess 12.3: $12.3^2 =$ _____ This value is too _____. So $\sqrt{150}$ is _____ than 12.3.

11. Guess 12.2: $12.2^2 =$ _____ This value is too _____. So $\sqrt{150}$ is _____ than 12.2.

12. Because 150 is closer to _____ than _____, $\sqrt{150}$ is closer to _____ than _____.

13. What is the length of the side of the window to the nearest tenth of a foot? _____

Look Back

14. Substitute the value from Exercise 13 into the area formula from Exercise 5.

   $A = s^2 = \boxed{}^2 =$ _____ Is your answer reasonable? _____

9

Holt Algebra 1

SECTION 1B
Ready to Go On? Skills Intervention
1-6 Properties of Real Numbers

Identifying Properties
Name the property that is illustrated in each equation.

A. $5 \cdot c = c \cdot 5$

Write the order of multiplication on the left side of the equation. _____

Write the order of multiplication on the right side of the equation. _____

Because you can multiply real numbers in any order, the equation

illustrates the _____.

B. $5 + (j + 3) = (5 + j) + 3$

Write the grouping of the expression on the left side of the equation. _____

Write the grouping of the expression on the right side of the equation. _____

Because grouping does not change the sum of real numbers, the equation illustrates the

_____.

Using the Distributive Property with Mental Math
Write the product using the Distributive Property. Then simplify.

4(197)

Break the larger factor into a sum or difference that contains a multiple of 10.

$4(197) = 4(\underline{\hspace{1cm}} - \underline{\hspace{1cm}})$ Round 197 to 200.

$ = \underline{\hspace{1cm}}(200) - \underline{\hspace{1cm}}(3)$ Use the Distributive Property.

$ = \underline{\hspace{1cm}} - \underline{\hspace{1cm}}$ Mentally multiply the products.

$ = \underline{\hspace{1cm}}$ Mentally subtract the second product from the first.

The product of 4(197) is _____.

Finding Counterexamples to Statements About Closure
Find a counterexample to show that the statement is false.

The set of odd numbers is closed under addition.

$a + b = \underline{\hspace{1cm}} + \underline{\hspace{1cm}}$ Find two odd numbers, a and b, such that the sum is not an odd number. Try $a = 1$ and $b = 3$.

$ = \underline{\hspace{1cm}}$ Since 4 is not an odd number, this is a counterexample.

The statement is false.

Holt Algebra 1

SECTION 1B **Ready to Go On? Skills Intervention**
1-7 Simplifying Expressions

Find these vocabulary words in Lesson 1-7 and the Multilingual Glossary.

Vocabulary			
order of operations	terms	like terms	coefficient

Simplifying Numerical Expressions
Simplify the expression.

$(8^2 - 1) + 3 \times 2$

$(8^2 - 1) + 3 \times 2$	What is the grouping symbol in the expression? _____
$(\underline{\hspace{1cm}} - 1) + 3 \times 2$	Evaluate the powers within the parentheses.
$\underline{\hspace{1cm}} + 3 \times 2$	Subtract within the parentheses.
$63 + \underline{\hspace{1cm}}$	Multiply.
$\underline{\hspace{1cm}}$	Add.

Combining Like Terms
Simplify the expression by combining like terms.

$7y + 9y$	$7y$ and $9y$ are like terms.
$\underline{\hspace{1cm}}y$	Add the coefficients.

Simplifying Algebraic Expressions
Use properties and operations to show that the first expression simplifies to the second expression.

$5(x + 2) - 3x + 1, 2x + 11$

Statements	Reasons
1. $5(x + 2) - 3x + 1$	
2. $\underline{\hspace{1cm}}x + \underline{\hspace{1cm}}(2) - 3x + 1$	Distributive Property
3. $5x + \underline{\hspace{1cm}} - 3x + 1$	Multiply.
4. $5x - \underline{\hspace{1cm}}x + \underline{\hspace{1cm}} + 1$	Commutative Property of Addition
5. $(5x - 3x) + (10 + 1)$	
6. $\underline{\hspace{1cm}}$	Combine like terms.

Holt Algebra 1

Name _____ Date _____ Class _____

Ready to Go On? Problem Solving Intervention

1-7 Simplifying Expressions

Order of operations:
- First, perform operations within grouping symbols;
- then, evaluate powers;
- then, perform multiplication and division from left to right;
- finally, perform addition and subtraction from left to right.

To find the area of the square that is not covered by the circle, you can use the expression $s^2 - \pi\left(\dfrac{d}{2}\right)^2$. If the side length of the square, s, is 12 m and the diameter of the circle, d, is 12 m, find the non-shaded area, to the nearest square meter. Use 3.14 for π.

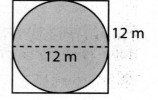

Understand the Problem

1. What is the expression you are to evaluate? _____

2. What are you trying to determine? _____

Make a Plan

3. What value will you substitute for s? _____ for d? _____ for π? _____

4. Is there more than one operation symbol in the expression? _____ If so, what

    will you need to do to evaluate the expression correctly? _____

Solve

5. Substitute the values from Exercise 3 for the variables and evaluate.

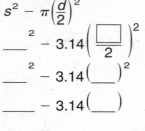

    ____² − 3.14$\left(\dfrac{\square}{2}\right)^2$ Substitute values for the variables.

    ____² − 3.14(____)²   Perform the operation within the parenthesis.

    ____ − 3.14(____)   Evaluate the powers.

    ____ − _____   Multiply.

    _____   Subtract.

6. What is the non-shaded area, to the nearest square meter? _____

Look Back

7. Use the drawing to find the area of the square. $A = s^2 = 12^2 =$ ____

    What is the area of the circle? $A = \pi r^2 = \pi(6)^2 =$ _____

    Subtract these two values and determine if your answer is correct.

    $A_{square} - A_{circle} =$ ____ − _____ = _____

Holt Algebra 1

SECTION 2A Ready to Go On? Skills Intervention
2-1 Solving One-Step Equations

Find these vocabulary words in Lesson 2-1 and the Multilingual Glossary.

Vocabulary		
equation	solution of an equation	solution set

Solving Equations by Using Addition or Subtraction
Solve each equation.

A. $d + 8 = 17$

$d + 8 = 17$ Since 8 is **added** to d, to **undo this addition,**

$\underline{- 8 \quad - 8}$ _____ 8 from both sides.

$d = 9$ The solution set is {_____}.

B. $q - 0.3 = 13.2$

$q - 0.3 = 13.2$ Since 0.3 is **subtracted** from q, to **undo this subtraction,**

$\underline{+ 0.3 \quad + 0.3}$ _____ 0.3 to both sides.

$q = 13.5$ The solution set is {_____}.

Solving Equations by Using Multiplication or Division
Solve each equation.

A. $3y = 39$

$3y = 39$ Since y is multiplied by 3, to **undo this multiplication,**

$\dfrac{3y}{3} = \dfrac{39}{3}$ _____ both sides by 3.

$y = 13$ The solution set is {_____}.

B. $-6 = \dfrac{w}{4}$

$-6 = \dfrac{w}{4}$ Since w is divided by 4, to **undo this division,**

$(4)(-6) = (4)\left(\dfrac{w}{4}\right)$ _____ both sides by 4.

$-24 = w$ The solution set is {_____}.

Holt Algebra 1

Ready to Go On? Problem Solving Intervention

SECTION 2A

2-1 Solving One-Step Equations

To find the solution to an equation, isolate the variable. To isolate the variable, use inverse, or opposite, operations to undo operations on the variable.

When Jeremy began his 9th grade year in school he was 5 ft 4 in. tall. When he was measured for his graduation gown at the end of his 12th grade year, he was 6 ft 3 in. tall. Write and solve an equation to find how many inches Jeremy grew over 4 years.

Understand the Problem

1. How tall was Jeremy at the beginning of his 9th grade year? _____

2. How tall was Jeremy at the end of his 12th grade year? _____

Make a Plan

3. What do you need to determine? _____

4. How many total inches is 5 ft 4 in.? _____

5. How many total inches is 6 ft 3 in.? _____

6. Let h represent the number of inches Jeremy grew in 4 years. Write an equation to represent this situation.

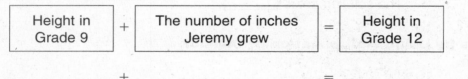

| Height in Grade 9 | + | The number of inches Jeremy grew | = | Height in Grade 12 |

_____ + _____ = _____

Solve

7. Solve the equation by isolating h.

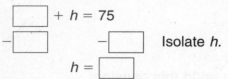

$$\boxed{} + h = 75$$
$$-\boxed{} \qquad -\boxed{} \quad \text{Isolate } h.$$
$$h = \boxed{}$$

8. The number of inches that Jeremy grew in 4 years is _____.

Look Back

9. Substitute the solution for h into the equation you wrote in Exercise 6.

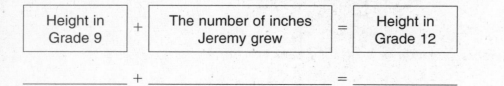

| Height in Grade 9 | + | The number of inches Jeremy grew | = | Height in Grade 12 |

_____ + _____ = _____

10. Does your solution make the equation true? _____

Holt Algebra 1

Name _____ Date _____ Class _____

Ready to Go On? Skills Intervention
2-2 Solving Two-Step Equations

Solving Two-Step Equations
Solve the equation. $5r + 15 = 155$

$5r + 15 = 155$

To isolate the variable r, subtract _____ from both sides.

$-\underline{} \quad -\underline{}$

Since r is multiplied by _____, then _____ both sides of the

$5r = \underline{}$

equation by _____.

$\dfrac{5r}{5} = \dfrac{\boxed{}}{\boxed{}}$

What is the value of r? _____

$r = \boxed{}$

Check: Substitute the value for r back into the original equation.

$5 \cdot \boxed{} + 15 = 155$

Does your answer check? _____

$\boxed{} = 155$

Solving Two-Step Equations That Contain Fractions
Solve the equation. $\dfrac{5}{8}n + 6 = 7$

$\dfrac{5}{8}n + 6 = 7$

To isolate the variable n, subtract _____ from both sides.

$-\underline{} \quad -\underline{}$

Since n is multiplied by _____, multiply both sides of the

$\dfrac{5}{8}n = \underline{}$

equation by the reciprocal, _____.

$\left(\dfrac{8}{\boxed{}}\right) \cdot \left(\dfrac{5}{8}n\right) = \boxed{} \cdot \dfrac{8}{5}$

What is the value of n? _____

$n = \dfrac{\boxed{}}{\boxed{}}$

To check your answer, substitute the value for n back into the

$\dfrac{5}{8} \cdot \dfrac{\boxed{}}{\boxed{}} + 6 = 7$

original equation. Does your answer check? _____

$\boxed{} = 7$

Solving Two-Step Equations That Contain Fractions
Solve the equation. $\dfrac{1}{3}y - \dfrac{1}{2} = \dfrac{7}{2}$

To simplify, multiply both sides by _____,
the LCD of the fractions. Distribute the LCD on the left.

$6 \cdot \left(\boxed{} - \boxed{}\right) = 6 \cdot \boxed{}$

Simplify.

$2y - 3 = 21$

To isolate y, add _____ to both sides.

$+\underline{} \; +\underline{}$

Since y is multiplied by _____, divide both sides by _____.

$2y = \boxed{}$

$\dfrac{2y}{2} = \dfrac{\boxed{}}{\boxed{}}$

What is the solution set?

$y = \left\{\boxed{}\right\}$

To check your answer, substitute the value for y back into the
original equation.

$\dfrac{1}{3}\left(\boxed{}\right) - \dfrac{1}{2} = \dfrac{7}{2}$ Does your answer check? _____

Holt Algebra 1

Name _____ Date _____ Class _____

Ready to Go On? Problem Solving Intervention
2-2 Solving Two-Step Equations

Equations that contain more than one operation require more than one step to solve. Use inverse operations and work backward to undo each operation one step at a time.

A fitness club offers membership for a joining fee of $99 and a monthly fee of $35. If Jenna has spent a total of $1009, how many months has Jenna been a member of the fitness club?

Understand the Problem

1. How much is the joining fee for the fitness club? _____

2. How much does the fitness club cost each month? _____

3. How much total has Jenna spent on the fitness club? _____

Make a Plan

4. What do you need to determine? _____

5. Let *m* represent the number of months that Jenna has been a member. Write an equation to represent the situation.

| Joining fee | + | Monthly fee | · | Number of months Jenna has been a member | = | Total amount spent |

_____ + _____ ·   *m*   = _____

Solve

6. Solve the equation by isolating *m*.

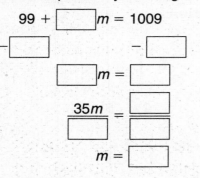

$$99 + \boxed{}m = 1009$$
$$-\boxed{} \qquad -\boxed{}$$
$$\boxed{}m = \boxed{}$$
$$\frac{35m}{\boxed{}} = \frac{\boxed{}}{\boxed{}}$$
$$m = \boxed{}$$

7. Jenna has been a member of the fitness club for _____ months.

Look Back

8. Substitute the solution for *m* into the equation you wrote in Exercise 5.

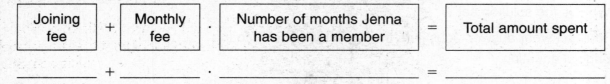

| Joining fee | + | Monthly fee | · | Number of months Jenna has been a member | = | Total amount spent |

_____ + _____ · _____ = _____

9. Does your solution make the equation true? _____

Holt Algebra 1

Name _____ Date _____ Class _____

Solving Multi-Step Equations
Solve.

$$\frac{3m - 5}{2} = 11$$

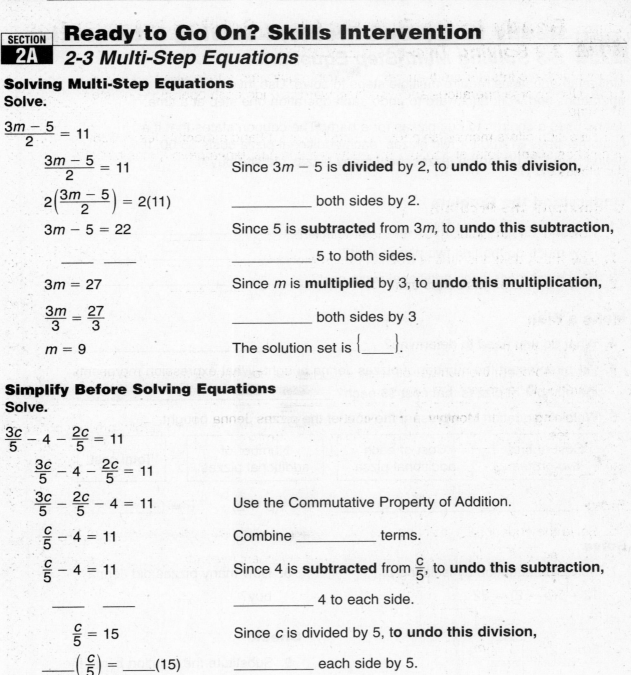

$\frac{3m - 5}{2} = 11$	Since $3m - 5$ is **divided** by 2, to **undo this division**,
$2\left(\frac{3m - 5}{2}\right) = 2(11)$	_____ both sides by 2.
$3m - 5 = 22$	Since 5 is **subtracted** from $3m$, to **undo this subtraction**,
____ ____	_____ 5 to both sides.
$3m = 27$	Since m is **multiplied** by 3, to **undo this multiplication**,
$\frac{3m}{3} = \frac{27}{3}$	_____ both sides by 3
$m = 9$	The solution set is $\{$____$\}$.

Simplify Before Solving Equations
Solve.

$$\frac{3c}{5} - 4 - \frac{2c}{5} = 11$$

$\frac{3c}{5} - 4 - \frac{2c}{5} = 11$	
$\frac{3c}{5} - \frac{2c}{5} - 4 = 11$	Use the Commutative Property of Addition.
$\frac{c}{5} - 4 = 11$	Combine _____ terms.
$\frac{c}{5} - 4 = 11$	Since 4 is **subtracted** from $\frac{c}{5}$, to **undo this subtraction**,
____ ____	_____ 4 to each side.
$\frac{c}{5} = 15$	Since c is divided by 5, **to undo this division**,
____$\left(\frac{c}{5}\right) =$ ____(15)	_____ each side by 5.
$c = 75$	The solution set is $\{$____$\}$.

Holt Algebra 1

SECTION 2A

Ready to Go On? Problem-Solving Intervention
2-3 Solving Multi-Step Equations

Multi-step equations require multiple steps to solve. Use inverse operations and work backward to undo each operation one step at a time.

Jenna uses a coupon to buy pizzas for a party. The coupon states that if a customer pays $12.00 for two pizzas, each additional pizza costs $5.00. If Jenna paid $32.00 for the pizzas, how many pizzas did she buy?

Understand the Problem

1. How much is the total bill? _____

2. How much do the first two pizzas cost? _____

3. How much does each additional pizza cost? _____

Make a Plan

4. What do you need to determine? _____

5. Let p represent the number of pizzas Jenna bought. What expression represents the number of pizzas that cost $5 each? _____

6. Write an equation to represent the cost of the pizzas Jenna bought.

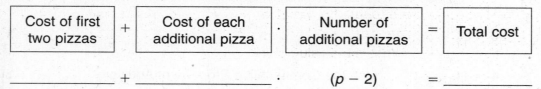

| Cost of first two pizzas | + | Cost of each additional pizza | · | Number of additional pizzas | = | Total cost |

_____ + _____ · $(p - 2)$ = _____

Solve

7. Solve the equation by isolating p.

$12 + 5(p - 2) = 32$

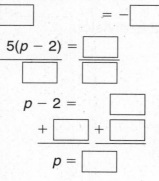

8. How many pizzas did Jenna buy? ____

Check

9. Substitute the solution p into the equation you wrote in Exercise 6.

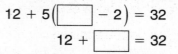

$12 + 5(\boxed{} - 2) = 32$

$12 + \boxed{} = 32$

10. Does your solution make the equation true? _____

Holt Algebra 1

Name _____ Date _____ Class _____

Find these vocabulary words in Lesson 2-4 and the Multilingual Glossary.

Vocabulary	
identity	contradiction

Simplifying Each Side Before Solving Equations
Solve the equation. $4(k - 3) = 3(3k + 6)$

Use the _____ Property to simplify this equation before you solve it.

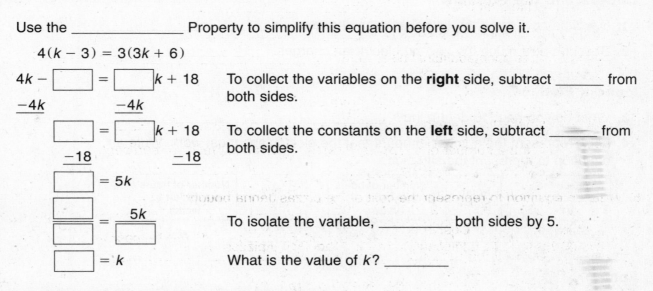

$4(k - 3) = 3(3k + 6)$

$4k - \boxed{} = \boxed{}k + 18$ To collect the variables on the **right** side, subtract _____ from both sides.
$-4k$ $-4k$

$\boxed{} = \boxed{}k + 18$ To collect the constants on the **left** side, subtract _____ from both sides.
-18 -18

$\boxed{} = 5k$

$\dfrac{\boxed{}}{\boxed{}} = \dfrac{5k}{\boxed{}}$ To isolate the variable, _____ both sides by 5.

$\boxed{} = k$ What is the value of k? _____

Infinitely Many Solutions or No Solutions
Solve the equation. $5(2x - 3) = 2(5x - 4)$

Use the _____ Property to simplify this equation before you solve it.

$5(2x - 3) = 2(5x - 4)$

$10x - \boxed{} = \boxed{}x - 8$ To collect the variables on the **right** side, subtract _____ from both sides.
$-10x$ $-10x$

$\boxed{} = -8$ Complete the resulting equation.

Is the resulting equation a true statement or a false statement? _____

What is the other name for a false statement given in the lesson? _____

How many values make this equation true? _____

Holt Algebra 1

Ready To Go On? Problem Solving Intervention

SECTION 2A

2-4 Solving Equations with Variables on Both Sides

To solve equations with variables on both sides, begin by collecting the variable terms on one side of the equation.

One electrician charges his customers a $60 service fee plus $35 per hour. Another electrician charges her customers $65 per hour. How many hours must the electricians work in order for the total cost of an electrician to be the same? What is the total cost?

Understand the Problem

1. Describe how much the first electrician charges. _____

2. Describe how much the second electrician charges. _____

Make a Plan

3. What do you need to determine? _____

4. Let *h* represent the number of hours that the electricians must work. Write an equation to represent the situation.

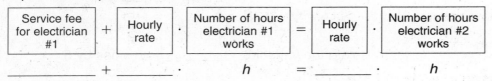

| Service fee for electrician #1 | + | Hourly rate | · | Number of hours electrician #1 works | = | Hourly rate | · | Number of hours electrician #2 works |

_____ + _____ ·   *h*   = _____ ·   *h*

Solve

5. On which side should you collect the variable terms? _____

6. Solve the equation by isolating *h*.

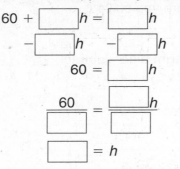

$$60 + \boxed{}h = \boxed{}h$$
$$-\boxed{}h \quad -\boxed{}h$$
$$60 = \boxed{}h$$
$$\frac{60}{\boxed{}} = \frac{\boxed{}h}{\boxed{}}$$
$$\boxed{} = h$$

7. The number of hours that the electricians need to work for the total cost to be the same is _____ hours.

8. What is the total cost for either of the electricians to work for this number of hours? _____

Look Back

9. Substitute the solution for *h* into the equation you wrote in Exercise 4.

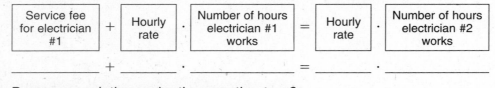

| Service fee for electrician #1 | + | Hourly rate | · | Number of hours electrician #1 works | = | Hourly rate | · | Number of hours electrician #2 works |

_____ + _____ · _____ = _____ · _____

10. Does your solution make the equation true? _____

Holt Algebra 1

Ready To Go On? Skills Intervention

SECTION 2B *2-5 Solving Proportions*

Find these vocabulary words in Lesson 2-5 and the Multilingual Glossary.

Vocabulary				
ratio	proportion	cross products	scale	scale drawing
rate	unit rate	scale model	conversion	factor

Solving Proportions
Solve each proportion.

A. $\dfrac{-22}{m} = \dfrac{11}{4}$

Complete the equation using cross products:

Multiply.

To isolate m, _____ both sides by _____.

What is the value of m? _____

To check your answer, substitute the solution in for m.

$\dfrac{-22}{m} = \dfrac{11}{4} \longrightarrow \dfrac{-22}{\boxed{}} = \dfrac{11}{4}$

Are the ratios equivalent? ____

$\dfrac{-22}{m} = \dfrac{11}{4}$

$4 \cdot \boxed{} = \boxed{} \cdot m$

$\boxed{} = 11m$

$\dfrac{\boxed{}}{\boxed{}} = \dfrac{11m}{\boxed{}}$

$\boxed{} = m$

B. Find 20% of 60.

Use a proportion.

Let x represent the part.

Find the cross products.

Since x is multiplied by 100, to undo the multiplication, divide both sides by ____.

$\dfrac{\boxed{}}{\text{whole}} = \dfrac{\boxed{}}{100}$

$\dfrac{x}{\boxed{}} = \dfrac{\boxed{}}{100}$

$\boxed{}\, x = \boxed{}$

$\dfrac{100x}{\boxed{}} = \dfrac{1200}{\boxed{}}$

$x = \boxed{}$

20% of 60 is $\boxed{}$

Holt Algebra 1

SECTION 2B Ready to Go On? Problem Solving Intervention
2-5 Solving Proportions

A comparison of two quantities by division is a ratio. Two ratios that are equivalent is a proportion.

The ratio of cats to dogs in the local animal shelter is 3:5. There are 60 dogs in the animal shelter. How many cats are in the animal shelter?

Understand the Problem

1. What is the ratio of cats to dogs? _____

2. How many dogs are in the shelter? _____

Make a Plan

3. What do you need to determine? _____

4. Complete the proportion: ratio of cats to dogs = $\dfrac{\text{number of cats}}{\boxed{}}$

5. If c represents the number of cats in the shelter, complete the proportion to find the number of cats: $\dfrac{\boxed{}}{5} = \dfrac{c}{\boxed{}}$

Solve

6. To solve the proportion, multiply both sides by _____.

7. Solve the equation for c.

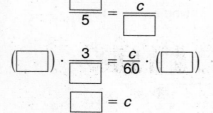

$$\dfrac{\boxed{}}{5} = \dfrac{c}{\boxed{}}$$

$$\left(\boxed{}\right) \cdot \dfrac{3}{\boxed{}} = \dfrac{c}{60} \cdot \left(\boxed{}\right)$$

$$\boxed{} = c$$

8. The number of cats in the shelter is _____.

Look Back

9. To check your solution, simplify the ratio of c to the number of dogs in the shelter.

$$\dfrac{c}{60} = \dfrac{\boxed{}}{60} = \dfrac{\boxed{}}{\boxed{}}$$

10. Is this the same as the ratio of cats to dogs, 3:5? _____

Holt Algebra 1

Name _____ Date _____ Class _____

Ready To Go On? Skills Intervention
2-6 Solving Literal Equations for a Variable

Find these vocabulary words in Lesson 2-6 and the Multilingual Glossary.

Vocabulary
formula   literal equation

Solving Literal Equations for a Variable

A. Solve $7u + v = w - 6$ for w.

Which side of the equation is w located? _____

What constant is on the same side of the equation as w? _____

Which operation is between the w and the constant? _____

To isolate w, _____ 6 to both sides of the equation.

Complete: $7u + v +$ ☐ $= w - 6 +$ ☐

$\qquad 7u + v +$ ☐ $= w$

B. Solve $j + k = 4(m - 10)$ for m.

Which side of the equation is m located? _____

What property do you use to simplify the equation first? _____

What is the resulting equation? $j + k =$ ___$m -$ ___

What constant is on the same side of the equation as $4m$? _____

Which operation is between the $4m$ and the constant? _____

To isolate $4m$, add _____ to both sides of the equation.

Complete to find the resulting equation.

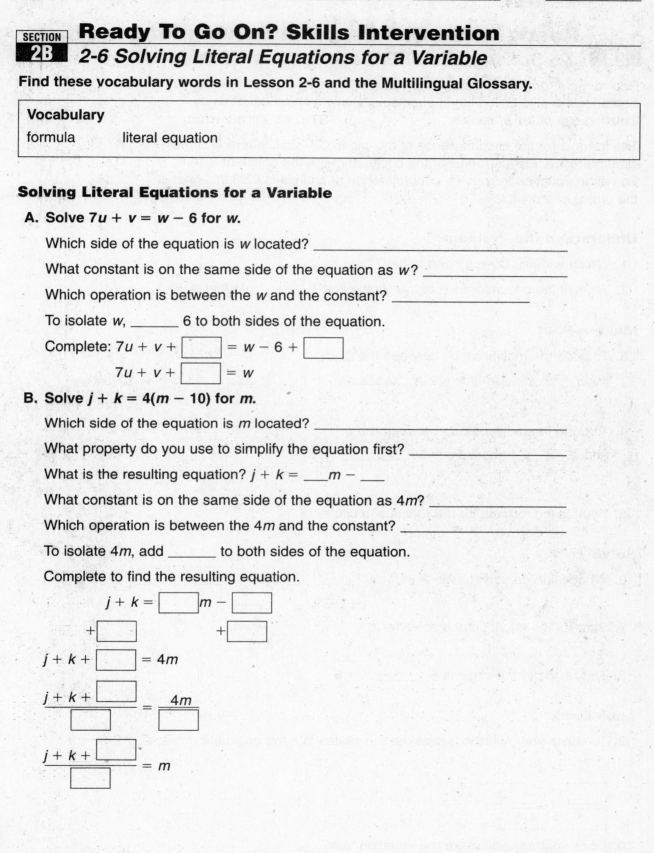

$\qquad j + k =$ ☐ $m -$ ☐

$\quad +$ ☐ $\qquad\qquad +$ ☐

$j + k +$ ☐ $= 4m$

$\dfrac{j + k + ☐}{☐} = \dfrac{4m}{☐}$

$\dfrac{j + k + ☐}{☐} = m$

Holt Algebra 1

Name _____ Date _____ Class _____

Ready to Go On? Problem Solving Intervention
2-6 Solving Literal Equations for a Variable

Rearrange a formula to isolate any variable by using inverse operations. Formulas are also called literal equations. Solve a literal equation by isolating one of the variables.

The formula for the circumference of a circle is $C = 2\pi r$, where C is the circumference, r is the radius of the circle, and π is the constant 3.14. Solve the equation for r. If the circumference of a circle is 62.8 in., what is the radius of the circle?

Understand the Problem

1. Which variable do you need to find? _____

2. What is the circumference of the given circle? _____ What is π? _____

Make a Plan

3. To undo the multiplication between the 2 and r, _____ both sides by _____.

$$C = 2\pi r$$

$$\frac{C}{\Box} = \frac{2\pi r}{\Box} \longrightarrow \frac{C}{\Box} = \pi r$$

4. To undo the multiplication between the π and r, _____ both sides by _____.

$$\frac{C}{2\pi} = \frac{\pi r}{\Box}$$

5. What is the formula for the radius of a circle, r?

$$\frac{C}{\Box} = r$$

Solve

6. What value do you substitute in for C? _____ and π? _____

7. Simplify the equation and solve for r.

$$\frac{\Box}{2 \cdot \Box} = r$$

8. The radius of the circle is _____.

$$\underline{\quad} = r$$

Look Back

9. To check your solution, substitute the values into the original formula, $C = 2\pi r$.

$$C = 2 \cdot \pi \cdot r$$

$$\Box = 2 \cdot \Box \cdot \Box$$

$$\Box = \Box$$

10. Does your solution make the equation true? _____

Holt Algebra 1

Ready to Go On? Skills Intervention

SECTION 2B *2-7 Solving Absolute-Value Equations*

Solving Absolute-Value Equations
Solve each equation.

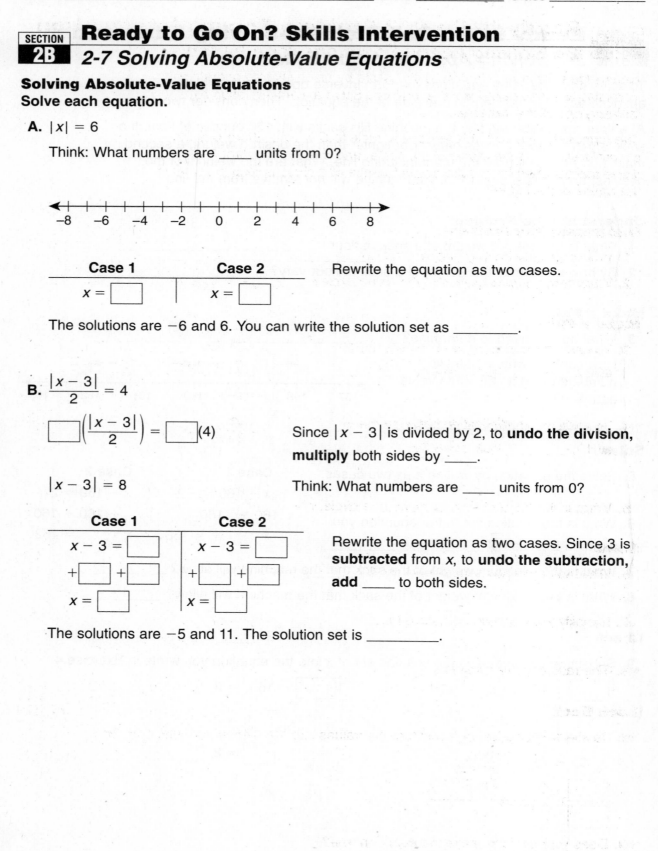

A. $|x| = 6$

Think: What numbers are _____ units from 0?

Case 1	Case 2
$x = \boxed{}$	$x = \boxed{}$

Rewrite the equation as two cases.

The solutions are -6 and 6. You can write the solution set as _____.

B. $\dfrac{|x - 3|}{2} = 4$

$\boxed{}\left(\dfrac{|x-3|}{2}\right) = \boxed{}(4)$

Since $|x - 3|$ is divided by 2, to **undo the division, multiply** both sides by _____.

$|x - 3| = 8$

Think: What numbers are _____ units from 0?

Case 1	Case 2
$x - 3 = \boxed{}$	$x - 3 = \boxed{}$
$+\boxed{}\ +\boxed{}$	$+\boxed{}\ +\boxed{}$
$x = \boxed{}$	$x = \boxed{}$

Rewrite the equation as two cases. Since 3 is **subtracted** from x, to **undo the subtraction, add** _____ to both sides.

The solutions are -5 and 11. The solution set is _____.

Holt Algebra 1

Ready to Go On? Problem-Solving Intervention

SECTION 2B

2-7 Solving Absolute-Value Equations

To solve absolute value equations, perform inverse operations to isolate the absolute value expression on one side of the equation. Then consider two cases.

At a flour-manufacturing plant, a machine fills sacks with 160 ounces of flour. If a sack is more than 2 ounces heavier or lighter than the desired weight, a second machine removes it from the manufacturing line. What are the weights of the heaviest and lightest sacks that the machine will *not* remove from the line?

Understand the Problem

1. What is the desired weight of a sack of flour? _____

2. By how much may the weight of a sack of flour vary? _____

Make a Plan

3. What do you need to determine? _____

4. How can you write these two numbers using an absolute value equation?

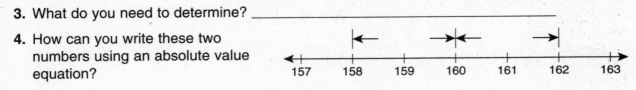

_____

Solve

5. Solve the equation by writing it as two cases.

Case 1	Case 2
$x - 160 = -2$	$x - 160 = 2$
$+ 160 + \quad 160$	$+ 160 + 160$
$x \qquad = 158$	$x \qquad = 162$

6. What is the solution set to the equation you wrote in Exercise 4? _____

7. What is the minimum weight of the sack that the machine will allow? _____

8. What is the maximum weight of the sack that the machine will allow? _____

Check

9. Substitute each value in the solution set of x into the equation you wrote in Exercise 4.

Ready To Go On? Skills Intervention
3-1 Graphing and Writing Inequalities

Find these vocabulary words in Lesson 3-1 and the Multilingual Glossary.

Vocabulary	
inequality	solution of an inequality

Graphing Inequalities

A. $b \le 7\frac{1}{2}$

What does the $\le$ symbol indicate? _____

Is $7\frac{1}{2}$ included in the solution set? _____

Should the circle drawn at $7\frac{1}{2}$ be solid or empty? _____

In which direction should the arrow point? _____

Graph the inequality. ◄──┼──┼──┼──┼──┼──┼──┼──┼──┼──┼──►
　　　　　　　　　　　 −2 −1　0　1　2　3　4　5　6　7　8

B. $r > -3$

What does the $>$ symbol indicate? _____

Is -3 included in the solution set? _____

So, a(n) _____ circle should be used and the arrow should point to the _____.

Graph the inequality. ◄──┼──┼──┼──┼──┼──┼──┼──┼──┼──┼──►
　　　　　　　　　　　 −5 −4 −3 −2 −1　0　1　2　3　4　5

Writing an Inequality from a Graph

A. ◄──┼──┼──●──┼──┼──┼──┼──┼──┼──┼──►
　　　 −5 −4 −3 −2 −1　0　1　2　3　4　5

Which direction does the arrow point?

_____

What does the solid circle mean?

_____

Which symbol should be used? _____

Write the inequality.

_____

B. ◄──┼──┼──┼──┼──┼──┼──┼──┼──○──┼──►
　　　 −5 −4 −3 −2 −1　0　1　2　3　4　5

Which direction does the arrow point?

_____

What does the empty circle mean?

_____

Which symbol should be used? _____

Write the inequality.

_____

Holt Algebra 1

SECTION	# Ready To Go On? Skills Intervention
3A	*3-2 Solving Inequalities by Adding and Subtracting*

Find this word in Lesson 3-2 and the Multilingual Glossary.

Vocabulary
equivalent inequality

Using Addition and Subtraction to Solve Inequalities
Solve each inequality and graph the solutions.

A. $y + 4 \leq 9$

Step 1: Solve for y.

$y + 4 \leq 9$ To isolate y, _____ 4 from both sides of the inequality.

$- \underline{} \quad - \underline{}$

$y \leq \underline{}$ Find the value of y.

Step 2: Graph the solution.

A(n) _____ circle should be used and the arrow should point to the _____.

$$\longleftarrow \! | \; | \; | \; | \; | \; | \; | \; | \; | \; | \; | \! \longrightarrow$$
$$-5 \; -4 \; -3 \; -2 \; -1 \;\; 0 \;\; 1 \;\; 2 \;\; 3 \;\; 4 \;\; 5$$

B. $x - 9 \geq -7$

Step 1: Solve for x.

$x - 9 \geq -7$ Isolate x by _____ 9 to both sides of the inequality.

$+ \underline{} \quad + \underline{}$

$x \geq \underline{}$

Step 2: Graph the solution.

A(n) _____ circle should be used and the arrow should point to the _____.

$$\longleftarrow \! | \; | \; | \; | \; | \; | \; | \; | \; | \; | \; | \! \longrightarrow$$
$$-5 \; -4 \; -3 \; -2 \; -1 \;\; 0 \;\; 1 \;\; 2 \;\; 3 \;\; 4 \;\; 5$$

C. $5 > p - 4$

Step 1: Solve for p.

$5 > p - 4$ Isolate p by _____ 4 to both sides of the inequality.

$+ \underline{} \quad + \underline{}$

$\underline{} > p$

Step 2: Graph the solution.

Another way to write this inequality is $p < \underline{}$.

A(n) _____ circle should be used and the arrow should point to the _____.

$$\longleftarrow \! | \; | \; | \; | \; | \; | \; | \; | \; | \; | \; | \! \longrightarrow$$
$$-10 \; -8 \; -6 \; -4 \; -2 \;\; 0 \;\; 2 \;\; 4 \;\; 6 \;\; 8 \;\; 10$$

Holt Algebra 1

Ready to Go On? Problem Solving Intervention

SECTION 3A *3-2 Solving Inequalities by Adding and Subtracting*

Solving one-step inequalities is much like solving one-step equations.

Kendra receives a weekly allowance of $15.00. She has already spent $11.50 on a movie ticket and a bag of popcorn. Write and solve an inequality to determine how much money Kendra can spend the rest of the week.

Understand the Problem

1. How much allowance does Kendra receive? _____

2. How much has Kendra spent so far this week? _____

Make a Plan

3. What do you need to determine?

_____

4. What inequality symbol represents *less than or equal to*? _____

Solve

5. Let *s* represent the amount of money Kendra can spend the rest of the week. Write an inequality to represent the situation.

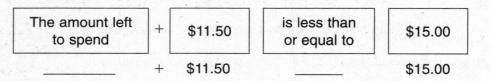

The amount left to spend	+	$11.50	is less than or equal to	$15.00
_____	+	$11.50	_____	$15.00

6. Solve for *s* by subtracting 11.50 from both sides of the inequality. $s \leq$ _____

7. The amount of money Kendra can spend the rest of the week is at most _____.

8. What is the least amount of money that Kendra can spend? _____

Look Back

9. Graph your solution on the number line.

$$-5 \; -4 \; -3 \; -2 \; -1 \; 0 \; 1 \; 2 \; 3 \; 4 \; 5$$

10. Choose a number that is included in your solution. _____

11. Substitute this number for *s* into the inequality you wrote in Exercise 5. _____

12. Does the number you chose in Exercise 10, make the inequality true or false? _____

13. Does your solution make sense? _____

Holt Algebra 1

Name _____ Date _____ Class _____

Ready To Go On? Skills Intervention
3-3 Solving Inequalities by Multiplying and Dividing

Multiplying or Dividing by a Positive Number

Solve $\frac{2}{5}y \le -4$. Then graph the solutions.

The variable, y, is being multiplied by _____, so you need to multiply by the

reciprocal of _____ on both sides of the inequality.

Step 1: Solve for y.

$$\frac{2}{5}y \le -4$$

_____ $\cdot \frac{2}{5}y \le -4 \cdot$ _____   Isolate y by _____ both sides of the inequality by $\frac{5}{2}$.

$$y \le \frac{-20}{2}$$ Divide.

$$y \le \text{\_\_\_\_\_}$$

Step 2: Graph the solution.

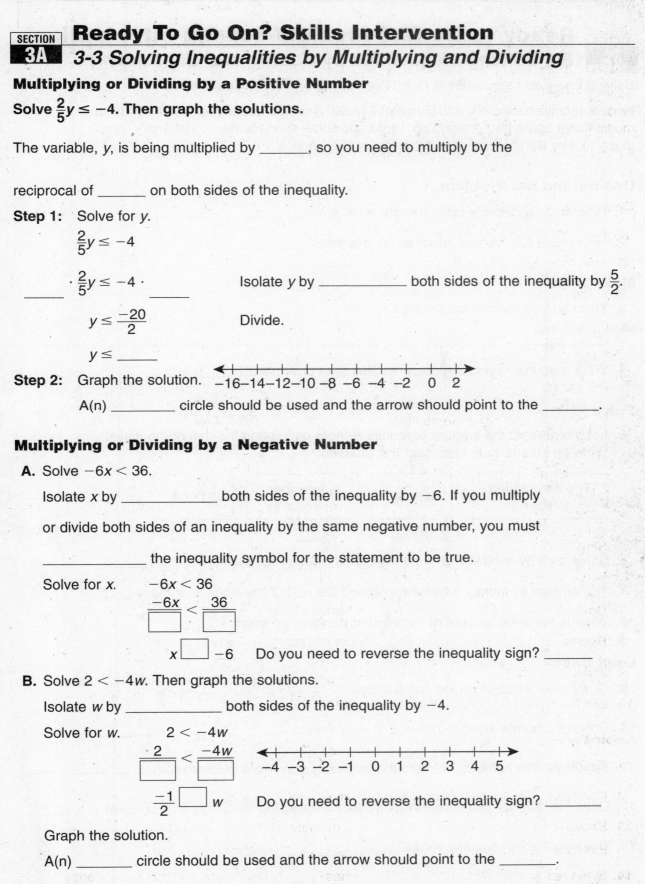

A(n) _____ circle should be used and the arrow should point to the _____.

Multiplying or Dividing by a Negative Number

A. Solve $-6x < 36$.

Isolate x by _____ both sides of the inequality by -6. If you multiply

or divide both sides of an inequality by the same negative number, you must

_____ the inequality symbol for the statement to be true.

Solve for x. $-6x < 36$

$$\frac{-6x}{\boxed{}} < \frac{36}{\boxed{}}$$

$x \boxed{} -6$ Do you need to reverse the inequality sign? _____

B. Solve $2 < -4w$. Then graph the solutions.

Isolate w by _____ both sides of the inequality by -4.

Solve for w. $2 < -4w$

$$\frac{2}{\boxed{}} < \frac{-4w}{\boxed{}}$$

$$\frac{-1}{2} \boxed{} w$$ Do you need to reverse the inequality sign? _____

Graph the solution.

A(n) _____ circle should be used and the arrow should point to the _____.

Holt Algebra 1

Name _____ Date _____ Class _____

Ready to Go On? Problem Solving Intervention
3-3 Solving Inequalities by Multiplying or Dividing

Solving one-step inequalities is much like solving one-step equations. To solve an inequality that contains multiplication or division, undo the operation by dividing or multiplying both sides of the inequality by the same number.

A piece of metal tubing is 90 inches long. Jamal needs to cut sections of tubing that are 12 inches long. What are the possible numbers of sections of tubing that Jamal can cut?

Understand the Problem

1. How much tubing does Jamal have? _____

2. How long does each section of tubing need to be? _____

3. What do you need to determine? _____

Make a Plan

4. What inequality symbol represents *at most*? _____

5. Let *t* represent the length of each section of tubing. Write an inequality for the situation.

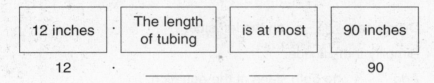

| 12 inches | · | The length of tubing | is at most | 90 inches |

| 12 | · | _____ | _____ | 90 |

Solve

6. Solve the inequality by isolating *t*.

$$12t \le 90$$
$$\frac{12t}{\boxed{}} \le \frac{90}{\boxed{}}$$
$$t \le \underline{}$$

7. Does Jamal want to cut the tubing into partial sections? _____

8. Round _____ to get the greatest number of sections of tubing Jamal can cut.

9. Jamal can cut the tubing into at most _____ sections.

10. List the number of sections Jamal can cut. _____ sections

Look Back

11. Graph your solution on the number line. ←—+——+——+——+——+——+——+——+——+——+——+——→
    −1 0 1 2 3 4 5 6 7 8 9

12. Choose a number that is included in your solution. _____

13. Because each section is 12 inches long, multiply the number you chose in Exercise 12 by 12. What is the result? _____

14. Is the result less than or equal to 90 inches? _____ Does your solution make sense? _____

Holt Algebra 1

Name _____ Date _____ Class _____

SECTION	# Ready To Go On? Skills Intervention
3B	***3-4 Solving Two-Step and Multi-Step Inequalities***

Solving Two-Step Inequalities

Solve the inequality $8 \geq 1 - 7r$ and graph the solutions.

$8 \geq 1 - 7r$

-5 -4 -3 -2 -1 0 1 2 3 4 5

$\underline{} \quad -\underline{}$

$\underline{} \geq -7r$ Isolate $-7r$ by _____ 1 from both sides.

$\dfrac{7}{\square} \geq \dfrac{7r}{\square}$ What is the inverse of multiplication? _____

$\underline{}\square r$ Do you need to reverse the sign? _____

To graph the solution, a(n) _____ circle should be used and the arrow should point to the _____.

Simplifying Before Solving Inequalities

Solve each inequality and graph the solutions.

A. $4(x - 3) > -2$

-5 -4 -3 -2 -1 0 1 2 3 4 5

$4(x - 3) > -2$

$4(x) - 4(3) > -2$ Distribute _____ on the left side.

$4x - \underline{} > -2$ Simplify the left side.

$4x > \underline{}$ Add _____ to both sides of the equation.

$\dfrac{4x}{\square} > \dfrac{\square}{4}$ Divide both sides by 4.

$x\,\square \underline{}$ Do you need to reverse the sign? _____ Graph the solution.

B. $\dfrac{5}{6}x + \dfrac{2}{3} > \dfrac{1}{6}$ What is the LCD of the fractions? _____

$\underline{}\left(\dfrac{5}{6}x + \dfrac{2}{3}\right) > \underline{}\left(\dfrac{1}{6}\right)$ Multiply both sides of the inequality by the LCD.

$\underline{}\left(\dfrac{5}{6}x\right) + \underline{}\left(\dfrac{2}{3}\right) > \underline{}\left(\dfrac{1}{6}\right)$ Distribute the LCD on the left side.

$5x + 4 > 1$

$5x > \underline{}$ Subtract _____ from both sides of the inequality.

$\dfrac{5x}{\square} > \dfrac{\square}{\square}$ Divide both sides by 5.

$x\,\square \underline{}$ Do you need to reverse the sign? _____

Graph the solution.

-2 -1 0 1 2

Holt Algebra 1

SECTION 3B Ready to Go On? Problem Solving Intervention
3-4 Solving Two-Step and Multi-Step Inequalities

Inequalities that contain more than one operation require more than one step to solve. Use inverse operations to undo the operations in the inequality one at a time.

George has scored 21 points and 17 points in his first two basketball games. How many points must he score in his third game to have an average of at least 20 points per game?

Understand the Problem

1. How many games has George played? _____

2. How many combined points has George scored in the games? _____

3. How many more games will George play? _____

Make a Plan

4. What are you trying to determine? _____

5. How many total points must George score to average 20 points for 3 games? _____

6. What inequality symbol represents *at least*? _____

7. Write an inequality to represent the situation where *x* equals the number of points in the third game. ____ + *x* ☐ 60

Solve

$$38 + x \geq 60$$

8. Solve the inequality.   − ____   − ____   Subtract to isolate *x*.

$$x \geq \text{____}$$

9. The number of points that George must score is at least _____.

Look Back

10. Graph your solution on the number line.   ← + + + + + + + + + + + →
                                              18 19 20 21 22 23 24 25 26 27 28

11. Choose a number that is included in your solution. _____

12. Find the average of the number you chose in Exercise 11, and the values 21, and 17. What is the result? _____

13. Is the result greater than or equal to 20? _____

14. Does your solution make sense? _____

Holt Algebra 1

SECTION 3B — Ready To Go On? Skills Intervention

3-5 Solving Inequalities with Variables on Both Sides

Solving Inequalities with Variables on Both Sides

Solve $x - 10 \geq 4x - 16$.

$$x - 10 \geq 4x - 16$$

$\underline{++}$ Isolate x by adding 10 to both sides.

$x \geq 4x - \underline{}$ Simplify.

$\underline{--}$ To isolate the constant term, subtract $4x$ from both sides.

$\underline{}x \geq \underline{}$

What is the inverse of multiplication? _____ Do you need to reverse the sign? _____

The solution is: _____

Simplifying Each Side Before Solving

Solve $4(3x - 1) < 2(x + 3)$.

$4(3x - 1) < 2(x + 3)$ Distribute _____ on the left side of the inequality.

$\underline{}(3x) - \underline{}(1) < \underline{}(x) + \underline{}(3)$ Distribute _____ on the right side of the inequality.

$12x - \underline{} < \underline{} + 6$ Simplify both sides of the inequality.

$\underline{-}x \quad -\underline{}x$ Subtract $2x$ from both sides so that the coefficient of x is positive.

$\underline{}x - \underline{} < 6$

$\underline{++}$ Add 4 to both sides of the equation.

$\underline{}x < \underline{}$ Divide both sides of the equation by 10.

Do you need to reverse the sign? _____ The solution is: _____

All Real Numbers as Solutions or No Solutions

Solve $3y + 4 > 3(y + 3)$.

$3y + 4 > 3(y + 3)$ Distribute 3 on the right side of the inequality. Simplify.

$3y + 4 > 3y + \underline{}$ The same variable term _____ appears on both sides of the inequality. Look at the other terms.

For any number $3y$, adding _____ will never result in a greater number than adding _____.

No values of y make the inequality _____.

There are no solutions. The solution set is _____.

Holt Algebra 1

Name _____ Date _____ Class _____

Ready to Go On? Problem Solving Intervention
3-5 Solving Inequalities with Variables on Both Sides

To solve inequalities that have variables on both sides of the inequality symbol, "collect" all the variable terms on one side of the inequality symbol and all the constant terms on the other side.

Hannah earns $150 per week plus $3 for each jersey she sells. Martin earns $136 per week plus $5 for every jersey he sells. For how many sales of jerseys will Martin make more money?

Understand the Problem

1. How much money does Hannah make per week before she sells any jerseys? _____

2. How much money does Hannah make per jersey sold? _____

3. How much money does Martin make per week before he sells any jerseys? _____

4. How much money does Martin make per jersey sold? _____

Make a Plan

Let j represent the number of jerseys sold.

5. Write an expression to represent the amount of money Hannah makes. ____ + $3j$

6. Write an expression to represent the amount of money Martin makes. 136 + ____

7. Who are you trying to determine will make more money? _____

8. Write an inequality to represent the situation. ____ + $3j$ ▢ 136 + ____

Solve

9. Solve the inequality by isolating j.

10. Martin has to sell more than _____ jerseys to make more money in one week than Hannah.

$$\underline{\quad} + 3j \;\square\; 136 + \underline{\quad}$$
$$\underline{-3j} \quad \underline{-3j}$$
$$150 \;\square\; 136 + \underline{\quad}\, j$$
$$\underline{-136} \quad \underline{-136}$$
$$\underline{\quad} \;\square\; 2j$$
$$\frac{\square}{2} < \frac{2j}{\square}$$
$$\underline{\quad} \;\square\; j$$

Look Back

11. Graph your solution on the number line.

−2 −1 0 1 2 3 4 5 6 7 8

12. Choose a number that is included in your solution. _____

13. Substitute this number in for j in the inequality you wrote in Exercise 8.

   What is the result? _____

14. Is the inequality true or false? _____ Does your solution make sense? _____

Holt Algebra 1

Name _____ Date _____ Class _____

Ready To Go On? Skills Intervention
3-6 Solving Compound Inequalities

Find these vocabulary words in Lesson 3-6 and the Multilingual Glossary.

Vocabulary		
compound inequality	intersection	union

Solving Compound Inequalities Involving AND
Solve $-3 \le x + 2 < 6$. Then graph the solution.

Write each compound inequality. $-3 \le x + 2$ AND _____

Solve each simple inequality. _____ $\le x$ AND $x <$ _____

How can you rewrite the first inequality? $x \ge$ _____

To graph this solution, should the circle drawn be solid or empty? _____

In which direction should the arrow point? _____

Graph the first inequality.

–5 –4 –3 –2 –1 0 1 2 3 4 5

Graph the second inequality.

–5 –4 –3 –2 –1 0 1 2 3 4 5

Graph the intersection by finding where the
two graphs overlap.

–5 –4 –3 –2 –1 0 1 2 3 4 5

Solving Compound Inequalities Involving OR
Solve the compound inequality $3 < d - 4$ OR $d + 4 < 1$ and graph the solution.

Solve each simple inequality.
$$3 < d - 4 \quad \text{OR} \quad d + 4 < 1$$
____ $< d$ OR $d <$ ____

For the first inequality, a(n) _____ circle
should be used and the arrow should point to the
_____.

–10–9–8–7–6–5–4–3–2–1 0 1 2 3 4 5 6 7 8 9 10

For the second inequality, a(n) _____ circle
should be used and the arrow should point to the
_____.

–10–9–8–7–6–5–4–3–2–1 0 1 2 3 4 5 6 7 8 9 10

Graph the union by combining the regions. This is
the graph of the compound inequality.

–10–9–8–7–6–5–4–3–2–1 0 1 2 3 4 5 6 7 8 9 10

Holt Algebra 1

Name _____ Date _____ Class _____

Ready to Go On? Problem Solving Intervention
3-6 Solving Compound Inequalities

When two simple inequalities are combined into one statement by the words AND or OR, the result is a compound inequality.

In the Kiddie Kingdom section of a local amusement park, guests must be between 42 and 54 inches tall to ride the Red Baron. Write a compound inequality to show the acceptable heights to ride the Red Baron. Graph the inequality.

Understand the Problem

1. What is the shortest acceptable height to ride the Red Baron? _____

2. What is the tallest acceptable height to ride the Red Baron? _____

3. What are you being asked to do?

   _____

Make a Plan

4. Translate the sentences into two mathematical inequalities. Let h represent the height.

   The acceptable ride height is greater than or equal to 42 inches. **AND** The acceptable ride height is less than or equal to 54 inches.

   h ☐ _____ h ☐ _____

Solve

5. Use the two inequalities from Exercise 4 to write a compound inequality.

   _____ ☐ h ☐ _____

6. To graph the inequality what kind of circle should be used to represent 42 inches?

   _____

7. Should the arrow point left or right? _____

8. What kind of circle should be used to represent 54 inches? _____

9. Should the arrow point left or right? _____

10. Graph the solution.

    38 40 42 44 46 48 50 52 54 56 58

Look Back

11. Select a point between 42 and 54 inches and see where it falls on the graph. _____

12. Select a point greater than 54 inches and see where it falls on the graph. _____

13. Does your inequality make sense? _____

Holt Algebra 1

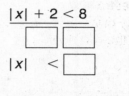

Ready to Go On? Skills Intervention

3-7 Solving Absolute-Value Inequalities

Solving Absolute-Value Inequalities Involving <
Solve the inequality and graph its solutions.

$|x| + 2 < 8$

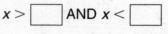

$|x| + 2 < 8$		Since 2 is added to $|x|$, to undo the addition,
$\boxed{}\ \boxed{}$		subtract ____ from both sides.
$|x| < \boxed{}$		Think: What values of x have absolute values less than ____?
$x > \boxed{}$ AND $x < \boxed{}$		Write as a compound inequality.
		The solution set is {x: ____ $< x <$ ____}.

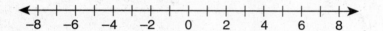

Solving Absolute-Value Inequalities Involving >
Solve the inequality and graph its solutions.

$|x - 3| - 11 \geq 5$

$|x - 3| - 11 \geq 5$	Since 11 is subtracted from $|x + 3|$, to undo the
$\ +\boxed{}\ +\boxed{}$	subtraction, add ____ to both sides.
$|x - 3| \geq \boxed{}$	Write as a compound inequality and solve each inequality.
$x - 3 \leq \boxed{}$ OR $x - 3 \geq \boxed{}$	Since 3 is subtracted from x, to undo the
$+\boxed{}\ +\boxed{}\quad +\boxed{}\ +\boxed{}$	subtraction, add ____ to both sides in each inequality.
$x \leq \boxed{}$ OR $x \geq \boxed{}$	Write a compound inequality.
	The solution set is {x: $x \leq$ ____ OR $x \geq$ ____}.

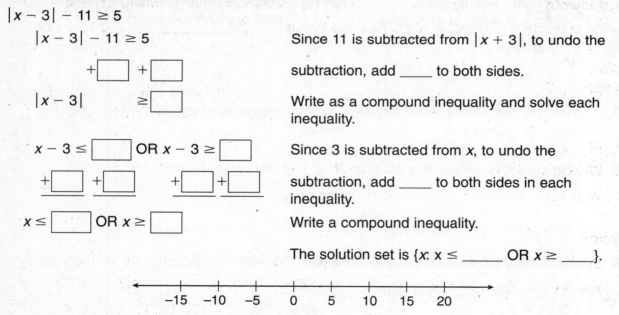

Holt Algebra 1

Name _____ Date _____ Class _____

To solve absolute-value inequalities, perform inverse operations to isolate the absolute-value expression on one side of the inequality. Then write the inequality as a compound inequality and solve each one.

A geologist measures the mass of an ore sample as 128.6 g using an electronic balance. The manufacturer of the balance states that the measured mass of a sample may vary by as much as 0.3 g. Write and solve an inequality for the range of the actual mass of the sample.

Understand the Problem

1. What is the measured mass of the sample? _____

2. The difference between the actual mass and the measured mass may be at

   most what value? _____

Make a Plan

3. What do you need to determine? _____

   _____

4. How can you write "the difference between the actual mass and the measured mass may

   be at most 0.3 g" using an absolute-value inequality? _____

Solve

5. $m - 128.6 \geq$ ▢ $m - 128.6 \leq$ ▢   Write the inequality as a compound

   $+$ ▢ $+$ ▢ $+$ ▢ $+$ ▢   inequality and solve each one.

   $m \quad \geq$ ▢ $m \quad \leq$ ▢

6. What is the solution set of the inequality? _____

7. What is the range of the possible mass of the sample? _____

Check

8. Substitute the maximum and minimum values of the solution set of m into the inequality

   you wrote in Exercise 4. $\left| \boxed{} - 128.6 \right| \leq 0.3$ $\left| \boxed{} - 128.6 \right| \leq 0.3$

                        $128.3 - 128.6 \geq -0.3$ $128.9 - 128.6 \leq 0.3$

                        $\boxed{} \geq -0.3$ $\boxed{} \leq 0.3$

Holt Algebra 1

SECTION
4A # Ready To Go On? Skills Intervention
4-1 Graphing Relationships

Find these vocabulary words in Lesson 4-1 and the Multilingual Glossary.

Vocabulary
continuous graph   discrete graph

Relating Graphs to Situations

An object rises from the ground at a constant rate for several minutes. The object stays at that elevation for several minutes before dropping down, then rising to its previous altitude before slowly descending back to the ground.

To relate a graph to a given situation, use key words in the description.

If a key word is "rose steadily" the line segment showing that description

should be slanting _____.

If a key word is "constant" the line segment should be a _____ line.

The table below lists the key words, in order, from the situation above.
Complete the table, using the graphs shown below.

Key Words	Segment Description	Graphs . . .
Rises from the ground	Slanting upward	Graphs B and C
Stays at that elevation	Horizontal	Graphs ____ and ____
Dropping down	Slanting _____	Graphs ____, B, and ____
Rising	Slanting _____	Graphs ____, ____, and ____
Slowly descending	Slanting _____	Graphs ____ and C

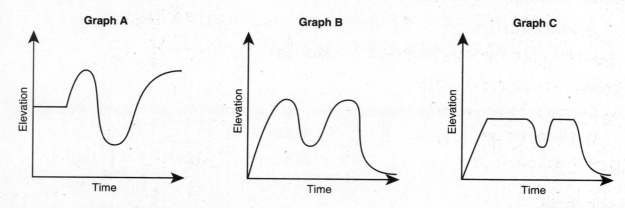

Which graph shows all the key phrases in order? _____

SECTION 4A Ready to Go On? Problem Solving Intervention
4-1 Graphing Relationships

Graphs with connected curves or lines are called continuous graphs. Graphs that only show distinct points are called discrete graphs.

Dennis has 100 raffle tickets to sell for a school fund-raiser. Each booklet has 10 raffle tickets. Sketch a graph to show how many raffle tickets he has left if he sells 1, 2, 3, 4 or 5 booklets of tickets.

Understand the Problem

1. How many tickets does Dennis have to sell? _____

2. Each booklet has how many raffle tickets? _____

3. If he sells one booklet, he has sold _____ tickets and 90 remain.

4. If he sells two booklets, he has sold 20 tickets and _____ tickets remain.

Make a Plan

5. What are you being asked to do? _____

   _____

6. Decide the type of graph you should draw. A _____ graph has

   connected lines or curves. A _____ graph has only distinct points.

   Since you can only count whole numbers of tickets sold, construct a _____ graph.

Solve

7. What should you title the graph? _____

8. Let the x-axis represent the number of booklets sold. The x-axis should

   be labeled from 0 to _____.

9. Let the y-axis represent the number of tickets remaining. The y-axis

   should be labeled from 0 to _____.

10. Complete the ordered pairs:

    (1, 90), (2, 80), (3, _____), (4, _____), (5, _____)

11. Plot the ordered pairs.

Look Back

12. If Dennis sells 3 books, how many tickets remain? _____

13. Is the point shown on your graph? _____

Tickets Remaining

Booklets Sold

Holt Algebra 1

Name _____ Date _____ Class _____

Ready To Go On? Skills Intervention
4-2 Relations and Functions

Find these vocabulary words in Lesson 4-2 and the Multilingual Glossary.

Vocabulary			
relation	domain	range	function

Finding the Domain and Range of a Relation
Give the domain and range of each relation.

A set of ordered pairs is called a _____.

The _____ of a relation is the set of first elements (or *x*-coordinates) of the ordered pairs.

The _____ of a relation is the set of second elements (or *y*-coordinates) of the ordered pairs.

A.

B.

List the ordered pairs: $(-3, \_\_\_)$; $(0, \_\_\_)$;

$(0, \_\_\_)$; $(3, \_\_\_)$

The domain is $\{-3, \_\_\_, \_\_\_\}$.

The range is $\{4, \_\_\_, \_\_\_\}$.

List the ordered pairs of the endpoints:

$(-3, \_\_\_)$; $(\_\_\_, 6)$

The domain is all *x*-values from _____ to ___, inclusive: $-3 \_\_ x \le \boxed{}$

The range is all *y*-values from 1 to ___, inclusive: $1 \_\_ y \_\_ \boxed{}$

Identifying Functions
Tell whether the relation is a function.

x	−4	−2	0	2	4
y	2	2	2	2	2

A function is a special type of relation that pairs each domain

value with exactly _____ range value.

List the ordered pairs $(-4, \_\_\_)$; $(-2, \_\_\_)$; $(\_\_\_, \_\_\_)$; $(\_\_\_, \_\_\_)$; $(\_\_\_, \_\_\_)$

The domain is $\{-4, \_\_\_\_, \_\_\_, \_\_\_, \_\_\_\}$. The range is $\{\_\_\_\}$.

Is a domain value (*x*-coordinates) paired with more than one range value? _____

Is the relation a function? _____

Holt Algebra 1

SECTION 4A Ready To Go On? Skills Intervention
4-3 Writing and Graphing Functions

Find these vocabulary words in Lesson 4-3 and the Multilingual Glossary.

Vocabulary			
independent variable	dependent variable	function rule	function notation

Using a Table to Write an Equation
Determine a relationship between the *x*- and *y*-values. Write an equation.

x	1	2	3	4
y	−5	−4	−3	−2

If $x = 1$, what can you subtract to get −5? $1 -$ ___ $= -5$

If $x = 1$, what can you multiply by to get −5? $1($____$) = -5$

Determine which relationship works for the other *x*- and *y*-values.

Subtracting: $2 - 6 =$ ____ $3 - 6 =$ ____ $4 - 6 =$ ____

Multiplying: $2(-5) =$ _____ $3(-5) =$ _____ $4(-5) =$ _____

Which relationship works so that when you input the *x*-values you get the *y*-values

in the table? _____

Write an equation: $y = x -$ _____

Writing Functions
Identify the independent and dependent variables. Write a rule in function notation.

A baker buys flour in 50-pound sacks that cost $18 each.

The cost depends on the number of sacks of flour purchased.

Dependent: _____   Independent: _____

Let *s* represent the number of sacks of flour purchased.

The function for the cost of the flour is $f($_____$) = 18$ _____.

Evaluating Functions
Evaluate the function $g(x) = 2x^2 - x$ for $x = -3$.

$g(-3) = 2($_____$)^2 - (-3)$ Substitute −3 for *x*.

$g(-3) = 2($_____$) - (-3)$ Evaluate the exponent.

$g(-3) =$ _____ $- (-3)$ Multiply.

$g(-3) =$ _____ $+$ _____   Add the opposite.

$g(-3) =$ _____   Simplify.

Holt Algebra 1

Ready to Go On? Problem Solving Intervention
4-3 Writing and Graphing Functions

You can graph a function by finding ordered pairs that satisfy the function.

The function $y = 9x$ represents how much money y Cameron earns in x hours. Graph the function.

Understand the Problem

1. What is the given function? _____

2. What variable represents hours? ___ What variable represents money? ___

3. If Cameron works 0 hours, how much money will she earn? ___

   If she works 1 hour how much will she earn? ___

4. So, the more Cameron works, the more _____ she will earn.

Make a Plan

5. Can Cameron earn negative money? _____ So, the domain values for this

   function should only be _____ numbers.

6. The graph will only be graphed in quadrant ___.

Solve

7. Complete the table for the given function values.

8. The x-coordinate of an ordered pair tells you to

   move _____ on the grid.

9. The y-coordinate of an ordered pair tells you to

   move _____ on the grid.

10. Graph each ordered pair.

x	$y = 9x$	(x, y)
0	$y = 9(0) = 0$	$(0, \_\_\_)$
1	$y = 9(1) = 9$	$(1, \_\_\_)$
2	$y = 9(\_\_\_) = 18$	$(2, \_\_\_)$
3	$y = 9(\_\_\_) = \_\_\_$	$(3, \_\_\_)$
4	$y = 9(\_\_\_) = \_\_\_$	$(\_\_\_, \_\_\_)$

Look Back

11. Use your graph to determine:

    What y-value corresponds with an x-value of 2? _____

    What y-value corresponds with an x-value of 4? _____

    What y-value corresponds with an x-value of 6? _____

12. If Cameron works more hours, does the graph show an increase or decrease in the amount of money she earns?

    _____

    Does this correspond to your understanding of the problem in Exercise 4? _____

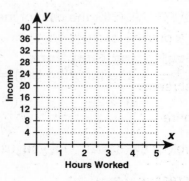

Holt Algebra 1

Name _____ Date _____ Class _____

Find these vocabulary words in Lesson 4-4 and the Multilingual Glossary.

Vocabulary		
scatter plot	correlation	positive correlation
negative correlation	no correlation	trend line

Graphing a Scatter Plot from Given Data
Graph a scatter plot using the given data.

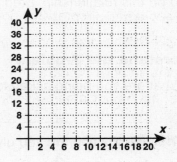

x	2	4	5	7	9	11
y	14	17	19	23	28	34

A _____ is a graph with points plotted to show a possible relationship between two sets of data.

List the sets of ordered pairs: (2, 14); (4, ___); (5, ___);

(___, ___); (___, ___); (___, ___).

When plotting an ordered pair the x-coordinate tells you to move _____ or _____

and the y-coordinate tells you to move ____ or _____.

To plot the point (2, 14) you move 2 units right from the origin and ____ units up.

To plot the point (4, 17) you move 4 units _____ from the origin and ____ units up.

To plot the point (5, 19) you move ____ units _____ from the origin and ____ units ____.
Plot the ordered pairs on the grid.

Describing Correlations from Scatter Plots
Describe the correlation illustrated by the above scatter plot.

A _____ describes a relationship between two sets of data.

In a positive correlation, both sets of data values _____.

In a _____ correlation, one set of data values increases as the other set decreases.

There is ____ correlation when the data values are scattered about.

Look at the scatter plot you just drew above. As the x-value _____ the y-value also

increases. Therefore, a _____ correlation exists between the two data sets.

Holt Algebra 1

Ready to Go On? Problem Solving Intervention

SECTION 4B

4-4 Scatter Plots and Trend Lines

You can graph a function on a scatter plot to show the relationship of data. Sometimes the function is a straight line. The line, called a **trend line** helps show the correlation between data sets more clearly. It can also be helpful when making predictions based on the data.

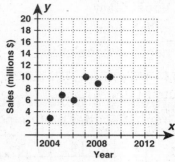

The scatter plot shows the estimated annual sales for a playhouse franchise of stores for the years 2004–2009. Based on this relationship, predict the total annual sales in 2012.

Understand the Problem

1. What are you being asked to predict?

   _____

2. What information are you given?

   _____

Make a Plan

3. What can be drawn on the scatter plot to help make a prediction? _____

4. Does your line have to go through all the data points? _____

5. When drawing a trend line, you want about the same number of points above

   and _____ the line.

Solve

6. Draw the trend line on the scatter plot above.

7. To make the prediction find the point on the line whose x-value is _____.
   The corresponding y-value is the predicted annual sales.

8. The estimated sales for the playground and playhouse franchise in 2012 are

   _____.

Look Back

9. The annual sales increase from year to year, based on the data.
   Is your answer a reasonable prediction of how much in sales the
   playground and playhouse franchise will collect in the year 2012? _____

10. Plot the point (2012, 16) on the grid. Does the point fall near your
    trend line? _____

Holt Algebra 1

Name _____ Date _____ Class _____

Find these vocabulary words in Lesson 4-5 and the Multilingual Glossary.

Vocabulary			
sequence	term	arithmetic sequence	common difference

Identifying Arithmetic Sequences

Determine whether the sequence 20, 12, 4, −4, ... appears to be an arithmetic sequence. If so, find the common difference and the next three terms.

A _____ is a list of numbers that often forms a pattern. Each number

in a sequence is called a _____.

Find the difference between successive terms:

12 − 20 = ____; 4 − 12 = ____; (−4) − 4 = ____

Is the difference the same between each set of terms? _____

If so, the common difference is ____.

Use the common difference to find the next three terms.

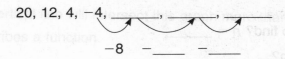

20, 12, 4, −4, _____, _____, _____

−8 − ____ − ____

Finding the nth Term of an Arithmetic Sequence

Find the 14th term of the arithmetic sequence 17, 8, −1, −10, ...

What is the common difference, d?

8 − 17 = ____

Write the rule to find the nth term:

_____

In the formula which variable represents

the first term? ____

What is a_1 in the above sequence?

____

The variable n represents the number of

term you are looking for, so $n = $ ____.

Solve for a_n.

$a_n = a_1 + (n − 1)d$

$a_n = $ ____ $+ (14 − 1)(−9)$ Substitute.

$a_n = $ ____ $+ 13(−9)$ Subtract.

$a_n = $ ____ − ____   Multiply.

$a_n = $ _____   Subtract.

The 14th term of the sequence is _____.

Holt Algebra 1

Name _____ Date _____ Class _____

Ready To Go On? Skills Intervention
5-2 Using Intercepts

Find these vocabulary words in Lesson 5-2 and the Multilingual Glossary.

Vocabulary

y-intercept   *x*-intercept

Graphing Linear Equations by Using Intercepts
Use intercepts to graph the line given by the equation $5x - 2y = 10$.

STEP 1: The *x*-intercept is the point where the line _____ the ____-axis.

The *y*-coordinate for the *x*-intercept is always ____.

Find the *x*-intercept of $5x - 2y = 10$.

$$5x - 2(\text{\_\_\_\_}) = 10 \qquad \text{Substitute } y = 0.$$

$$5x - (\text{\_\_\_\_}) = 10 \qquad \text{Multiply.}$$

$$5x = 10$$

$$x = \text{\_\_\_\_}$$

The point where $5x - 2y = 10$ crosses the *x*-axis is (____, 0).

STEP 2: The *y*-intercept is the point where the line _____ the ____-axis.

The *x*-coordinate for the *y*-intercept is always ____.

Find the *y*-intercept of $5x - 2y = 10$.

$$5(\text{\_\_\_\_}) - 2y = 10 \qquad \text{Substitute } x = 0.$$

$$(\text{\_\_\_\_}) - 2y = 10 \qquad \text{Multiply.}$$

$$-2y = 10$$

$$y = \text{\_\_\_\_}$$

The point where $5x - 2y = 10$ crosses the *y*-axis is (0, ____).

STEP 3: The *x*-intercept is (____, 0). Plot this point on the

coordinate system. The *y*-intercept is (0, ____). Plot this point

on the coordinate system. Connect these two intercepts with

a straight line.

Name _____ Date _____ Class _____

Ready to Go On? Problem Solving Intervention
5-2 Using Intercepts

The intercepts of the graph of a linear function are specific points on the line. They are the points where the line intersects each axis.

Jaime earns a monthly allowance of $50. He currently owes his mom $250 for money she let him borrow. The function $f(x) = 50x - 250$ represents Jaime's current allowance status, where x = months. Graph the function and find its intercepts. What does each intercept represent?

Understand the Problem

1. What does x represent? _____

2. What does $f(x)$ represent? _____

Make a Plan

3. Use the function $f(x) = 50x - 250$ to complete the table.

x	0	1	2	3	4	5
y	−250					0

Solve

4. Graph the ordered pairs from the table.

5. Name the ordered pair of the y-intercept. _____

6. The y-intercept represents the amount of _____

Jaime owes his _____.

7. Name the ordered pair of the x-intercept. _____

8. The x-intercept represents the number of _____ that will

pass before Jaime has paid off his mom.

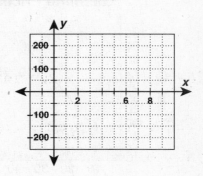

Look Back

9. To check your answer, substitute the intercepts into the function.

x-intercept: _____ y-intercept: _____

$f(\_\_\_) = 50(\_\_\_) - 250$ $f(\_\_\_) = 50(\_\_\_) - 250$

$f(\_\_\_) = \_\_\_\_ - 250$ $f(\_\_\_) = \_\_\_ - 250$

$f(\_\_\_) = \_\_\_$ $f(\_\_\_) = \_\_\_\_$

10. Do the intercepts make the function true? _____

Holt Algebra 1

SECTION 5A Ready To Go On? Skills Intervention
5-3 Slope

Finding Slope from Graphs and Tables
Find the slope of the line. Then tell what the **slope represents.**

A.

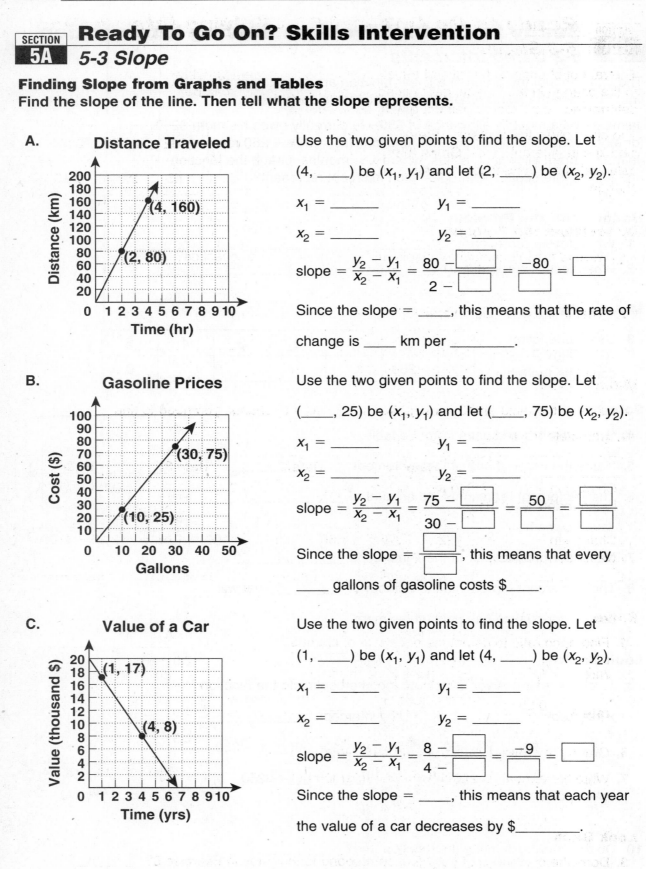

Distance Traveled

Use the two given points to find the slope. Let

(4, _____) be (x_1, y_1) and let (2, _____) be (x_2, y_2).

$x_1 = $ _____ $y_1 = $ _____

$x_2 = $ _____ $y_2 = $ _____

$\text{slope} = \dfrac{y_2 - y_1}{x_2 - x_1} = \dfrac{80 - \boxed{}}{2 - \boxed{}} = \dfrac{-80}{\boxed{}} = \boxed{}$

Since the slope = _____, this means that the rate of

change is _____ km per _____.

B.

Gasoline Prices

Use the two given points to find the slope. Let

(_____, 25) be (x_1, y_1) and let (_____, 75) be (x_2, y_2).

$x_1 = $ _____ $y_1 = $ _____

$x_2 = $ _____ $y_2 = $ _____

$\text{slope} = \dfrac{y_2 - y_1}{x_2 - x_1} = \dfrac{75 - \boxed{}}{30 - \boxed{}} = \dfrac{50}{\boxed{}} = \dfrac{\boxed{}}{\boxed{}}$

Since the slope = $\dfrac{\boxed{}}{\boxed{}}$, this means that every

_____ gallons of gasoline costs $_____.

C.

Value of a Car

Use the two given points to find the slope. Let

(1, _____) be (x_1, y_1) and let (4, _____) be (x_2, y_2).

$x_1 = $ _____ $y_1 = $ _____

$x_2 = $ _____ $y_2 = $ _____

$\text{slope} = \dfrac{y_2 - y_1}{x_2 - x_1} = \dfrac{8 - \boxed{}}{4 - \boxed{}} = \dfrac{-9}{\boxed{}} = \boxed{}$

Since the slope = _____, this means that each year

the value of a car decreases by $_____.

Holt Algebra 1

Ready to Go On? Problem Solving Intervention

SECTION 5A *5-3 Slope*

The rate of change is the ratio of the change in the dependent variable to the change in the independent variable. The rate of change can be determined from ordered pairs, a graph, or an equation.

The chart gives the average price of gasoline in different years. Graph this data and show the annual rates of change.

Year	2000	2001	2002	2003	2004
Cost ($)	1.20	1.50	1.65	2.00	2.15

Understand the Problem

1. What is the independent variable, the year or the cost of gasoline?

   _____

2. What is the dependent variable, the year or the cost of gasoline?

   _____

Make a Plan

3. Look at the table and determine how many rates of change you need to find. _____

4. Complete the table:

	Rate 1	**Rate 2**	**Rate 3**	**Rate 4**
Change in Independent Variable	2001 − 2000 = _____	2002 − 2001 = _____	2003 − 2002 = _____	2004 − 2003 = _____
Change in Dependent Variable	1.50 − 1.20 = _____	1.65 − 1.50 = _____	2.00 − 1.65 = _____	2.15 − 2.00 = _____

Solve

5. Find each ratio to determine each rate of change:

   rate 1 $= \dfrac{0.3}{1} =$ _____   **rate 2** $= \dfrac{\boxed{}}{1} =$ _____

   rate 3 $= \dfrac{0.35}{\boxed{}} =$ _____   **rate 4** $= \dfrac{\boxed{}}{1} =$ _____

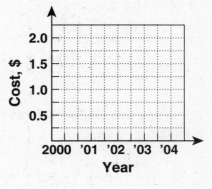

6. Graph the ordered pairs from the data table.

7. Write the annual rate of change on the graph between each point.

Look Back

8. Does the steepness of each line correspond to the rates in Exercise 5? _____

Holt Algebra 1

Name _____ Date _____ Class _____

Find these vocabulary words in Lesson 5-4 and the Multilingual Glossary.

Vocabulary	
direct variation	constant of variation

Identifying Direct Variations from Ordered Pairs

Tell whether the relationship is a direct variation. If so, identify the constant of variation.

x	3	5	7	9
y	12	20	28	36

Find $\frac{y}{x}$ for each ordered pair.

(3, 12): $\frac{y}{x} = \frac{12}{3} =$ ☐

(5, 20): $\frac{y}{x} = \frac{20}{5} =$ ☐

(7, 28): $\frac{y}{x} = \frac{\Box}{\Box} =$ ☐

(9, 36): $\frac{y}{x} = \frac{\Box}{\Box} =$ ☐

Is $\frac{y}{x}$ the same for each ordered pair? _____

So, this is an example of a _____.

Writing and Solving Direct Variation Equations

The value of y varies directly with x, and y = 8 when x = 10.
Find y when x = 24.

Since y varies directly with x, you can use the formula y = ____x.

It is given that y = 8 when x = ____.

Substitute these values into the direct variation formula: 8 = k(____)

STEP 1: Solve for k.

8 = 10k

$\dfrac{8}{\Box} = \dfrac{10}{\Box}k$

$\dfrac{4}{\Box} = k$

Substitute this value for k into the equation y = kx.

$y = \dfrac{\Box}{\Box}x$

STEP 2: Find y when x = 24.

Substitute 24 in for x and solve for y.

$y = \dfrac{\Box}{\Box}x$

$y = \dfrac{4}{5}(\underline{})$

$y = \dfrac{(\Box)}{5}$

$y = $ _____

STEP 3: Complete: When x = 24, y = _____.

Holt Algebra 1

SECTION 5B

Ready To Go On? Skills Intervention
5-5 Slope-Intercept Form

Graphing by Using Slope and *y*-intercept.
Graph the line given a slope of $\frac{2}{5}$ and *y*-intercept of −2.

STEP 1: The *y*-intercept is ____, so the line contains the point

(____, −2).

Plot the *y*-intercept: (____, −2)

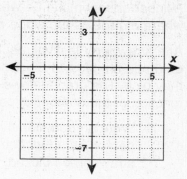

STEP 2: Slope $= \dfrac{\text{change in } y}{\text{change in } x} = \dfrac{2}{5}$

Count ____ units up and ____ units right from (0, −2)

and plot another point.

STEP 3: Connect these two points with a straight line.

Writing Linear Equations in Slope-Intercept Form
Write the equation, −2*x* + *y* = 1, in slope-intercept form, and then graph.

To write an equation in slope-intercept form, isolate the variable, _____.

−2*x* + *y* = 1

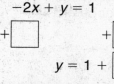   Add 2*x* to both sides.

$y = 1 + \boxed{}$ Solve for *y*.

Determine the slope and *y*-intercept. Remember that *y* = *mx* + *b*.

m = _____   *b* = _____

STEP 1: The *y*-intercept is ____, so the line contains the point

(____, 1).

Plot the *y*-intercept: (____, 1)

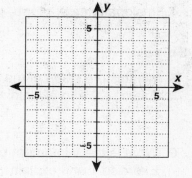

STEP 2: Slope $= \dfrac{\text{change in } y}{\text{change in } x} = \dfrac{2}{1}$

Count ____ units up and ____ unit right from (0, 1) and plot another point.

STEP 3: Connect these two points with a straight line.

Holt Algebra 1

SECTION 5B Ready to Go On? Problem Solving Intervention
5-5 Slope-Intercept Form

A linear equation can be written in slope-intercept form, $y = mx + b$, where m repeats the slope and b repeats the y-intercept.

At a strawberry festival, each person is charged a $4.00 entrance fee plus $1.50 per pound for the strawberries that they pick. The graph shows the total cost per person as a function of the number of pounds of strawberries picked.

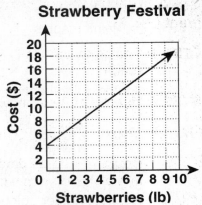

Strawberry Festival

a. Write an equation that represents the total cost per person as a function of the number of pounds of strawberries picked.

b. Identify the slope and the y-intercept and describe the meaning of each in this situation.

Understand the Problem

1. How much does it cost to enter the strawberry festival? _____

2. How much does each pound of strawberries cost? _____

Make a Plan

3. Let y represent the total cost and x represent the number of pounds of strawberries. Complete the equation: Cost is equal to $4.00 entrance fee plus $1.50 per pound.

    _____ = _____ + 1.5 · _____

4. In slope-intercept form, $y = mx + b$, $m =$ _____ and $b =$ _____ .

Solve

5. What is the slope of the equation in Exercise 3? _____ Use Exercise 2 and explain what the slope of this equation means.

    _____

6. What is the y-intercept of the equation in Exercise 3? _____ Use Exercise 1 and explain what the y-intercept of this equation means.

    _____

Look Back

7. Substitute 0 in for x into the equation from Exercise 3.

    $y = 4 + 1.5(\boxed{}) \longrightarrow y = \boxed{}$

    Is the result the same as the y-intercept? _____

Holt Algebra 1

Name _____ Date _____ Class _____

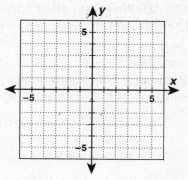

SECTION 5B — Ready To Go On? Skills Intervention
5-6 Point-Slope Form

Using Slope and a Point to Graph
Graph the line with a slope of −3 that contains the point (−2, 4).

STEP 1: The given point is (____, 4). Plot this point on the graph.

STEP 2: Use the slope to move from (____, 4) to another point.

Slope = $\dfrac{\text{change in } y}{\text{change in } x} = \dfrac{-3}{1}$

Count ____ units down and ____ unit right from (−2, 4) and plot another point.

STEP 3: Connect these two points with a straight line.

Using Two Points to Write an Equation
Write an equation in slope-intercept form for the line that passes through the points (−6, −6) and (2, 10).

To write an equation in slope-intercept form you need to know the value of

the _____ and the *y*-intercept.

STEP 1: Find the slope. Let (−6, ____) be (x_1, y_1) and let (2, ____) be (x_2, y_2).

Slope = $m = \dfrac{y_2 - y_1}{x_2 - x_1} = \dfrac{10 - (\boxed{})}{\boxed{} - (-6)} = \dfrac{\boxed{}}{8} = \boxed{}$

STEP 2: Choose one of the points (−6, −6) or (2, 10). If you do not want

to use negative coordinates, choose the point (____, ____).

Substitute this point for (x_1, y_1) and the slope from **STEP 1** into

the point-slope formula: $y - \boxed{} = \boxed{}(x - x_1)$.

$m = $ ____ $x_1 = \boxed{}$ $y_1 = 10$

$y - 10 = \boxed{}(x - \boxed{})$

STEP 3: Solve this equation for *y* to write $y - 10 = \boxed{}(x - \boxed{})$
it in slope-intercept form.

$y - 10 = 2x - \boxed{}$

$ + 10 \qquad + 10$

$y = 2x + \boxed{}$

Holt Algebra 1

Ready To Go On? Skills Intervention

SECTION 5B

5-7 Slopes of Parallel and Perpendicular Lines

Identifying Parallel Lines
Identify which lines are parallel.

$y = -\frac{1}{2}x$; $y = \frac{1}{2}x + 3$;

$y = \frac{1}{2}x$; $y - 5 = \frac{1}{2}(x + 8)$

Complete the table.

Equation	Slope = m	y-intercept = b
$y = -\frac{1}{2}x$		
$y = \frac{1}{2}x + 3$		
$y = \frac{1}{2}x$		
$y - 5 = \frac{1}{2}(x + 8)$ $y - 5 = \frac{1}{2}x + \boxed{}$ $y = \frac{1}{2}x + \boxed{}$		

Parallel lines have the _____ slope.

How many equations have the same slope but different y-intercepts?

_____

Which equations are parallel?

_____

Identifying Perpendicular Lines
Identify which lines are perpendicular.

$y = -5x - 1$; $y = \frac{1}{5}x$; $y = 5x - 9$; $x = -5$

Complete the table.

Equation	Slope = m	y-intercept = b
$y = -5x - 1$		
$y = \frac{1}{5}x$		
$y = 5x - 9$		
$x = -5$		

The product of the slopes of

perpendicular lines is _____.

What is the product of -5 and $\frac{1}{5}$?

_____

What is the product of 5 and $\frac{1}{5}$?

_____

The slopes of which two equations have a product of -1?

_____

So, which two equations are perpendicular?

_____

Holt Algebra 1

Name _____ Date _____ Class _____

Ready to Go On? Skills Intervention
6-1 Solving Systems by Graphing

Find these vocabulary words in Lesson 6-1 and the Multilingual Glossary.

> **Vocabulary**
>
> systems of linear equations   solution of a system of linear equations

Identifying Solutions of Systems

Tell whether the ordered pair is a solution of the given system.

$(3, -2) \begin{cases} 2x + y = 4 \\ x + y = 1 \end{cases}$

Substitute ____ for x and ____ for y.

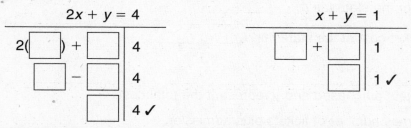

The ordered pair $(3, -2)$ makes both equations true, so $(3, -2)$ is a

_____ of the system.

Solving a System of Linear Equations by Graphing

Solve the system $\begin{cases} y = -\frac{1}{2}x + 2 \\ 2x + y = -1 \end{cases}$ **by graphing. Check your answer.**

Rewrite the second equation in slope-intercept form by adding $-2x$ to both sides of the equation.

$y = -2x - 1$

Graph the system. The solution appears to be at $(-2, 3)$.

Check your answer.

Substitute ____ for x and ____ for y.

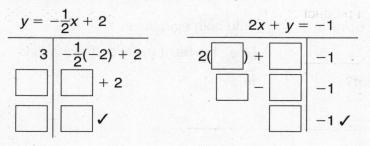

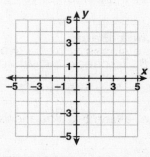

The solution is $(-2, 3)$.

Holt Algebra 1

Ready to Go On? Problem Solving Intervention

SECTION 6A *6-1 Solving Systems by Graphing*

The solution to a system of linear equations is the point where the graphs of the two lines intersect.

The local county fair charges $7.00 admission and $0.50 per ticket to ride the rides. The state fair charges $5.00 admission and $1.50 per ticket to ride the rides. For how many tickets will the total cost be the same at both fairs? What is that cost?

Understand the Problem

1. How much is the admission for the local county fair? _____

   How much does each ride ticket cost at the local county fair? _____

2. How much is the admission for the state fair? _____

   How much does each ride ticket cost at the state fair? _____

Make a Plan

Let *x* represent the number of tickets purchased and *y* represent the total cost.

   Total cost is price per ticket times number of tickets plus admission

3. Equation for local county fair: $\boxed{} = \boxed{} x + 7$

4. Equation for state fair: $\boxed{} = \boxed{} x + 5$

Solve

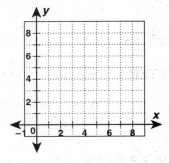

5. Graph the system of equations $\begin{cases} \boxed{} = \boxed{} x + 7 \\ \boxed{} = \boxed{} x + 5 \end{cases}$

6. What is the ordered pair where the two lines intersect?

   _____

7. If a person buys _____ tickets, the cost at both fairs is the same: _____.

Look Back

8. To check, substitute the intersection point, _____, into both equations.

   $y = 0.5x + 7$ $y = 1.5x + 5$ Does the point make both equations

   ____ = 0.5(____) + 7   ____ = 1.5(____) + 5   true? _____

   ____ = ____   ____ = ____

Holt Algebra 1

SECTION 6A Ready To Go On? Skills Intervention
6-2 Solving Systems by Substitution

Solving a System of Linear Equations by Substitution
Solve each system by substitution.

A. $\begin{cases} y = -x + 3 \\ y = \frac{2}{3}x - 2 \end{cases}$

STEP 1 Substitute $-x + 3$ for ____ in the second equation and solve for x.

STEP 2

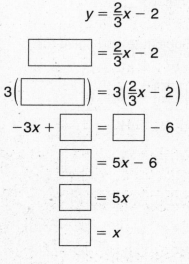

$$y = \frac{2}{3}x - 2$$

$$\boxed{} = \frac{2}{3}x - 2$$

$$3\left(\boxed{}\right) = 3\left(\frac{2}{3}x - 2\right)$$

$$-3x + \boxed{} = \boxed{} - 6$$

$$\boxed{} = 5x - 6$$

$$\boxed{} = 5x$$

$$\boxed{} = x$$

STEP 3 Solve for the other variable, y.

You know from Step 2 that $x = \boxed{}$.

$$y = -x + 3$$

$$y = -\left(\boxed{}\right) + 3$$

$$y = \boxed{}$$

The solution to the system of equations

is (____, 0).

B. $\begin{cases} x + y = 4 \\ x + 2y = -2 \end{cases}$

STEP 1 Solve the equation $x + y = 4$ for x.

$$x + y = 4$$

$$x = 4 - \boxed{}$$

STEP 2 Substitute $4 - y$ for ____ in the second equation.

$$x + 2y = -2$$

$$\boxed{} + 2y = -2$$

STEP 3 Solve for ____.

$$4 - y + 2y = -2$$

$$4 + \boxed{} = -2$$

$$y = \boxed{}$$

STEP 4 Solve for the other variable, x.

$$x + y = 4$$

$$x + \boxed{} = 4$$

$$x = \boxed{}$$

The solution to the system is (10, 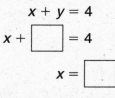).

Holt Algebra 1

SECTION 6A **Ready To Go On? Skills Intervention**

6-3 Solving Systems by Elimination

Elimination using Addition

Solve $\begin{cases} x + 4y = 16 \\ 5x - 4y = 8 \end{cases}$ by elimination.

STEP 1 Combine the two equations by addition.

$$x + 4y = 16$$
$$5x - 4y = 8$$

$\boxed{} + \boxed{} = 24$ Which variable is eliminated? ____

STEP 2 Solve for ____.

$$6x = 24$$

$$\frac{6x}{\boxed{}} = \frac{24}{\boxed{}}$$

$$x = \boxed{}$$

STEP 3 Substitute and solve for ____.

$$x + 4y = 16$$

$$\boxed{} + 4y = 16$$

$$4y = \boxed{}$$

$$y = \boxed{}$$

STEP 4 The solution to the system is (4, ____).

Elimination using Multiplication First

Solve $\begin{cases} 3x - y = 4 \\ x + 4y = 10 \end{cases}$ by elimination.

STEP 1 To eliminate *y*, multiply the

first equation by ____.

$4(3x - y) = 4(4)$ → $\boxed{}x - \boxed{}y = \boxed{}$

$x + 4y = 10$ → $x + 4y = 10$

STEP 2 Combine the two equations using _____.

$\boxed{}x - \boxed{}y = \boxed{}$

$x + 4y = 10$

$\boxed{}x + \boxed{} = 26$

STEP 3 Solve for *x*.

$$13x = 26$$

$$\frac{\boxed{}x}{\boxed{}} = \frac{26}{\boxed{}}$$

$$x = \boxed{}$$

STEP 4 Substitute and solve for *y*.

$$x + 4y = 10$$

$$\boxed{} + 4y = 10$$

$$4y = \boxed{}$$

$$y = \boxed{}$$

STEP 5 The solution to the system of equations is (2, ____).

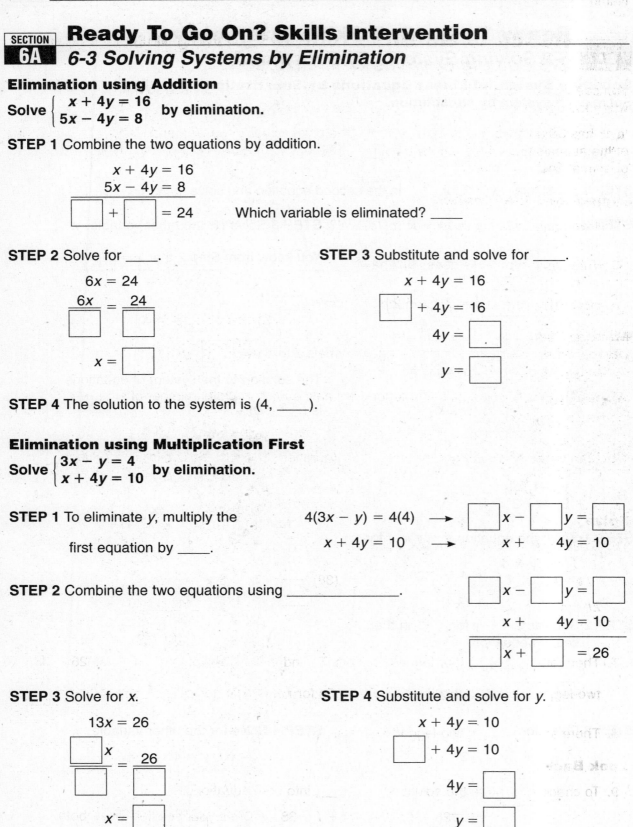

Holt Algebra 1

Name _____ Date _____ Class _____

Ready to Go On? Problem Solving Intervention

6-3 Solving Systems by Elimination

You can multiply one or both of the equations in a system by a number so that when the equations are combined, one of the variables is eliminated.

Jack has 38 animals on his farm. Some of the animals have two legs and some of the animals have 4 legs. If Jack counted 128 legs total, how many of each type of animal does he have?

Understand the Problem

1. How many animals does Jack have total? _____

2. What type of animals does Jack have? _____

3. How many legs did Jack count on his farm? _____

Make a Plan

Let t represent the number of two-legged animals and f represent the number of four-legged animals.

4. Two-legged animals plus four-legged animals equals the total number of animals.

$$t \quad + \quad \text{_____} \quad = \quad \text{_____}$$

5. (2)(number of two-legged animals) + (4)(number of 4-legged animals) = Total legs

$$2(t) \quad + \quad 4(\text{_____}) \quad = \quad \text{_____}$$

Solve

6. To eliminate t multiply the first equation by _____.

$$t + f = 38 \longrightarrow \boxed{}(t + f) = \boxed{}(38) \longrightarrow \boxed{}t + \boxed{}f = \boxed{}$$
$$2t + 4f = 128 \longrightarrow 2t + 4f = 128 \longrightarrow \underline{\quad 2t + \quad 4f = 128 \quad}$$
$$2f = 52$$
$$f = 26$$

7. There are _____ four-legged animals. To find the number of two-legged animals, substitute _____ in for f and solve for t.

$$t + 26 = 38$$
$$t = \boxed{}$$

8. There are _____ two-legged animals.

Look Back

9. To check, substitute the solution, _____, into both equations.

$$2t + 4f = 128 \qquad t + f = 38 \qquad \text{Does your solution make both}$$
$$2(\text{\_\_\_}) + 4(\text{\_\_\_}) = 128 \qquad \text{\_\_\_} + \text{\_\_\_} = 38 \qquad \text{equations true? _____}$$
$$\text{\_\_\_\_\_} = 128 \qquad \text{\_\_\_\_\_} = 38$$

Holt Algebra 1

Name _____ Date _____ Class _____

Ready To Go On? Skills Intervention
6-4 Solving Special Systems

Find these vocabulary words in Lesson 6-4 and the Multilingual Glossary.

Vocabulary			
inconsistent system	consistent system	independent system	dependent system

Systems with No Solution

Solve $\begin{cases} y = 4x - 3 \\ -4x + y = 8 \end{cases}$.

Consider $y = 4x - 3$.

What is the slope of this equation?

_____

What is the y-intercept of this equation?

$(0, \underline{\hspace{1cm}})$

Consider $-4x + y = 8$.
Solve the equation for y.
$-4x + y = 8$
$y = \boxed{} + 8$

What is the slope of this equation? _____

What is the y-intercept of this equation? $(0, \underline{\hspace{1cm}})$

The slopes of both equations are _____. The y-intercepts of the equations are

_____. The lines are _____ so the lines do not _____. Therefore

there is no _____.

Classifying Systems of Linear Equations

Classify the system $\begin{cases} y = -\dfrac{1}{3}x + 6 \\ x + 3y = 18 \end{cases}$. **Give the number of solutions.**

Consider $y = -\dfrac{1}{3}x + 6$.

What is the slope of this equation? _____

What is the y-intercept of this equation?

$(0, \underline{\hspace{1cm}})$

Consider $x + 3y = 18$.

To identify the slope and y-intercept solve the

equation for _____.

$$x + 3y = 18$$
$$3y = 18 - \boxed{}$$
$$\frac{3y}{\boxed{}} = \frac{18 - \boxed{}}{\boxed{}}$$
$$y = \boxed{} - \frac{1}{3}x$$

What is the slope of this equation? _____

What is the y-intercept of this equation? $(0, \underline{\hspace{1cm}})$

The slopes of both equations are _____. The y-intercepts of equations are

_____. Since the lines overlap this system has _____ many solutions.

This system is called _____ and _____.

Holt Algebra 1

SECTION 6A · Ready To Go On? Skills Intervention

6-5 Applying Systems

Writing Systems of Linear Equations

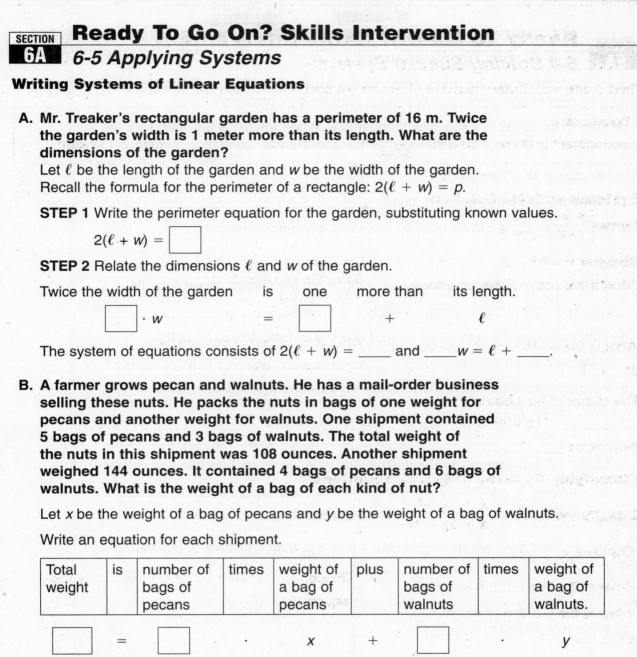

A. Mr. Treaker's rectangular garden has a perimeter of 16 m. Twice the garden's width is 1 meter more than its length. What are the dimensions of the garden?

Let ℓ be the length of the garden and w be the width of the garden.
Recall the formula for the perimeter of a rectangle: $2(\ell + w) = p$.

STEP 1 Write the perimeter equation for the garden, substituting known values.

$2(\ell + w) = \boxed{}$

STEP 2 Relate the dimensions ℓ and w of the garden.

Twice the width of the garden	is	one	more than	its length.
$\boxed{} \cdot w$	$=$	$\boxed{}$	$+$	ℓ

The system of equations consists of $2(\ell + w) = $ _____ and _____ $w = \ell + $ _____.

B. A farmer grows pecan and walnuts. He has a mail-order business selling these nuts. He packs the nuts in bags of one weight for pecans and another weight for walnuts. One shipment contained 5 bags of pecans and 3 bags of walnuts. The total weight of the nuts in this shipment was 108 ounces. Another shipment weighed 144 ounces. It contained 4 bags of pecans and 6 bags of walnuts. What is the weight of a bag of each kind of nut?

Let x be the weight of a bag of pecans and y be the weight of a bag of walnuts.

Write an equation for each shipment.

Total weight	is	number of bags of pecans	times	weight of a bag of pecans	plus	number of bags of walnuts	times	weight of a bag of walnuts.
$\boxed{}$	$=$	$\boxed{}$	$\cdot$	x	$+$	$\boxed{}$	$\cdot$	y
$\boxed{}$	$=$	$\boxed{}$	$\cdot$	x	$+$	$\boxed{}$	$\cdot$	y

The system of equations consists of _____ = _____ $x + $ _____ y and

_____ = _____ $x + $ _____ y.

Holt Algebra 1

SECTION 6A Ready To Go On? Problem-Solving Intervention
6-5 Applying Systems

A two-digit number can be represented by the expression $10t + u$. Using this idea and a system of equations, you can solve number-digit problems.

The sum of the digits of a two-digit number is 8. When the digits are reversed, the new number is 18 more than the original number. What is the original number?

Understand the Problem

1. What are you being asked to find? _____

2. What expression can be used to represent a two-digit number? _____

Make a Plan

3. If $10t + u$ represents the original number, what expression represents the

   new two-digit number when the digits are reversed? _____

4. You know that the sum of the digits t and u is 8. How do you write this

   statement as an equation? _____

5. What do you know about the relationship between the original number and
   the new number?

   _____

6. Using the expressions for the original and new numbers, how can you restate

   your answer to Exercise 5 as an equation? _____

Solve

Use the equations you wrote in Exercise 4 and 6 to form a system of equations.
Solve for t and u.

$t =$ _____ and $u =$ _____

7. What is the original number? _____

Check

8. As stated in the problem, the sum of the digits is ____ + ____ = ____. ✓

9. When the digits are reversed, the new number is _____.

10. Is your answer to Exercise 9 a number that is 18 more than the original number?

    _____ ✓

Holt Algebra 1

Name _____ Date _____ Class _____

Ready To Go On? Skills Intervention

SECTION 6B *6-6 Solving Linear Inequalities*

Find these vocabulary words in Lesson 6-6 and the Multilingual Glossary.

Vocabulary

linear inequality   solution of a linear inequality

Identifying Solutions of Inequalities

Tell whether the ordered pair, (−4, −2), is a solution of the inequality, $y \le -3x + 6$.

To be a solution to the inequality, the ordered pair must make the inequality _____.

Substitute the ordered pair (−4, −2) into the inequality. Let $x =$ _____ and $y =$ _____.
$y \le -3x + 6$

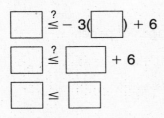

Does the ordered pair (−4, −2) make the inequality true? _____

Therefore the ordered pair (−4, −2) _____ a solution to the inequality $y \le -3x + 6$.

Graphing Linear Inequalities in Two Variables

Graph the solutions of the linear inequality, $y > -2x - 3$.

The inequality, $y > -2x - 3$, is in _____ form.

The _____ line is given by the equation y _____ $-2x - 3$.

The slope of this line is _____. The y-intercept of this line is (0, _____).

Use the slope and y-intercept to plot the boundary line.

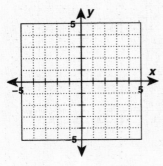

Start at the point (0, _____) and go up _____ units and left _____ unit. Plot the point.

Make the boundary line a _____ line because the inequality symbol is not "or equal to."

The inequality symbol is _____, so should the solutions be located in the half-plane above or below the line? _____ Shade this region to represent the solutions.

Check: Choose the point (0, 0) and substitute it into the inequality.

$y > -2x - 3 \longrightarrow 0 > -2(0) - 3 \longrightarrow 0 > -3$

Does the point make the inequality true? _____ Did you shade correctly? _____

Holt Algebra 1

SECTION 6B

Ready to Go On? Problem Solving Intervention

6-6 Solving Linear Inequalities

A solution to a linear equality lies in a half-plane with other ordered pairs that make the inequality true.

Janel has $10 to buy pencils and paper. Pencils sell for $1.50 per dozen and paper sells for $0.50 per package. Write a linear inequality to represent the situation. Then graph the linear inequality and give two possible combinations of pencils and paper that Janel can buy.

Understand the Problem

1. How much money does Janel have? _____

2. A dozen pencils cost _____ and a package of paper cost _____.

Make a Plan

Let *x* represent the dozens of pencils and *y* represent the number of packages of paper.

3. (1.50)(dozens of pencils) + (0.50)(packages of paper) ≤ $10

   _____ · *x*   +   (0.50) · _____   ≤ _____

4. Write the inequality in slope-intercept form:

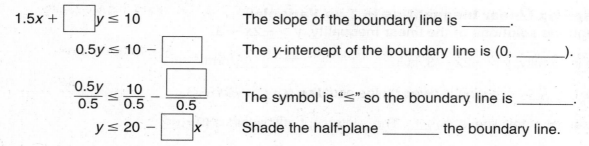

   $1.5x + \boxed{}y \le 10$ The slope of the boundary line is _____.

   $0.5y \le 10 - \boxed{}$ The *y*-intercept of the boundary line is (0, _____).

   $\dfrac{0.5y}{0.5} \le \dfrac{10}{0.5} - \dfrac{\boxed{}}{0.5}$ The symbol is "≤" so the boundary line is _____.

   $y \le 20 - \boxed{}x$ Shade the half-plane _____ the boundary line.

Solve

5. Graph the inequality and shade the correct half-plane.

6. Choose two combinations: (2, ____) and (____, 5).

Look Back

7. Substitute your combinations into the inequality from Exercise 3.

   $y \le 20 - 3x$ $y \le 20 - 3x$

   ____ ≤ 20 − 3(____)   ____ ≤ 20 − 3(____)

   ____ ≤ ____   ____ ≤ ____

   So Janel can buy 2 dozen pencils and _____ packages of paper or 1 dozen pencils and

   _____ packages of paper.

Holt Algebra 1

Ready To Go On? Skills Intervention

SECTION 6B — 6-7 *Solving Systems of Linear Inequalities*

Find these vocabulary words in Lesson 6-7 and the Multilingual Glossary.

Vocabulary

system of linear inequalities   solution of a system of linear inequalities

---

Identifying Solutions of Systems of Linear Inequalities

Tell whether the ordered pair (−3, 1) is a solution of the system, $\begin{cases} y < -x + 3 \\ y \geq x - 2 \end{cases}$.

To be a solution to the system of inequalities, the ordered pair (−3, 1) has to make

both inequalities _____. Let $x =$ _____ and let $y =$ _____.

Substitute $x = -3$ and $y = 1$ into $y < -x + 3$.	Substitute $x = -3$ and $y = 1$ into $y \geq x - 2$.
_____ < _____ + 3	_____ ≥ _____ − 2
_____ < _____ + 3	_____ ≥ _____
_____ < _____	
The point (−3, 1) makes this inequality _____.	The point (−3, 1) makes this inequality _____.

Since the point (−3, 1) makes both inequalities _____, it is a _____ to the system.

Solving a System of Linear Inequalities by Graphing

Graph the system of inequalities $\begin{cases} y > -x + 3 \\ y \leq 2x \end{cases}$. **Give two ordered**

pairs that are solutions and two that are not solutions.

$y > -x + 3$ The y-intercept is (0, _____)

and the slope = _____. Use this information

to draw a _____ line. Because the symbol

is _____ than, shade the half-plane

_____ the line.

$y \leq 2x$ The

y-intercept is (0, _____)

and the slope = _____. Use this

information to draw a _____ line. Because

the symbol is _____ than or equal to,

shade the half-plane _____ the line.

Look at the graph. Are (2, 3) and (4, 1) solutions? _____

Are (0, 0) and (1, −1) solutions? _____

Did you shade the graph correctly? _____

Holt Algebra 1

SECTION 6B — Ready to Go On? Problem Solving Intervention
6-7 Solving Systems of Linear Inequalities

The solutions to a system of linear inequalities are located in the intersection of the half-planes.

As a fundraiser, the chess club sells hotdogs and hamburgers. They make $1 for every hotdog and $2 for every hamburger they sell. The club cannot sell more than 100 hotdogs or 200 hamburgers. The club's goal is to make at least $200 in total profit. Show and describe possible combinations of hotdogs and hamburgers that can be sold to meet the goal.

Understand the Problem

1. How much does the club earn from each hotdog? _____ Each hamburger? _____

2. How many hotdogs do they have to sell? _____ Hamburgers? _____

3. How many inequalities need to be written? _____

Make a Plan

Let x represent the number of hotdogs and y represent the number of hamburgers.

4.

The club cannot sell more than 100 hotdogs.	The club cannot sell more than 200 hamburgers.	Profit from hotdogs + Profit from hamburgers ≥ 200
$x \leq$ _____	$y \leq$ _____	$1x +$ [___]$y \geq$ [___]

5. Graph each inequality on the coordinate system.

Inequality	Boundary Line	Dashed or Solid Line	Shaded Region
$x \leq$ _____	Vertical line at $x =$ _____	_____ line	Shade to the _____ of the line.
$y \leq$ _____	Horizontal line at $y =$ _____	_____ line	Shade _____ the line.
$1x +$ [___]$y \geq$ [___]	x-intercept: (200, 0) y-intercept: (0, 100)	_____ line	Shade above the line.

Solve

6. Graph each inequality and shade the correct half-planes.

7. Are the points (50, 100), (75, 150), and (80, 175) located in

   the intersection of all three regions? _____

Look Back

8. Check that the x-coordinates of each point are less than 100 and that the y-coordinates

   are less than 200. Does each point make the inequality $x + 2y \geq 200$ true? _____

Holt Algebra 1

Name _____ Date _____ Class _____

Ready To Go On? Skills Intervention
7-1 Integer Exponents

Evaluating Expressions with Zero and Negative Exponents

Zero Exponent: Any nonzero number raised to the zero power is ____.

$4^0 =$ ____

Negative Exponent: A nonzero number raised to a negative exponent is

equal to one divided by that number raised to the _____ exponent.

$3^{-4} = \dfrac{1}{3^{\square}}$

Evaluate each expression for the given value(s) of the variable(s).

A. $a^{-3}b^2$ for $a = 2$ and $b = 3$

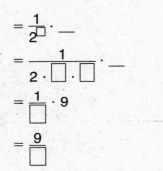

____$^{-3} \cdot 3^{\square}$ Substitute ___ for a and ___ for b.

$= \dfrac{1}{2^{\square}} \cdot$ ____ Use the definition $x^{-n} = \dfrac{1}{x^n}$ and simplify.

$= \dfrac{1}{2 \cdot \square \cdot \square} \cdot$ ____ Write the power in the denominator as a product.

$= \dfrac{1}{\square} \cdot 9$ Evaluate the power in the denominator.

$= \dfrac{9}{\square}$ Simplify.

B. $x^0 y^{-3}$ for $x = 7$ and $y = -5$

____$^0 \cdot (-5)^{\square}$ Substitute ____ for x and ____ for y.

$= $ ____ $\cdot \dfrac{1}{(-5)^{\square}}$ Any nonzero number raised to the zero power is ____ and $x^{-n} = \dfrac{1}{x^n}$.

$= 1 \cdot \dfrac{1}{\boxed{}}$ Evaluate the power.

$= \dfrac{\boxed{}}{}$ Simplify.

Simplifying Expressions with Zero and Negative Exponents

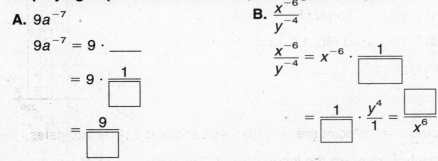

A. $9a^{-7}$

$9a^{-7} = 9 \cdot$ ____

$= 9 \cdot \dfrac{1}{\boxed{}}$

$= \dfrac{9}{\boxed{}}$

B. $\dfrac{x^{-6}}{y^{-4}}$

$\dfrac{x^{-6}}{y^{-4}} = x^{-6} \cdot \dfrac{1}{\boxed{}}$

$= \dfrac{1}{\boxed{}} \cdot \dfrac{y^4}{1} = \dfrac{\boxed{}}{x^6}$

Holt Algebra 1

Ready To Go On? Skills Intervention

SECTION 7A

7-2 Powers of 10 and Scientific Notation

Find this vocabulary word in Lesson 7-2 and the
Multilingual Glossary.

Vocabulary
scientific notation

Positive Integer Exponent: If n is a positive integer, find the
value of 10^n by starting with 1 and moving the decimal point
_____ places to the right.

Negative Integer Exponent: If n is a negative integer, find the value
of 10^n by starting with 1 and moving the decimal point _____ places to
the left.

Evaluating Powers of 10

Find the value of 10^7.

Is the exponent positive or negative? _____

Start with _____ and move the decimal point _____ places to the _____.

100 ‿‿‿‿‿   So, 10^7 = _____.

Writing Powers of 10

Write each number as a power of 10.

A. 0.00001

0.00001   The decimal point is _____ places to the _____ of 1, so

should the exponent be positive or negative? _____

$0.00001 = 10^{—}$

B. 10,000,000,000

1 0 0 0 0 0 0 0 0 0 0.   The decimal point is _____ places to the _____ of 1, so

should the exponent be positive or negative? _____

$10{,}000{,}000{,}000 = 10^{—}$

Multiplying Powers of 10

Find the value of 16.3×10^6.

Move the decimal point _____ places to the _____.

16 3 0 0 0 0 0. = _____

Holt Algebra 1

SECTION 7A Ready To Go On? Skills Intervention
7-3 Multiplication Properties of Exponents

Finding Product of Powers

Product of Powers Property: The product of two powers with the same base equals

that base raised to the _____ of the exponents. For example $5^4 \cdot 5^2 = 5^{4+2}$.

Simplify.

A. $2^7 \cdot 2^3$ What is the base of each expression? _____

   $2^7 \cdot 2^3 = 2^{—} + 3 = 2^{—}$ Add the exponents.

B. $a^4 \cdot a^{-3} \cdot a^2$ Are the bases the same? _____ So, _____ the exponents.

   $a^{4-3+—} = a^{—}$

Finding Powers of Powers

Power of a Power Property: A power raised to another power equals that base

raised to the _____ of the exponents. For example $(4^3)^5 = 4^{3 \cdot 5} = 4^{15}$.

Power of a Product Property: A product raised to a power equals the _____ of

each factor raised to that _____. For example $(2^2 y^3)^4 = (2^2)^4 (y^3)^4 = 2^8 y^{12}$.

Simplify.

A. $(2x^3)^4$

   $(2)^4 \cdot (\underline{\quad})^4$ Use the Power of a Product Property.

   $16 \cdot x^{3 \cdot —}$ When you raise a power to another power, _____ exponents.

   $16 \cdot x^{—}$ Simplify.

B. $(-5a^3)^2$

   $(\underline{\quad})^2 \cdot (a^3)^{—}$ Use the Power of a Product Property.

   $\underline{\quad\quad} \cdot (a^{3 \cdot —})$ Simplify.

   $25a^{—}$

C. $(ab^2)^3 \cdot (a^4 b^2)^2$

   $a^3 b^{—} \cdot a^{4 \cdot 2} b^{—}$ Use the Power of a Product Property.

   $a^3 b^{—} \cdot a^8 b^{—}$ Simplify.

   $a^{3+8} b^{——}$ Use the Product of Powers Property.

   $a^{11} b^{—}$ Simplify.

Holt Algebra 1

SECTION 7A Ready to Go On? Problem Solving Intervention
7-3 Multiplication Properties of Exponents

A number written in scientific notation has two parts that are multiplied. The first part is a number that is greater than or equal to 1 and less than 10. The second part is a power of 10.

Light travels at a speed of 3.0×10^8 meters per second. If light travels for 4.5 seconds, how far does it travel? Write your answer in scientific notation and in standard form.

Understand the Problem

1. What number(s) are given in scientific notation? _____

2. What number(s) are given in standard form? _____

3. What are you being asked to find? _____

Make a Plan

4. What operation must be used to solve the problem? _____

5. Write the multiplication expression. $4.5 \cdot (3.0 \times$ ____$)$

Solve

6. What is the product of the expression? $(4.5)(3.0) \times 10^8 =$ _____ $\times 10^8$

7. What units should your answer have? _____

8. Is the answer 13.5×10^8 written in scientific notation? _____

   a. How many places does the decimal point need to be moved? _____

   b. In what direction does the decimal point need to be moved? _____

   c. Write the answer in scientific notation. _____ $\times 10^9$

9. Write the answer in standard form.

   a. How many places does the decimal point need to be moved? _____

   b. In what direction does the decimal point need to be moved? _____

   c. Write the answer in standard form. _____ meters

Look Back

10. Estimate your answer to see if it is correct.

    What does 4.5 round to? _____

    What is $(5 \cdot 3) \times 10^8$? _____

11. Is your estimate close to your numeric answers in Exercises 8c and 9c? _____

Holt Algebra 1

Ready To Go On? Skills Intervention
7-4 Division Properties of Exponents

Finding Quotients of Powers

Quotient of Powers Property: The quotient of two nonzero powers with

the same base equals the base raised to the _____ of

the exponents. For example $\frac{5^8}{5^3} = 5^{8-3}$.

Simplify $\frac{3a^7y^{10}}{a^2y^8}$.

When finding the quotient of two powers you _____ the exponents.

$$\frac{3a^7y^{10}}{a^2y^8} = 3a^{7-2}y^{—————} = 3a^{—}y^{—}$$

Dividing Numbers in Scientific Notation

Simplify $(3 \times 10^8) \div (6 \times 10^5)$ and write the answer in scientific notation.

$(3 \times 10^8) \div (6 \times 10^5) = \dfrac{\boxed{} \times 10^8}{\boxed{} \times 10^5}$ Rewrite as a quotient.

$= \dfrac{\boxed{}}{6} \times \dfrac{10^8}{10^{—}}$ Write as a product of quotients.

$= \underline{\quad\quad} \times 10^{—}$ Simplify each quotient and simplify the exponent.

$= 5 \times \underline{\quad\quad} \times 10^{—}$ Write 0.5 in scientific notation.

$= 5 \times 10^{—}$ Add the exponents.

Finding Positive Powers of Quotients

Positive Power of a Quotient Property: A quotient raised to a positive power

equals the quotient of each base raised to that _____.

Simplify $\left(\dfrac{3a^4}{6a^2b^2}\right)^2$.

$\left(\dfrac{3a^4}{6a^2b^2}\right)^2 = \dfrac{(3a^4)^{—}}{(6a^2b^2)^{—}}$ Use the Power of a Quotient Property.

$= \dfrac{(3)^2(a^4)^{—}}{(6)^2(a^2)^{—}(b^2)^{—}}$ Use the Power of a Product Property.

$= \dfrac{\boxed{}a^{4\cdot—}}{\boxed{}(a^{2\cdot—})(b^{2\cdot—})}$ Simplify and Use the Power of a Power Property.

$= \dfrac{\boxed{}a^{—}}{\boxed{}(a^{—})(b^{—})} = \dfrac{a^4}{4b^{—}}$ Simplify.

Name _____ Date _____ Class _____

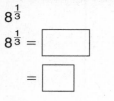

Ready To Go On? Skills Intervention
SECTION 7B *7-5 Fractional Exponents*

Find this vocabulary word in Lesson 7-5 and the Multilingual Glossary.

Vocabulary
index

Simplifying $b^{\frac{1}{n}}$
Simplify the expression.

$8^{\frac{1}{3}}$

$8^{\frac{1}{3}} = \boxed{}$ Use definition of $b^{\frac{1}{n}}$ as $(\sqrt[n]{b})$. Think: $?^3 =$ _____.

$= \boxed{}$

Simplifying Expressions with Fractional Exponents
Simplify the expression.

$16^{\frac{5}{4}}$

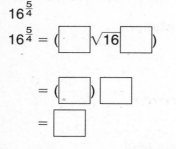

$16^{\frac{5}{4}} = \left(\boxed{}\sqrt{16}\boxed{}\right)$ Use the definition of $b^{\frac{m}{n}}$ as $(\sqrt[n]{b})^m$.

Think $?^4 =$ _____.

$= \left(\boxed{}\right)\boxed{}$ Evaluate the expression.

$= \boxed{}$

Using Properties of Exponents to Simplify Expressions
Simplify. All variables represent nonnegative numbers.

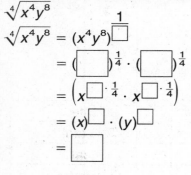

$\sqrt[4]{x^4 y^8}$

$\sqrt[4]{x^4 y^8} = (x^4 y^8)^{\frac{1}{\boxed{}}}$ Use the definition of $b^{\frac{1}{n}}$.

$= \left(\boxed{}\right)^{\frac{1}{4}} \cdot \left(\boxed{}\right)^{\frac{1}{4}}$ Power of a Product Property

$= \left(x^{\boxed{} \cdot \frac{1}{4}} \cdot x^{\boxed{} \cdot \frac{1}{4}}\right)$ Power of a Product Property

$= (x)^{\boxed{}} \cdot (y)^{\boxed{}}$ Simplify exponents.

$= \boxed{}$

Holt Algebra 1

Name _____ Date _____ Class _____

Ready To Go On? Skills Intervention
7-6 Polynomials

Find these vocabulary words in Lesson 7-6 and the Multilingual Glossary.

Vocabulary		
monomial	degree of a monomial	polynomial
degree of a polynomial	standard form of a polynomial	leading coefficient
quadratic	cubic	binomial	trinomial

Finding the Degree of a Monomial
Find the degree of the monomial.

$6c^4b^3$

Add the exponents of the variables: ____ + ____ = ____.

The degree of a monomial is the sum of the exponents of the variables.

The degree of $6c^4b^3$ is ____.

Writing Polynomials in Standard Form
Write the polynomial in standard form and give the leading coefficient.

$-4a^2 + 12 + a^6 + 7a^3$

Identify the degree of each term: $\underbrace{-4a^2}_{2} + \underbrace{12}_{0} + \underbrace{a^6}_{} + \underbrace{7a^3}_{}$

Arrange in descending order: $a^6 +$ ____ − ____ $+ 12$

What is the leading coefficient? ____

Classifying Polynomials
Classify each polynomial according to its degree and number of terms.

A. $6x^3 + 3x^2 - 5$ Degree: 3 Terms: ____

What is the name for an expression with a

degree of 3? _____

What is the name for an expression having

3 terms? _____

$6x^3 + 3x^2 - 5$ is a _____ trinomial.

B. $8 - 5y^2 + y - 6y^4$ Degree: ____ Terms: 4

$8 - 5y^2 + y - 6y^4$ is a quartic _____ .

Degree	Name
0	Constant
1	Linear
2	Quadratic
3	Cubic
4	Quartic

Terms	Name
1	Monomial
2	Binomial
3	Trinomial
4 or more	Polynomial

Holt Algebra 1

Ready To Go On? Skills Intervention

SECTION 7B 7-7 Adding and Subtracting Polynomials

Adding Polynomials
Add.

A. $(4x^3 - 3x) + (5x^3 + 4x - 7)$

Which terms are like terms? $4x^3$ and _____; $-3x$ and _____

$(4x^3 + $ _____ $) + (-3x + $ _____ $) + (-7)$ Group like terms.

_____ $x^3 + $ _____ $- 7$ Combine like terms.

B. $(8y^7 - 4y^3) + (2y^5 + 3)$

Which terms are like terms? _____

Arrange the terms in descending order:

$8y^7 + $ _____ $- $ _____ $+ 3$

Subtracting Polynomials
Subtract.

Remember that subtracting polynomials is the same as _____ the opposite.

A. $(8y^3 + 6y^2) - (3y^2 + 2y)$

Identify like terms: $6y^2$ and _____

Rewrite the subtraction as addition of the opposite. $(8y^3 + 6y^2) + (-3y^2 - $ _____ $)$

Rearrange terms so that like terms are together. $8y^3 + ($ _____ $- 3y^2) - $ _____

Combine like terms. $8y^3 + $ _____ $- $ _____

B. $(w^2 - 4) - (-3w^3 + 7w)$

Are there any like terms? _____

Rewrite the subtraction as addition of the opposite. $(w^2 - 4) + ($ _____ $- 7w)$

Combine like terms and arrange in descending order. $3w^3 + $ _____ $- $ _____ $- 4$

C. $(8n^3 - 3n) - (2n^3 - 7)$

$(8n^3 - 3n) + (-2n^3 + $ _____ $)$ Rewrite subtraction as addition of the opposite.

Use the vertical method and align like terms. Use 0 for place holders.

$$
\begin{array}{cccccc}
 & 8n^3 & + & 0n^2 & - \underline{} & + & 0 \\
- & \underline{} & + & 0n^2 & + & 0n & + \underline{} \\
\hline
 & \underline{} & & & - \underline{} & + & 7
\end{array}
$$
    Add.

Holt Algebra 1

Name _____ Date _____ Class _____

SECTION 7B Ready To Go On? Skills Intervention
7-8 Multiplying Polynomials

Multiplying Monomials

Multiply $(a^3b^4)(-7a^2b^3)$.

$-7(a^3 \cdot$ ____$)(b^4 \cdot$ ____$)$ Rearrange terms so that like bases are together.

$= -7a{-}b{-}$ Should you add or subtract exponents? _____

Multiplying a Polynomial by a Monomial

Multiply $3xy(7x^2 + 4x^2y)$.

$3xy(7x^2 + 4x^2y)$

$= 3xy($____$) +$ ____$(4x^2y)$ Distribute $3xy$.

$= (3 \cdot 7)(x \cdot$ ____$)y + (3 \cdot$ ____$)(x \cdot$ ____$)(y \cdot$ ____$)$ Group like bases together.

$=$ ____$x^3y +$ _____   Multiply.

Multiplying Binomials

Multiply $(4x^2 + 3y)(2x^2 + y)$.

What does FOIL mean? _____

_____

$4x^2(2x^2) +$ _____$(y) +$ _____$(2x^2) +$ _____(y) Use the FOIL method.

$= 8x^4 +$ _____ $+$ _____ $+ 3y^2$ Multiply.

$= 8x^4 +$ _____ $+$ _____   Combine like terms.

Multiplying Polynomials

Multiply $(a^2 + 2a)(7a^2 - 5a - 3)$.

To multiply polynomials with more than two terms you can use the Distributive Property several times or multiply vertically.

$(a^2 + 2a)(7a^2 - 5a - 3)$ Use the Distributive Property.

$= a^2(7a^2 - 5a - 3) +$ ____$($____ $-$ ____ $-$ ____$)$

$= a^2(7a^2) +$ ____$(-5a) +$ ____$(-3) +$ ____$(7a^2) +$ ____$(-5a) +$ ____(-3) Distribute again.

$= 7a^4 -$ _____ $- 3a^2 +$ _____ $- 10a^2 -$ _____   Multiply.

$= 7a^4 +$ _____ $-$ _____ $- 6a$ Combine like terms.

Holt Algebra 1

SECTION 7B Ready To Go On? Skills Intervention
7-9 Special Product of Binomials

Find these vocabulary words in Lesson 7-9 and the Multilingual Glossary.

Vocabulary
perfect-square trinomial   difference of two squares

Finding Products in the Form $(a + b)^2$.

A. Multiply $(x + 9)^2$.

What is the rule for $(a + b)^2$? $a^2 + 2$___$+ b^2$

Let $a = x$ and $b =$ ___.

$(x + 9)^2 = (x)^2 + 2($___$)(9) + ($___$)^2$

$\qquad = x^2 +$ ___ $x +$ ___

B. Multiply $(3x + 5y)^2$.

Let $a = 3x$ and $b =$ ___.

$(3x + 5y)^2 = (3x)^2 + 2($___$)(5y) + ($___$)^2$

$\qquad = $ ___$x^2 +$ ___$xy +$ ___y^2

Finding Products in the Form $(a - b)^2$.

A. Multiply $(x - 5)^2$.

What is the rule for $(a - b)^2$? $a^2 - 2$___$+$ ___^{2}

Let $a = x$ and $b =$ ___.

$(x - 5)^2 = (x)^2 - 2($___$)(5) + ($___$)^2$

$\qquad = x^2 -$ ___$x +$ ___

B. Multiply $(4x - 3)^2$.

Let $a =$ ___ and $b =$ ___.

$(4x - 3)^2 = (4x)^2 - 2($___$)($___$) + ($___$)^2$

$\qquad = $ ___$x^2 -$ ___$x +$ ___

Finding Products in the Form $(a + b)(a - b)$.

A. Multiply $(x + 8)(x - 8)$.

What is the rule for a difference of two squares $(a + b)(a - b)$? $a^2 -$ ___

Let $a = x$ and $b =$ ___.

$(x + 8)(x - 8) = (x)^2 -$ ___^{2}

$\qquad = x^2 -$ ___   Simplify.

B. Multiply $(3x + 4)(3x - 4)$.

Let $a = 3x$ and $b =$ ___.

$(3x + 4)(3x - 4) = ($___$)^2 - (4)^2$

$\qquad = $ ___$x^2 -$ ___   Simplify.

Holt Algebra 1

Ready to Go On? Problem Solving Intervention

SECTION 7B

7-9 Special Products of Binomials

A circular fish pond has a radius of $(x - 12)$ feet. Write a polynomial that represents the area of the fish pond. The formula for the area of a circle is $A = \pi r^2$, where r represents the radius of the circle. Leave the symbol π in your answer.

Understand the Problem

1. What are you being asked to find? _____

2. What piece of information are you given regarding the pond?
   _____

3. How do you find the area of a circle? _____

Make a Plan

4. Write an expression representing the area of the fish pond. _____

5. What are two possible ways that $(x - 12)^2$ can be simplified?

   _____

   _____

Solve

6. What is $(x - 12)^2$? $x^2 -$ _____ $+$ _____

7. Write an expression representing the area of the pond. $\pi x^2 -$ _____ $+$ _____

Look Back

8. Suppose that $x = 20$. What would the length of the radius be $(x - 12)$? _____

9. What would the area of the pond equal using $A = \pi r^2$?

   $$A = \pi \underline{\quad}^2$$

   $$A = \underline{\quad} \pi$$

10. What is the value of the expression in Exercise 7, using $x = 20$?

    $$A = \pi x^2 - 24\pi x + 144\pi$$

    $$= \pi(20)^2 - 24\pi(\underline{\quad}) + 144\pi$$

    $$= \underline{\quad}\pi - \underline{\quad}\pi + 144\pi$$

    $$= \underline{\quad}\pi$$

11. Are your answers to Exercises 9 and 10 the same? _____

Holt Algebra 1

Ready To Go On? Skills Intervention
8-1 Factors and Greatest Common Factors

Find these vocabulary words in Lesson 8-1 and the Multilingual Glossary.

Vocabulary	
prime factorization	greatest common factor

Writing Prime Factorizations
Write the prime factorization of 48.

What is a prime number? _____

Method 1 Factor tree
Choose any two factors of 48 to begin.
Keep finding factors until each branch
ends in a prime factor.
Circle the prime factors.

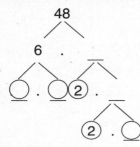

Method 2 Ladder diagram
Choose a prime factor of 48 to begin.
Keep dividing by prime factors until the
quotient is 1.

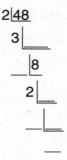

The prime factorization of 48 is $2 \cdot 2 \cdot$ __ $\cdot$ __ $\cdot$ __ or 2—$\cdot$ __.

Finding the GCF of Monomials
Find the GCF of each pair of monomials.

A. $9a^3$ and $3a$

$9a^3 = 3 \cdot$ __ $\cdot a \cdot$ __ $\cdot$ __   Write the prime factorization of each coefficient and
                                            write the powers as products.

$3a = 3 \cdot$ ___   Align the common factors.

What are the factors common to both monomials? 3 and __

Multiply the common factors. The GCF of $9a^3$ and $3a$ is ___.

B. $24x^3$, $30x^5$

$24x^3 = 2 \cdot 2 \cdot$ __ $\cdot$ __ $\cdot$ $x \cdot$ __ $\cdot$ __   Write the prime factorization of each
                                                          coefficient and write the powers as products.

$30x^5 =$ $2 \cdot$ __ $\cdot$ __ $\cdot x \cdot x \cdot$ __ $\cdot$ __ $\cdot$ __   Align the common factors.

What are the factors common to both monomials? 2, __ and ___

Multiply the common factors. The GCF is ____.

Holt Algebra 1

SECTION 8A Ready To Go On? Problem Solving Intervention
8-1 Factors and Greatest Common Factors

Factors that are shared by two or more numbers are called common factors. The largest common factor is called the GCF, or greatest common factor.

A softball league bought new equipment for the teams. The league bought 40 balls and 24 bats. How many teams are there if all the equipment is distributed evenly between the teams? How many bats and balls does each team receive?

Understand the Problem

1. How many bats and balls were purchased? _____ bats and _____ balls

2. How is the equipment divided? _____

3. What are you being asked to find? _____
   _____

Make a Plan

4. If the equipment is to be divided evenly between teams then 40 and 24 must be
   _____ by the same number.

5. What are the factors of 24: 1, 2, _____

   40: 1, 2, 4, _____

Solve

6. Which factors are common to 24 and 40? 1, 2, _____, _____

7. What is the largest common factor? _____

8. So, there are _____ softball teams.

9. Since there are 40 balls and _____ teams, how many balls does each team receive? _____

10. Since there are 24 bats and _____ teams, how many bats does each team receive? _____

Look Back

11. How many balls does each team receive? _____ How many teams are there? _____
    What is the product of number of teams and number of balls? _____

12. How many bats does each team receive? _____ How many teams are there? _____
    What is the product of number of teams and numbers of bats? _____

13. Do your answers to Exercises 11 and 12 match the information in the problem
    statement? _____

Holt Algebra 1

Name _____ Date _____ Class _____

Factoring by Using the GCF
Factor each polynomial. Check your answer.

A. $8y^3 + 24y^2$

Find the GCF of each term.

$8y^3 = 2 \cdot \_\_ \cdot \_\_ \cdot y \cdot \_\_ \cdot \_\_$

$24y^2 = 2 \cdot \_\_ \cdot \_\_ \cdot \_\_ \cdot y \cdot \_\_$

The GCF is $2 \cdot \_\_ \cdot \_\_ \cdot \_\_ \cdot \_\_ = 8\_\_\_\_$.

Write terms as products using the GCF as a factor. $y(8y^2) + 3_____$

Use the Distributive Property to factor out the GCF. $8y^2(\_\_ + \_\_)$

Check: Multiply to check your answer. $8y^2(\_\_ + \_\_) = 8y^3 + 24y^2$

B. $4x^2 + 20x + 28$

Find the GCF of each term.

$4x^2 = 2 \cdot \_\_ \cdot \_\_ \cdot \_\_$

$20x = 2 \cdot \_\_ \cdot \_\_ \cdot \_\_$

$28 = 2 \cdot \_\_ \cdot \_\_$

The GCF is $2 \cdot \_\_ = \_\_$.

Write terms as products using the GCF as a factor. $x^2(4) + 4\_\_\_\_\_ + \_\_(7)$

Use the Distributive Property to factor out the GCF. $4(\_\_\_ + 5x + \_\_)$

Check: Multiply to check your answer. $4(\_\_\_ + 5x + \_\_) = 4x^2 + 20x + 28$

Factoring by Grouping
Factor the polynomial, $4a^3 + 8a^2 - 3a - 6$, by grouping. Check your answer.

Group terms that have a common number of variables as a factor. $(4a^3 + 8a^2) + (-3a - 6)$

What is the GCF of $4a^3$ and $8a^2$? _____   What is the GCF of $-3a$ and -6? _____

Write each group with the GCF. $\_\_\_\_(a + \_\_) + (-3)(a + \_\_)$

Factor out the common factor of $a + 2$. $(a + 2)(\_\_\_\_\_ - \_\_)$

Multiply to check your solution.

$(a + 2)(\_\_\_\_\_ - \_\_) = \_\_(4a^2) + \_\_(-3) + \_\_(4a^2) + \_\_(-3)$

$= \_\_\_\_\_ - 3a + \_\_\_\_\_ - 6$ Multiply.

$= \_\_\_\_\_ + 8a^2 - \_\_\_ - 6$ Rewrite in descending order.

Holt Algebra 1

SECTION 8A Ready To Go On? Skills Intervention
8-3 Factoring $x^2 + bx + c$

Factoring $x^2 + bx + c$ When c is Positive.
Factor each trinomial. Check your answer.

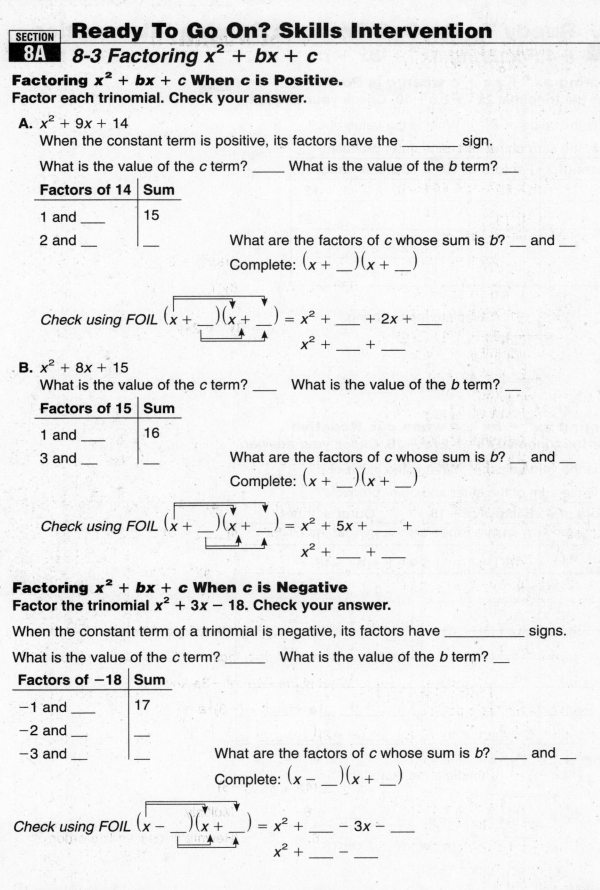

A. $x^2 + 9x + 14$

When the constant term is positive, its factors have the _____ sign.

What is the value of the c term? _____ What is the value of the b term? __

Factors of 14	Sum
1 and ___	15
2 and __	__

What are the factors of c whose sum is b? __ and __

Complete: $(x + \_\_)(x + \_\_)$

Check using FOIL $(x + \_\_)(x + \_\_) = x^2 + \_\_\_ + 2x + \_\_\_$

$x^2 + \_\_\_ + \_\_\_$

B. $x^2 + 8x + 15$

What is the value of the c term? ___ What is the value of the b term? __

Factors of 15	Sum
1 and ___	16
3 and __	__

What are the factors of c whose sum is b? __ and __

Complete: $(x + \_\_)(x + \_\_)$

Check using FOIL $(x + \_\_)(x + \_\_) = x^2 + 5x + \_\_\_ + \_\_\_$

$x^2 + \_\_\_ + \_\_\_$

Factoring $x^2 + bx + c$ When c is Negative
Factor the trinomial $x^2 + 3x - 18$. Check your answer.

When the constant term of a trinomial is negative, its factors have _____ signs.

What is the value of the c term? _____ What is the value of the b term? __

Factors of −18	Sum
−1 and ___	17
−2 and __	__
−3 and __	__

What are the factors of c whose sum is b? _____ and __

Complete: $(x - \_\_)(x + \_\_)$

Check using FOIL $(x - \_\_)(x + \_\_) = x^2 + \_\_\_ - 3x - \_\_\_$

$x^2 + \_\_\_ - \_\_\_$

Holt Algebra 1

Ready To Go On? Problem Solving Intervention

SECTION 8A *8-4 Factoring $ax^2 + bx + c$*

Factoring $ax^2 + bx + c$ when c is Positive.
Factor the trinomial $2x^2 + 9x + 10$. Check your answer.

What is the value of a? __ What is the value of c? ___

What is the sum of the inner and outer products? __

Factors of 2	Factors of 10	Outer + Inner
$1 \cdot 2$	$1 \cdot 10$	$1 \cdot 10 + 2 \cdot 1 = 12$
$1 \cdot 2$	$10 \cdot 1$	$1 \cdot 1 + 2 \cdot \_\_\_ = 21$
$1 \cdot 2$	$5 \cdot \_\_$	$1 \cdot 2 + 2 \cdot \_\_ = \_\_\_$
$1 \cdot 2$	$2 \cdot \_\_$	$1 \cdot 5 + 2 \cdot \_\_ = \_\_$

$(x + \_\_)(2x + \_\_)$ Complete the factoring.

Check $(x + \_\_)(2x + \_\_) = 2x^2 + \_\_\_ + \_\_\_ + \_\_\_$
$= 2x^2 + \_\_\_ + 10$

Factoring $ax^2 + bx + c$ when c is Negative
Factor the trinomial $4x^2 + 21x - 18$. Check your answer.

What is the value of a? __ What is the value of c? _____

What is the sum of the inner and outer products? _____

Factors of 4	Factors of −18	Outer + Inner
$1 \cdot 4$	$1(-18)$	$1 \cdot -18 + 4 \cdot 1 = -14$
$1 \cdot 4$	$-18(1)$	$1 \cdot 1 + 4 \cdot -18 = \_\_\_\_$
$1 \cdot 4$	$2 \cdot \_\_\_\_$	$1 \cdot -9 + 4 \cdot \_\_ = \_\_\_$
$1 \cdot 4$	$-9 \cdot \_\_$	$1 \cdot \_\_ + 4 \cdot \_\_\_ = \_\_\_\_$
$1 \cdot 4$	$3 \cdot \_\_\_\_$	$1 \cdot \_\_\_ + 4 \cdot \_\_ = \_\_\_\_$
$1 \cdot 4$	$-6 \cdot \_\_$	$1 \cdot \_\_ + 4 \cdot \_\_\_ = \_\_$
$1 \cdot 4$	$-3 \cdot \_\_$	$1 \cdot \_\_ + 4 \cdot \_\_\_ = \_\_$
$1 \cdot 4$	$6 \cdot \_\_\_$	$1 \cdot \_\_\_ + 4 \cdot \_\_ = \_\_\_$

$(x + \_\_)(4x - \_\_)$ Complete the factoring.

Check $(x + \_\_)(4x - \_\_) = 4x^2 - \_\_\_ + \_\_\_\_ - \_\_\_$
$= 4x^2 + \_\_\_\_ - 18$

Holt Algebra 1

SECTION 8B Ready To Go On? Skills Intervention
8-5 Factoring Special Products

Recognizing and Factoring Perfect-Square Trinomials

A trinomial is a perfect square if the first and the _____ terms are perfect

squares. The _____ term is two times one factor from the first term and one
factor from the last term.

Determine whether each trinomial is a perfect square.
If so, factor it. If not, explain why.

A. $x^2 + 14x + 42$

Method 1 Factor.

Factors of 42	Sum
1 and 42	43
2 and 21	___
___ and 14	___
6 and ___	___

Is $x^2 + 14x + 42$ a perfect square

trinomial? _____ Why? _____

_____

B. $9x^2 - 24x + 16$

Method 2 Use the pattern.

$9x^2 - 24x + 16$

$3x \cdot 3x - 2(3x \cdot \_\_) + 4 \cdot 4$

The trinomial is a perfect _____.

$a = 3x, b = \_\_$

$(3x)^2 - 2(\_\_\_)(4) + 4^2$ Write the trinomial
as $a^2 - 2ab + b^2$.

$(\_\_\_ - 4)^2$ Write as $(a - b)^2$.

Determine whether each binomial is the difference of two squares. If so, factor
it. If not explain why.

A. $x^2 - 16$

$(x \cdot x) - (4 \cdot \_\_)$ The polynomial is the difference of two _____.

$a = x, b = 4$

$(x + 4)(x - \_\_)$ Write the polynomial as $(a + b)(a - b)$.

So $x^2 - 16 = (x + \_\_)(x - \_\_)$.

B. $9x^6 - 17y^2$

Is $9x^6$ a perfect square? _____

Is $-17y^2$ a perfect square? _____

Is $9x^6 - 17y^2$ the difference of two squares? _____

Why? _____

Holt Algebra 1

Ready To Go On? Problem Solving Intervention

SECTION 8B *8-5 Factoring Special Products*

If a trinomial is a perfect square, it can be factored to determine measurements of real-world objects.

A community garden, rectangular in shape, has an area of $(25x^2 + 20x + 4)$ ft^2. The dimensions of the garden are approximately $ax + b$, where a and b are whole numbers. Find an expression for the perimeter of the garden. Then find the perimeter where $x = 12$.

Understand the Problem

1. What is the shape of the garden? _____

2. What is the area of the garden? _____

3. What kind of numbers are a and b? _____.

4. What are you being asked to find? _____

_____ and _____

Make a Plan

5. The formula for the area of a rectangle is: Area = length × _____

6. What must be done to the trinomial to find the length and width? _____

Solve

7. Does the trinomial $25x^2 + 20x + 4$ have a common factor? _____

8. Is $25x^2 + 20x + 4$ a perfect square trinomial? _____ So, $a =$ _____ and $b = 2$.

9. What are the factors of the perfect square trinomial? _____

10. Since the length and width of the garden are equal, what is the actual shape of

the garden? _____

11. The formula for the perimeter of a square is $P = 4s$.

  a. What should you substitute in the perimeter formula for s? _____

  b. Simplify $4(5x + 2)$ to find an expression for the perimeter. _____

12. Evaluate the expression when $x = 12$. What is the perimeter? _____

Look Back

13. Using the perimeter from Exercise 12, what is the length of one side of the square?

_____ Use this side length to find the area. _____

14. Evaluate $25x^2 + 20x + 4$ for $x = 12$: $25(12)^2 + 20(12) + 4 =$ _____

15. Are the areas in Exercises 13 and 14 equal? _____

Holt Algebra 1

SECTION 8B Ready To Go On? Skills Intervention
8-6 Choosing a Factoring Method

Determining Whether an Expression Is Completely Factored
Tell whether each expression is completely factored. If not, factor it.

A. $4x^2 + 2x - 6 = 2(2x^2 + x - 3)$

The greatest common factor is ___.

Is $(2x^2 + x - 3)$ factorable? _____

Is $2(2x^2 + x - 3)$ completely factored? _____

Factor: $2(2x^2 + x - 3) \Rightarrow 2(2x + ___)(x - ___)$

B. $42x - 14x^3 = 14(3x - x^3)$

What is the greatest common factor? _____

Is the polynomial factored completely? _____

Factor: $42x - 14x^3 \Rightarrow 14x(\_\_ - \_\_^2)$

Can the polynomial be factored any further? _____

Factoring by Multiple Methods
Factor the polynomial $6x^3 + 21x^2 + 15x$ completely. Check your answer.

Consider $6x^3 + 21x^2 + 15x$.

What is the GCF? _____

Factor out the GCF: $3x(\_\_\_\_\_ + \_\_\_\_\_ + 5)$

What is the value of a? __   What is the value of c? __,

The Outer + Inner terms = __.

Factors of 2	Factors of 5	Outer + Inner
$1 \cdot 2$	$5 \cdot 1$	$1 \cdot 1 + 2 \cdot 5 = $ ___
$1 \cdot 2$	$1 \cdot$ ___	$1 \cdot$ ___ $+ 2 \cdot$ ___ $=$ ___

Complete the binomial: $(x + \_\_)(2x + \_\_)$

Write as a factored polynomial: $3x(x + 1)(2x + \_\_)$

Check: $3x(x + 1)(2x + 5)$

$= 3x(2x^2 + \_\_\_\_\_ + \_\_\_\_\_ + 5)$ FOIL

$= 3x(2x^2 + \_\_\_\_\_ + 5)$ Combine like terms.

$= 6x^- + \_\_x^2 + \_\_x$ Distribute the $3x$.

Is this the original polynomial? _____

Holt Algebra 1

SECTION
9A
Ready To Go On? Skills Intervention
9-1 Quadratic Equations and Functions

Find these vocabulary words in Lesson 9-1 and the Multilingual Glossary.

Vocabulary					
quadratic equation	quadratic function	parabola	vertex	minimum	maximum

Identifying Quadratic Functions

The quadratic function $y = x^2$ does not have constant first differences. It

has constant _____ differences. This is true for all quadratic
functions.

A. Tell whether the point (−2, 7) is on the graph of $y = 2x^2 − 1$. Explain.

Substitute (−2, 7) into $y = ax^2 − 1$.

$y = 2x^2 − 1$ 　　　　　　　　Is the point (−2, 7) on the graph of $y = 2x^2 − 1$?

_____ $= 2($_____$)^2 − 1$ 　　　_____

_____ $= 2 \cdot$ _____ $− 1$ 　　　How do you know?

_____ $=$ _____ $− 1$ 　　　_____

$7 =$ _____ ✓ 　　　_____

B. Graph the function $y = \frac{1}{2}x^2 − 4$ and give the domain and range.

Make a table of values. Choose values of x and use them to find values of y.
Graph the points and connect with a smooth curve.

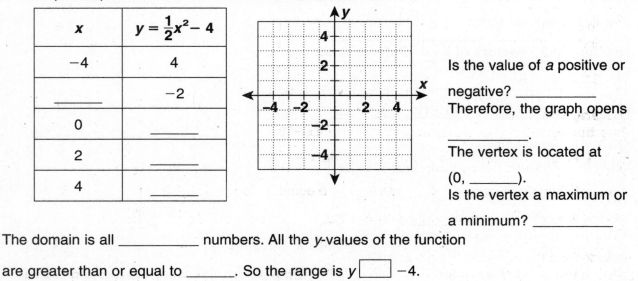

x	$y = \frac{1}{2}x^2 − 4$
−4	4
_____	−2
0	_____
2	_____
4	_____

Is the value of a positive or

negative? _____
Therefore, the graph opens

_____.

The vertex is located at

(0, _____).
Is the vertex a maximum or

a minimum? _____

The domain is all _____ numbers. All the y-values of the function

are greater than or equal to _____. So the range is $y \boxed{} −4$.

Holt Algebra 1

Name _____ Date _____ Class _____

9-2 Characteristics of Quadratic Functions

Find these vocabulary words in Lesson 9-2 and the Multilingual Glossary.

Vocabulary
zero of a function   axis of symmetry

Finding Zeros of Quadratic Functions From Graphs
Find the zeros of the quadratic function from its graph. Then find its axis of symmetry.

The zero of a function is an *x*-value that makes the function equal to zero.
The zero of a function is the same as an *x*-intercept.

A quadratic function may have one, _____, or no zeros.

The axis of symmetry always passes through the _____ of the parabola.

A.

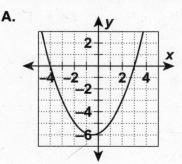

B.

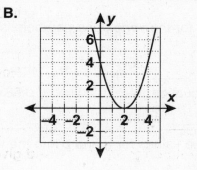

Where does the graph cross the *x*-axis?

____ and ____
To determine the axis of symmetry,
find the average of the zeros.

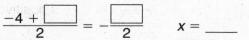

$$\frac{-4 + \boxed{}}{2} = -\frac{\boxed{}}{2} \qquad x = \underline{\quad}$$

Where does the graph cross the *x*-axis?

____
In this case, the *x*-coordinate is the
axis of symmetry.

$x = \underline{\quad}$

Finding the Vertex of a Parabola
Find the vertex of the parabola $y = -2x^2 + 4x - 3$.

Step 1 Find the *x*-coordinate using the formula $x = -\frac{b}{2a}$.

What does *a* equal? ____ What does *b* equal? ____

$$x = \frac{-b}{2a} = -\frac{4}{2(\boxed{})} = -\frac{4}{\boxed{}} = \underline{\quad}$$

Step 2 Find the corresponding *y*-coordinate.

$y = -2x^2 + 4x - 3$

$y = -2(\underline{\quad})^2 + 4(\underline{\quad}) - 3$

$y = -2 + \underline{\quad} - 3 = \underline{\quad}$

Step 3 Write the coordinates as an ordered
pair. The vertex is (1, ____).

Holt Algebra 1

Ready To Go On? Problem Solving Intervention

9-2 Characteristics of Quadratic Functions

The x-coordinate of the vertex of a parabola can be found by $x = -\dfrac{\boxed{}}{2a}$.

The height above water of a curved arch support for a bridge can be modeled by $y = -0.004x^2 + 0.68x + 0.6$, where x is the distance in feet from where the arch support enters the water. How tall is the arched bridge?

Understand the Problem

1. What are you being asked to find? _____

2. What formula are you given? _____

Make a Plan

3. The _____ represents the highest point of a parabola.

4. The formula for the vertex of a parabola is $x = -\dfrac{\boxed{}}{2a}$.

Solve

5. Given the equation $y = -0.004x^2 + 0.68x + 0.6$,

$a =$ _____ and $b =$ _____.

6. Substitute the values for a and b into the vertex formula.

$x = -\dfrac{\boxed{}}{2a}$

$x = -\dfrac{\boxed{}}{2(-0.004)} =$ _____

7. Find the corresponding y-coordinate. $y = -0.004x^2 + 0.68x + 0.6$

$= -0.004(\underline{})^2 + 0.68(\underline{}) + 0.6$

$= \underline{}$

8. The height of the bridge is _____ feet.

Look Back

9. Graph the function $y = -0.004x^2 + 0.68x + 0.6$ on a graphing calculator. Viewing window: x-values -5 to 200 by 25, y-values -10 to 50 by 10.

10. Use the Calc feature on your calculator and determine the maximum point on

the parabola. _____

11. Do your heights in Exercise 8 and Exercise 10 match? _____

Holt Algebra 1

Ready To Go On? Skills Intervention

SECTION 9A *9-3 Graphing Quadratic Functions*

Graphing a Quadratic Function

Graph $y = 2x^2 + 4x + 1$.

Step 1 Find the axis of symmetry.

$x = -\dfrac{b}{2a}$ What does a equal? _____ What does b equal? _____

$x = -\dfrac{4}{2(\boxed{})} = -\dfrac{4}{\boxed{}} = $ _____   Substitute known values and solve for x.

Step 2 Find the vertex. Substitute the x-coordinate into the equation.

$y = 2x^2 + 4x + 1$

$y = 2(\underline{})^2 + 2(\underline{}) + 1$

$y = 2 - \underline{} + 1$

$y = \underline{}$ The vertex is (_____, _____).

Step 3 Find the y-intercept.

$y = 2x^2 + 4x + 1$ Identify c. _____

The y-intercept is 1; the graph passes through (0, _____).

Step 4 Find two more points on the same side of the axis of symmetry as the point containing the y-intercept. Use -3 and -2.

Let $x = -3$

$y = 2x^2 + 4x + 1$

$y = 2(\underline{})^2 + 4(\underline{}) + 1$

$y = 2(\underline{}) - \underline{} + 1$

$y = \underline{}$

The point is $(-3, \underline{})$.

Let $x = -2$

$y = 2x^2 + 4x + 1$

$y = 2(\underline{})^2 + 4(\underline{}) + 1$

$y = 2(\underline{}) - \underline{} + 1$

$y = \underline{}$

The point is $(-2, \underline{})$.

Step 5 Graph the axis of symmetry, vertex, y-intercept, and the two other points.

Step 6 Now, reflect the points across the axis of symmetry to graph points on the other side of the parabola. Connect the points with a smooth curve.

Holt Algebra 1

SECTION 9B Ready To Go On? Skills Intervention
9-4 Solving Quadratic Equations by Graphing

Find this vocabulary word in Lesson 9-4 and the Multilingual Glossary.

┌─────────────────────────┐
│ **Vocabulary**   │
│ quadratic equation   │
└─────────────────────────┘

Solving Quadratic Equation by Graphing
Solve each equation by graphing the related function.

A. $x^2 - 4$

Step 1 Write the related function. $y = x^2 -$ ____

Step 2 Graph the function.

The axis of symmetry is $x =$ ____.

The vertex is $(0,$ ____$)$.

Two other points are $(-1,$ ____$)$ and $(-3,$ ____$)$.
Graph the points and reflect them across the axis of symmetry.

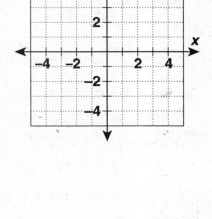

Step 3 Find the zeros. The zeros appear to be -2 and ____.

Check

$x^2 - 4 = 0$			$x^2 - 4 = 0$	
$(-2)^2 - 4$	0		$(2)^2 - 4$	0
$4 - 4$	0		$4 - 4$	0
0	0		0	0

B. $x^2 + 3x - 10$

Step 1 Write the related function. $y = x^2 +$ ____ $-$ ____

Step 2 Graph the function.

The axis of symmetry is $x =$ _____.

The vertex is $(-1.5,$ _____$)$.

Two other points are $(-4,$ _____$)$ and $(-3,$ _____$)$.
Graph the points and reflect them across the axis of symmetry.

Step 3 Find the zeros. The zeros appear to be _____ and _____.

Check

$x^2 + 3x - 10 = 0$			$x^2 + 3x - 10 = 0$	
$(-5)^2 + 3($_____$) - 10$	0		$(2)^2 + 3($_____$) - 10$	0
$25 -$ _____ $- 10$	0		$4 +$ _____ $- 10$	0
0	0		0	0

Holt Algebra 1

Ready To Go On? Problem Solving Intervention

SECTION 9B

9-4 Solving Quadratic Equations by Graphing

Given a quadratic equation, you can write and graph the related function to determine the zeros of the function.

The height of a water rocket is launched upward with an initial velocity of 48 feet per second. Its height h, from the ground can be approximated by $h = -16t^2 + 48t$, where t is the time in seconds. Find the time it takes for the rocket to reach the ground after it is launched.

Understand the Problem

1. What are you being asked to determine?

   _____

2. What equation approximates the height? _____

Make a Plan

3. Write the related function and graph the function.

   The related function: $h = -16t^2 + 48t$

   $\qquad\qquad\qquad\quad\ 0 = -16t^2 + 48t$

   $\qquad\quad$ _____ $= -16t^2 + 48t$

Solve

4. Graph the function from Exercise 3. Use a graphing calculator.

5. Use the TRACE key to estimate the zeros.

   The zeros appear to be _____ and _____.

6. The rocket leaves the launch pad at _____ seconds and reaches the ground in

   _____ seconds.

7. The rocket is in the air for about _____ seconds.

Look Back

8. Substitute your value in Exercise 7 for t and see if the answer checks.

   $0 = -16t^2 + 48t$

0	$-16(\underline{\quad})^2 + 48(\underline{\quad})$
0	$-16(\underline{\quad}) + \underline{\quad}$
0	$-144 + \underline{\quad}$
0	0 ✓

Holt Algebra 1

SECTION 9B Ready To Go On? Skills Intervention
9-5 Solving Quadratic Equations by Factoring

Using the Zero Product Property

If the product of two quantities equal zero, at least one of the quantities equals

_____. If a quadratic equation is written in standard form, $ax^2 + bx + c = 0$,

then to solve the equation, you may need to _____ before using the Zero
Product Property.

Using the Zero Product Property.

A. $(x + 7)(x + 3) = 0$

$x +$ ____ $= 0$ or $x + 3 =$ ____   Use the _____ Property.

$x = -7$ or $x =$ ____   Solve each equation.

Check: $x = -7$ Check: $x = -3$
$\quad(x + 7)(x + 3) = 0$ $\quad(x + 7)(x + 3) = 0$
$\quad$(____ $+ 7)($____ $+ 3) = 0$ (____ $+ 7)($____ $+ 3) = 0$
$\quad\quad(0)($____$) = 0$ $\quad(4)($____$) = 0$
$\quad\quad\quad 0 = 0$ $\quad\quad 0 = 0$

B. $x(x - 3) = 10$

$x^2 -$ ____ $= 10$ Multiply.

$x^2 - 3x - 10 =$ ____   Write the equation in _____ form

$(x -$ ____$)(x +$ ____$) = 0$ Factor.

$x - 5 = 0$ or $x +$ ____ $= 0$ Use the Zero Product Property.

$x =$ ____   or $x =$ ____   Solve each equation.

C. $(x + 5)(x - 8) = -22$

$x^2 -$ ____ $+ 5x -$ ____ $= -22$ Multiply using the FOIL method.

$x^2 -$ ____ $- 40 = -22$ Combine like terms.

$x^2 - 3x -$ ____ $= 0$ Write the equation in standard form.

$(x -$ ____$)(x +$ ____$) = 0$ _____ the trinomial.

$x -$ ____ $= 0$ or $x +$ ____ $= 0$ Use the Zero Product Property.

$x =$ ____   or $x =$ ____   Solve each equation.

Holt Algebra 1

Ready To Go On? Problem Solving Intervention

SECTION 9B

9-6 Solving Quadratic Equations by Factoring

A bottle rocket is launched upward with an initial velocity of 48 feet per second. The rocket's height h, in feet, after t seconds is given by $h = -16t^2 + 48t$. When will the rocket hit the ground?

Understand the Problem

1. Which direction is the bottle rocket launched? _____

2. What is the initial velocity of the rocket? _____

3. What is the height represented by in the problem? _____

4. What is the time represented by in the problem? _____

5. What is the equation given that models the launched rocket? _____

6. What are you asked to find? _____

Make a Plan

7. Which variable does the equation need to be solved for? _____

8. When the rocket hits the ground what does h equal? _____

   Write the equation substituting this value for h. _____

Solve

9. What is the GCF of the equation in Exercise 8? _____

10. Factor out the GCF and rewrite the equation in Exercise 8. _____

11. Using the Zero Product Property, solve.

    $-16t = 0$ $t - 3 = 0$

        $t =$ _____ $t =$ _____

12. Which value for t is the only one that makes sense, why?

    _____

13. How long will it take for the rocket to hit the ground? _____

Look Back

14. Substitute your answer in Exercise 13 into the original equation, $0 = -16(\_\_\_)^2 + 48(\_\_\_)$.

15. Does the value found satisfy the equation to make it true? _____

Holt Algebra 1

Name _____ Date _____ Class _____

Using Square Roots to Solve Quadratic Equations

Every positive real number has _____ square roots, one _____ and

one _____. When you take the square root of a positive real number and the
sign of the square root is not indicated, you must find both the positive and negative

square root. This is indicated by ____ $\sqrt{}$. The square root of _____ is neither
positive nor negative.

Solve using square roots. Round to the nearest hundredth if necessary.

A. $6x^2 = 216$

$$\frac{6x^2}{\boxed{}} = \frac{216}{\boxed{}}$$

Divide each side by ____.

$$x^2 = \underline{}$$

$$\sqrt{x^2} = \sqrt{\underline{}}$$

Solve for x by taking the _____ of both sides.

$$x = \pm\underline{}$$

Use ____ to show both square roots.

B. $18 = x^2 - 31$

$$18 = x^2 - 31$$

$$\underline{+\ 31} \qquad +\underline{}$$

Add ____ to each side of the equation.

$$\underline{} = x^2$$

$$\sqrt{\underline{}} = \sqrt{x^2}$$

Solve for x by taking the square root of both sides.

$$x = \underline{}$$

Use $\pm$ to show both square roots.

C. $5x^2 + 6 = 34$

$$5x^2 + 6 = 34$$

$$\underline{-} \qquad -\underline{}$$

Subtract ____ from each side of the equation.

$$5x^2 = \underline{}$$

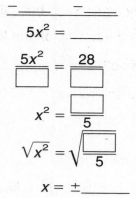

$$\frac{5x^2}{\boxed{}} = \frac{28}{\boxed{}}$$

Divide each side by ____.

$$x^2 = \frac{\boxed{}}{5}$$

$$\sqrt{x^2} = \sqrt{\frac{\boxed{}}{5}}$$

Solve for x by taking the _____ of each side.

$$x = \pm\underline{}$$

Use $\pm$ to show _____ square roots. Round to
the nearest hundredth.

Holt Algebra 1

Name _____ Date _____ Class _____

SECTION 9B Ready To Go On? Skills Intervention
9-7 Completing the Square

Find this vocabulary word in Lesson 9-7 and the
Multilingual Glossary.

Vocabulary
completing the square

Solving $x^2 + bx = c$ by Completing the Square
Solve each equation by completing the square.

A. $x^2 + 12x = 45$

Step 1 Write the equation in the form $x^2 + bx = c$. _____

Step 2 What is the value of b in the equation? ____ What is $\left(\dfrac{b}{2}\right)^2$? ____

Step 3 $x^2 + 12x +$ ____ $= 45 +$ ____   Complete the square by adding 36 to both sides.

Step 4 $(x + 6)^2 =$ ____   Factor the perfect-square trinomial on the left.

Step 5 $x +$ ____ $= \pm$ ____   Take the square root of both sides.

Step 6 $x + 6 =$ ____   or $x + 6 = -$ ____   Write and solve two equations.

$\qquad$ $x = 3$ $\qquad\qquad$ $x =$ ____   Solve for x.

The solutions of the equation are ____ and _____.

Check: Substitute the solutions into the original equation $x^2 + 12x = 45$ and solve.

$\qquad$ $x = 3$ $\qquad\qquad\qquad$ $x =$ ____

$\qquad$ (____)$^2 + 12($____$) = 45$ $\qquad$ (____)$^2 + 12($_____$) = 45$

$\qquad\qquad$ ____ $= 45$ $\qquad\qquad\qquad$ ____ $= 45$

Do your solutions check? _____

B. $x^2 - 11 = 4x$

Step 1 Write the equation in the form $x^2 + bx = c$. $x^2 -$ ____ $= 11$

Step 2 What is the value of b in the equation? ____ What is $\left(\dfrac{b}{2}\right)^2$? ____

Step 3 $x^2 - 4x +$ ____ $= 11 +$ ____   Complete the square by adding 4 to both sides.

Step 4 $(x - 2)^2 =$ ____   Factor the perfect-square trinomial on the left.

Step 5 $x -$ ____ $= \pm\sqrt{}$ Take the square root of both sides.

Step 6 $x - 2 = \sqrt{}$ or $x - 2 = -\sqrt{}$ Write and solve two equations.

$\qquad$ $x = 2 + \sqrt{}$ or $x = 2 - \sqrt{}$

The solutions of the equation are _____ and _____.

Check: You can use a graphing calculator to check your answer.

Holt Algebra 1

Using the Quadratic Formula

A. Solve $x^2 + 7x + 2 = 0$ using the Quadratic Formula.

What is the quadratic formula?

$$x = \frac{-b \pm \sqrt{^2 - 4c}}{2a}$$

In the equation $x^2 + 7x + 2 = 0$, $a =$ ____ $b =$ ____ and $c =$ ____.

Substitute for a, b, and c in the quadratic formula.

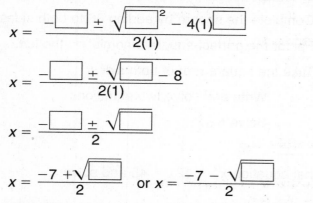

$$x = \frac{-\boxed{} \pm \sqrt{\boxed{}^2 - 4(1)\boxed{}}}{2(1)}$$

$$x = \frac{-\boxed{} \pm \sqrt{\boxed{} - 8}}{2(1)}$$ Simplify.

$$x = \frac{-\boxed{} \pm \sqrt{\boxed{}}}{2}$$

$$x = \frac{-7 + \sqrt{\boxed{}}}{2} \quad \text{or} \quad x = \frac{-7 - \sqrt{\boxed{}}}{2}$$

B. Solve $3x = x^2 - 10$ using the Quadratic Formula.

Write the equation in standard form. $x^2 - 3x - 10 = 0$

In the equation $x^2 - 3x - 10 = 0$, $a =$ ____, $b =$ ____, and $c =$ ____.

Substitute for a, b, and c in the quadratic formula.

$$x = \frac{-(\underline{}) \pm \sqrt{(\underline{})^2 - 4(1)(\underline{})}}{2(1)}$$

$$x = \frac{-(\underline{}) \pm \sqrt{\underline{} + \underline{}}}{2(1)}$$ Simplify.

$$x = \frac{-(\underline{}) \pm \sqrt{\underline{}}}{2(1)}$$

$$x = \frac{3 + \underline{}}{2} \quad \text{or} \quad x = \frac{3 - \underline{}}{2}$$

$$x = \frac{\underline{}}{2} \quad \text{or} \quad x = \frac{\underline{}}{2}$$

$$x = \underline{} \quad \text{or} \quad x = \underline{}$$

Holt Algebra 1

Name _____ Date _____ Class _____

Find this vocabulary word in Lesson 9-9 and the Multilingual Glossary.

Vocabulary
discriminant

Using the Discriminant
Find the number of solutions of $3x^2 - 4x + 5 = 0$.

If $b^2 - 4ac$ is positive, the equation has ____ real solutions.

If $b^2 - 4ac = 0$, the equation has ____ real solution.

If $b^2 - 4ac$ is negative, the equation has _____ real solutions.

For the equation $3x^2 - 4x + 5 = 0$, $a =$ ____, $b =$ ____, and $c =$ ____.

Substitute values for a, b, and c into the discriminant.

$b^2 - 4ac = (\underline{})^2 - 4 \cdot (\underline{})(\underline{})$

$ = 16 - \underline{}$

$ = \underline{}$

The equation $3x^2 - 4x + 5 = 0$ has ____ real solutions.

Using the Discriminant to Find the Number of x-intercepts
Find the number of x-intercepts of $y = x^2 - 6x + 9$.

If $b^2 - 4ac$ is positive, the related function has ____ x-intercepts.

If $b^2 - 4ac = 0$, the related function has ____ x-intercepts.

If $b^2 - 4ac$ is negative, the related function has _____ x-intercepts.

For the function $y = x^2 - 6x + 9$, $a =$ ____, $b =$ ____, and $c =$ ____.

Substitute values for a, b and c into the discriminant.

$b^2 - 4ac = (\underline{})^2 - 4(\underline{})(\underline{})$

$ = 36 - \underline{}$

$ = \underline{}$

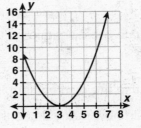

The function $y = x^2 - 6x + 9$ has ____ x-intercept.

Holt Algebra 1

Name _____ Date _____ Class _____

The equation of motion describes the location of a moving object as a function of time. You can use the discriminant to find the number of solutions of this equation at any given location. You can then use the number of solutions to predict the number of times the object is at that location during its motion.

The nozzle of a water jet in a fountain is 0.5 m above the pool. A burst of water leaves the jet straight upward. The height *h* of the burst of water above the pool is described by the equation $h = -4.9t^2 + 20t + 0.5$. Will the water ever be at a height of 10 m? Use the discriminant to explain your answer.

Understand the Problem

1. What are you being asked to find? _____

_____

2. What is the height equation when the burst is at 10 m? ____ = _____ .

   $t^2 +$ ____ $\cdot t +$ ____

Make a Plan

3. Rewrite the equation in step 2 in standard form. _____

4. What can you determine using the discriminant of the equation in step 3?

_____

Solve

5. What are the values of *a*, *b*, and *c* in the discriminant of the equation $0 = -4.9t^2 + 20t - 9.5$?

   $a =$ _____, $b =$ _____, and $c =$ _____

6. Evaluate the discriminant, $b^2 - 4ac$.

   ____^{2} $- 4 \cdot ($____$)($____$) =$ _____ $-$ _____ $=$ _____.

7. Because the discriminant is positive, how many solutions does the equation have? ____

8. Explain how many times the water will be at a height of 10 m. _____

_____

_____

Check

9. How could you check for two solutions to the equation? _____

_____

Holt Algebra 1

Ready To Go On? Skills Intervention

SECTION 10A *10-1 Inverse Variation*

Find this vocabulary word in Lesson 10-1 and the
Multilingual Glossary.

> **Vocabulary**
>
> inverse variation

Identifying Inverse Variation
Tell whether the relationship is an inverse variation. Explain.

A.

x	2	3	4
y	6	4	3

Find *xy* for each ordered pair.

2(___) = 12

___(4) = 12

4(___) = ___

The product *xy* is a constant so the

relationship ____ an inverse variation.

B.

x	3	4	5
y	15	20	25

Write the function rule.

$y =$ ___ x Every *x*-term is multiplied by

___ to get the *y*-term.

Can the relationship be written in

$y = \frac{k}{x}$ form? ____ So this relationship

_____ an inverse variation.

Graphing an Inverse Variation
Write and graph the inverse variation in which *y* = 3 when *x* = 2.

Step 1 Find *k*.

$k = xy$ Write the rule for constant of variation.

$= 2($___$)$ Substitute ___ for *x* and ___ for *y*.

$=$ ___

Step 2 Use the value *k* to write an inverse variation equation.

$y = \frac{k}{x}$ Write the rule for inverse variation.

$y = \dfrac{\boxed{}}{x}$ Substitute 6 for ___.

Step 3 Use the equation to make a table
of values. Complete the table.

x	−3	___	___	___	1	___	3
y	−2	−3	−6	Undef.	___	3	___

Step 4 Plot the points and connect them with smooth curves.

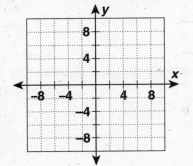

Holt Algebra 1

Name _____ Date _____ Class _____

Inverse variation implies that when one quantity increases the other quantity will _____.

A group of college students build decks over the summer for extra money. The time required to completely build a deck varies inversely as the number of people who are involved in the building. If it takes 4 hours for 6 people to build the deck, how long will it take 2 people to build the same deck assuming they work at the same rate?

Understand the Problem

1. In the first situation, how many people are building the deck? _____

2. How long does it take to completely build the first deck? _____

3. In the second situation, how many people are building the deck? _____

4. What are you asked to find?

_____

Make a Plan

5. What is the relationship between the number of workers and the amount of time?

_____

_____

6. Write the Product Rule for Inverse Variation. _____

7. What do you substitute for $x_1 y_1$? _____

8. What do you substitute for x_2? _____

Solve

9. Using the Product Rule for Inverse Variation, solve for y_2.

$(6)(4) = (2)(y_2)$

___ $= y_2$

10. How long will it take 2 people to build the deck at the same rate as the first deck was built? _____

Look Back

11. Substitute the time found for y_2 in Exercise 9 into the original equation for the Product Rule for Inverse Variation. $(6)(4) = 2(\boxed{})$

$24 = $ ___

Is your answer correct? _____

Holt Algebra 1

Ready To Go On? Skills Intervention

SECTION 10A *10-2 Rational Functions*

Find these vocabulary words in Lesson 10-2 and the Multilingual Glossary.

Vocabulary

rational function   excluded value   discontinuous function   asymptote

Identifying Excluded Values

Identify any excluded values for each rational function.

A. $y = \dfrac{9}{x}$

Set the denominator equal to 0.

$x = 0$

The excluded value is ___.

B. $\dfrac{x - 1}{x^2 + x - 6}$

Factor the denominator. $(x + \underline{\quad})(x - \underline{\quad})$

Set the denominator equal to 0.

$(x + \underline{\quad})(x - \underline{\quad}) = 0$

The excluded values are ____ and ___.

Graphing Rational Functions Using Asymptotes

Identify the excluded values and the vertical and horizontal asymptotes for the rational function $y = \dfrac{2}{x - 4} + 3$. **Then graph the function.**

$0 = x - 4$ To identify the excluded value, set the denominator of the function equal to zero.

$\underline{\quad} = x$ Solve for x.

A rational function in the form $y = \dfrac{a}{x + b} + c$ has a _____ asymptote at

the excluded value, or $x = -b$, and a _____ asymptote at $y = c$.

　　Vertical asymptote: $x = \underline{\quad}$ Horizontal asymptote $y = \underline{\quad}$

On the coordinate grid, graph the asymptotes using dashed lines.

Make a table of values. Choose x-values on both sides of the vertical asymptote.

x	0	2	___	___	8
y	2.5	___	undefined	4	___

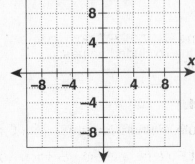

Plot the points and connect them with smooth curves.

The curves will get very close to the asymptotes, but will not touch them.

Holt Algebra 1

Ready To Go On? Skills Intervention

SECTION 10A *10-3 Simplifying Rational Expressions*

Find this vocabulary word in Lesson 10-3 and the
Multilingual Glossary.

Vocabulary
rational expression

Identifying Excluded Values

Find any excluded value of each rational expression.

A. $\dfrac{11}{k-3}$

$k - 3 =$ ___   Set the denominator equal to _____.

$k =$ ___   Solve for k.

The excluded value is ___.

B. $\dfrac{7x}{12x + x^2}$

$12x + x^2 =$ ___   Set the _____ equal to zero.

$x(_____) = 0$ Factor.

$x =$ ___ or $x =$ _____   Use the Zero Product Property and solve for x.

The excluded values are ___ and _____.

Simplifying Rational Expressions

Simplify the rational expression $\dfrac{4 - x^2}{x^2 - x - 2}$, if possible. Identify any
excluded values.

$\dfrac{4 - x^2}{x^2 - x - 2} = \dfrac{(2 - x)(\_\_\_ + x)}{(x - \_\_\_)(x + \_\_\_)}$ Factor the numerator and denominator.

$= \dfrac{-(x - \_\_\_)(x + \_\_\_)}{(x - 2)(x + \_\_\_)}$ Factor -1 from $(2 - x)$.

$= \dfrac{-(x - 2)(x + 2)}{(x - 2)(x + 1)}$ Divide out the common factor _____.

$= \underline{\hspace{3cm}}$ Simplify.

Determine the excluded values.

$x + 1 =$ ___   Set the denominator equal to zero.

$x =$ ____   Solve for x.

The excluded value is ____.

Holt Algebra 1

Name _____ Date _____ Class _____

Ready To Go On? Skills Intervention
10-4 Multiplying and Dividing Rational Expressions

Multiplying Rational Expressions.

Multiply $\dfrac{16b^4c^3}{3ac} \cdot \dfrac{15a^3b}{4b^3c^2}$. Simplify your answer.

$\dfrac{16(\underline{})a^3(b \cdot \underline{})c^3}{3(4)\underline{}b^3(c \cdot \underline{})}$ Multiply the numerators and denominators. Arrange the expression so like variables are together.

$\dfrac{\boxed{}a^{\square}b^{\square}c^3}{\boxed{}ab^3c^{\square}}$ Simplify.

$\underline{}a{-}b^2c^0$ Divide out common factors. Use properties of exponents.

$\underline{}a{-}b^2$ Simplify. Remember that $c^0 = 1$.

Multiplying Rational Expressions Containing Polynomials

Multiply $\dfrac{m^2 - m - 12}{m^2 - 9m + 20} \cdot \dfrac{m^2 - 10m + 25}{5m + 15}$. Simplify your answer.

$\dfrac{(m-4)(m+3)}{(m-\underline{})(m-\underline{})} \cdot \dfrac{(m-5)(m-\underline{})}{5(m+\underline{})}$ Factor.

$\dfrac{(m\cancel{-4})(m+3)}{(m-\underline{})(m\diagdown\underline{})} \cdot \dfrac{(m-5)(m-\underline{})}{5(m+\underline{})}$ Divide out common factors.

$\dfrac{m-\boxed{}}{\boxed{}}$ Simplify.

Dividing by Rational Expressions and Polynomials

Divide $\dfrac{2y^2 + 11y + 12}{y} \div \dfrac{2y^2 - y - 6}{y^4 - y^3}$. Simplify your answer.

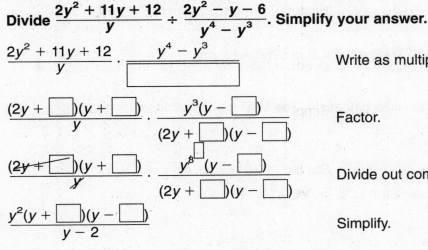

$\dfrac{2y^2 + 11y + 12}{y} \cdot \boxed{}$ Write as multiplication by the reciprocal.

$\dfrac{(2y+\boxed{})(y+\boxed{})}{y} \cdot \dfrac{y^3(y-\boxed{})}{(2y+\boxed{})(y-\boxed{})}$ Factor.

$\dfrac{(\cancel{2y+\boxed{}})(y+\boxed{})}{y} \cdot \dfrac{y^{\cancel{3}}(y-\boxed{})}{(2y+\boxed{})(y-\boxed{})}$ Divide out common factors.

$\dfrac{y^2(y+\boxed{})(y-\boxed{})}{y-2}$ Simplify.

Holt Algebra 1

Name _____ Date _____ Class _____

SECTION 10B # Ready To Go On? Skills Intervention
10-5 Adding and Subtracting Rational Expressions

Subtracting Rational Expressions with Like Denominators

Subtract $\dfrac{x^2 + 7x}{x - 3} - \dfrac{5x + 15}{x - 3}$. Simplify your answer.

$\dfrac{x^2 + 7x}{x - 3} - \dfrac{5x + 15}{x - 3} = \dfrac{x^2 + 7x - (\boxed{} + \boxed{})}{x - 3}$ Add the opposite.

$= \dfrac{x^2 + 7x - \boxed{} - \boxed{}}{x - 3}$ Distribute the negative.

$= \dfrac{x^2 + \boxed{}x - \boxed{}}{x - 3}$ Combine like terms.

$= \dfrac{(x - \boxed{})(x + \boxed{})}{x - 3}$ Factor.

$= x + \underline{}$ Simplify.

Adding and Subtracting with Unlike Denominators
Add or Subtract. Simplify your answer.

A. $\dfrac{3x}{4x^2} + \dfrac{7}{9x^3}$

Step 1 Identify the LCD. $4x^2 = 2 \cdot \underline{} \cdot x \cdot \underline{}$

$9x^3 = 3 \cdot \underline{} \cdot x \cdot \underline{} \cdot \underline{}$

$LCD = 2 \cdot \underline{} \cdot 3 \cdot \underline{} \cdot x \cdot \underline{} \cdot \underline{} = \underline{}x^3$

Step 2 Multiply each term by an appropriate form of 1. $\dfrac{3x}{4x^2} \cdot \left(\dfrac{\boxed{}x}{\boxed{}x}\right) + \dfrac{7}{9x^3} \cdot \left(\dfrac{\boxed{}}{4}\right)$

Step 3 Write each expression using the LCD. $\dfrac{\boxed{}x^2}{36x^3} + \dfrac{\boxed{}}{36x^3}$

Step 4 Add the numerators. $\dfrac{\boxed{}x^2 + \boxed{}}{36x^3}$

Step 5, 6 No factoring is needed. The problem is in simplest form.

B. $\dfrac{3}{x - 4} - \dfrac{7}{4 - x}$

Step 1 The denominators are opposite binomials. The LCD can be either $x - \underline{}$ or $\underline{} - x$.

Step 2 Multiply the second term by $\dfrac{-1}{-1}$. $\dfrac{3}{x - 4} - \dfrac{7}{4 - x} \cdot \dfrac{\boxed{}}{\boxed{}}$

Step 3 Write each expression using the LCD. $\dfrac{3}{x - 4} - \dfrac{(\boxed{})}{\boxed{}}$

Step 4 Subtract the numerators. $\dfrac{3 - (\boxed{})}{x - 4}$

Step 5, 6 No factoring is needed. Just simplify. $\dfrac{\boxed{}}{x - 4}$

Holt Algebra 1

Ready To Go On? Skills Intervention

SECTION 10B *10-6 Dividing Polynomials*

Dividing a Polynomial by a Monomial
Divide. $(2x^3 + 6x^2 - 8x + 10) \div 2x$

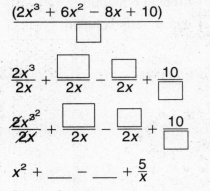

$\dfrac{(2x^3 + 6x^2 - 8x + 10)}{\boxed{}}$ Write as a rational expression.

$\dfrac{2x^3}{2x} + \dfrac{\boxed{}}{2x} - \dfrac{\boxed{}}{2x} + \dfrac{10}{\boxed{}}$ Divide each term in the polynomial by the monomial.

$\dfrac{2x^{3^2}}{\cancel{2x}} + \dfrac{\boxed{}}{2x} - \dfrac{\boxed{}}{2x} + \dfrac{10}{\boxed{}}$ Divide out common factors.

$x^2 + \underline{} - \underline{} + \dfrac{5}{x}$ Simplify.

Polynomial Long Division
Divide using long division. $(28 + 4x^2 - 23x) \div (x - 4)$

Step 1 $x - 4\overline{)4x^2 - \boxed{} + \boxed{}}$ Write in long division form with expressions in standard form.

Step 2 $x - 4\overline{)4x^2 - 23x + 28}^{\boxed{}x}$ Divide the first term of the dividend $4x^2$ by the first term of the divisor x to get the first term of the quotient.

Step 3 $x - 4\overline{)4x^2 - 23x + 28}^{\boxed{}x}$
$\ 4x^2 - \boxed{}x$ Multiply the first term of the quotient $4x$ by the binomial divisor $(x - 4)$. Place the product under the dividend, aligning like terms.

Step 4 $x - 4\overline{)\ 4x^2 - 23x + 28}^{\boxed{}x}$
$-\left(4x^2 - \boxed{}x\right)$
$0 - \boxed{}$ Subtract the product from the dividend.

Step 5 $x - 4\overline{)\ 4x^2 - 23x + 28}^{\boxed{}x}$
$-\left(4x^2 - \boxed{}x\right) \downarrow$
$0 - \boxed{} + \boxed{}$ Bring down the next term in the dividend.

Step 6 $x - 4\overline{)\ 4x^2 - 23x + 28}^{\boxed{}x - \boxed{}}$
$-\left(4x^2 - \boxed{}x\right)$
$- \boxed{} + \boxed{}$
$-(-7x + 28))$
0 Repeat Steps 2–5 as necessary.

Holt Algebra 1

SECTION 10B Ready To Go On? Skills Intervention

10-7 Solving Rational Equations

Find this vocabulary word in Lesson 10-7 and the
Multilingual Glossary.

Vocabulary

rational equation

extraneous solution

Solving Rational Equations by Using Cross Products

Solve $\dfrac{6}{x+7} = \dfrac{1}{x+2}$. Identify any extraneous solutions.

$6(x + \underline{\quad}) = x + \underline{\quad}$ Multiply cross products.

$6x + \underline{\quad} = x + \underline{\quad}$ Distribute 6 on the left side.

$\underline{\quad}x + \underline{\quad} = 7$ Subtract x from both sides.

$\underline{\quad}x = \underline{\quad}$ Subtract 12 from both sides.

$x = \underline{\quad}$ Divide both sides by 5.

Solve Rational Equations by Using the LCD.

Solve $\dfrac{8}{n^2} = \dfrac{14}{n} + 4$. Identify any extraneous solutions. Check your answer.

Step 1 Find the LCD. Include every factor of the denominators.

     The LCD is n^2.

Step 2 Multiply both sides of the equation by the LCD. Distribute on the left side.

$$n^2\left(\dfrac{8}{n^2}\right) = \underline{\quad}\left(\dfrac{14}{n} + 4\right)$$

$$8 = \underline{\quad}n + \underline{\quad}n^2$$

Step 3 Simplify and solve.

$8 = 14n + 4n^2$

$0 = 4n^2 + 14n - \underline{\quad}$

$0 = \underline{\quad}(2n^2 + \underline{\quad}n - \underline{\quad})$

$0 = 2(2n - \underline{\quad})(n + \underline{\quad})$

$0 = 2n - \underline{\quad}$ or $n + \underline{\quad} = 0$

$\underline{\quad} = n$ or $n = -4$

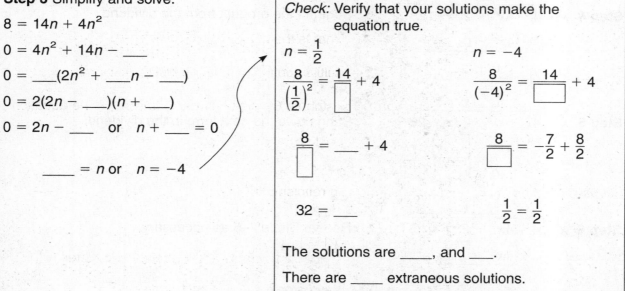

Check: Verify that your solutions make the
        equation true.

$n = \dfrac{1}{2}$ $n = -4$

$\dfrac{8}{\left(\frac{1}{2}\right)^2} = \dfrac{14}{\boxed{}} + 4$ $\dfrac{8}{(-4)^2} = \dfrac{14}{\boxed{}} + 4$

$\dfrac{8}{\boxed{}} = \underline{\quad} + 4$ $\dfrac{8}{\boxed{}} = -\dfrac{7}{2} + \dfrac{8}{2}$

$32 = \underline{\quad}$ $\dfrac{1}{2} = \dfrac{1}{2}$

The solutions are $\underline{\quad}$, and $\underline{\quad}$.

There are $\underline{\quad}$ extraneous solutions.

Holt Algebra 1

Ready To Go On? Problem Solving Intervention

SECTION 10B *10-7 Solving Rational Equations*

A rational equation is an equation that contains one or more rational expressions.

Mort can refinish a wood table in 6 hours. It takes his business partner Rebecca 10 hours to refinish the same table. How long will it take them to refinish the table if they work together?

Understand the Problem

1. What are you being asked to determine? _____
_____

2. Mort refinishes the table in ____ hours, so he completes $\frac{1}{6}$ of the table per hour.

3. Rebecca refinishes the table in ____ hours, so she completes _____ of the table per hour.

Make a Plan

4. Mort's rate, times the number of hours worked, plus Rebecca's rate, times the number of hours worked, equals the complete time to refinish the table.

Let h = the number of hours worked.

   Mort's rate + Rebecca's rate = complete job

   _____ + _____ = 1

Solve

5. Solve the rational equation.

   $\frac{1}{6}h + \frac{1}{10}h = 1$ What is the LCD? ____

   $\underline{\quad}\left(\frac{1}{6}h + \frac{1}{10}h\right) = \underline{\quad} \cdot 1$ Multiply both sides by the LCD.

   $10h + \underline{\quad} = 60$ Distribute 60 on the left side and solve the equation.

   $\underline{\quad} = 60$

   $h = \dfrac{60}{\boxed{}} = \boxed{}\ \frac{3}{4}$

6. Mort and Rebecca, working together, can refinish the table in _____ hours.

Look Back

7. In $3\frac{3}{4}$ hours, Mort completes $\frac{15}{4} \cdot \underline{\quad} = \dfrac{\boxed{}}{8}$ of the table and Rebecca completes

   $\frac{15}{4} \cdot \dfrac{1}{\boxed{}} = \dfrac{\boxed{}}{8}$ of the table. Together, they complete $\frac{5}{8} + \frac{3}{8}$ or 1 table.

Holt Algebra 1

SECTION 10B — Ready To Go On? Skills Intervention
10-8 Applying Rational Equations

Writing Rational Equations

A. Silas helps pick grapes during the harvest season. As an experienced grape harvester, he can pick a bushel of grapes in 6 minutes. Fran is a less experienced harvester. It takes her 9 minutes to pick a bushel of grapes. How long will it take them to pick 1 bushel of grapes if they work together?

The sum of the amount of grapes picked by Silas and the amount of grapes picked by Fran as they work together equals 1 bushel.

The amount of grapes Silas picks equals the product of his picking rate and the time.

The amount of grapes Fran picks equals the product of her picking rate and the time.

Step 1 Write the expression for the rate at which Silas picks grapes.

$$\frac{1 \text{ bushel}}{6 \text{ min}} = \frac{1}{\underline{}} \text{ bushel per minute}$$

Step 2 Write the expression for the amount of grapes Silas picks in time t.

$$\frac{1}{\underline{}} \cdot t$$

Step 3 Write the expression for the rate at which Fran picks grapes.

$$\frac{1 \text{ bushel}}{\underline{} \text{ min}} = \frac{1}{\underline{}} \text{ bushel per minute}$$

Step 4 Write the expression for the amount of grapes Fran picks in time t.

$$\frac{1}{\underline{}} \cdot t$$

Step 5 Write an equation to show that the sum of the amounts of grapes that Silas and Fran each pick in time t equals the amount that they both pick in time t.

$$\frac{1}{6} \cdot t + \frac{1}{9} \cdot t = \underline{}$$

Step 6 Solve the equation for t.

B. Silas and Fran continue to pick grapes at their same rates. Complete the equation that you could solve to find the time that it takes them to pick 5 bushels of grapes together.

$$\frac{}{6} \cdot t + \frac{1}{\underline{}} \cdot t = \underline{}$$

Holt Algebra 1

Ready To Go On? Problem Solving Intervention

SECTION 10B *10-8 Applying Rational Equations*

You can use rational equations to calculate amounts of substances used to prepare solutions of given concentrations.

A lab technician has 60 milliliters of a solution that is 50% ethanol. He needs a solution that is 75% ethanol. How many milliliters of ethanol should he add?

Understand the Problem

1. What are you being asked to find? _____

    _____

2. What volume of ethanol is in 60 milliliters of a solution that is 50% ethanol? _____

3. If the volume of ethanol added to the original solution is represented by *v*, what

    expression represents the volume of ethanol in the new solution? _____

4. In terms of *v*, what expression represents the total volume of the new solution? _____

Make a Plan

5. Construct a table that shows the volume of ethanol and the total volume of the solution.

	Ethanol (mL)	Total (mL)
Original	30	60
New	30 + *v*	60 + *v*

6. Write an equation to express the 75% concentration of the new

    solution in terms of the volume of ethanol and the total volume of the solution.

    _____

Solve

5. Solve this equation for *v*.

$$\frac{30 + v}{60 + v} = 0.75$$

$$0.25v = 15$$

$$v = \_\_\_\_$$

The technician must add _____ milliliters of ethanol to the 60 milliliters of the 50% solution.

Check

6. If 60 mL is substituted into the concentration formula,
    is the new concentration 75%? _____

$$\frac{30 + \_\_\_}{60 + \_\_\_} = \frac{\_\_\_}{\_\_\_} = \_\_\_\_$$

Holt Algebra 1

Ready To Go On? Skills Intervention

SECTION 11A *11-1 Square-Root Functions*

Find this vocabulary word in Lesson 11-1 and the
Multilingual Glossary.

Vocabulary
square-root function

Finding the Domain of Square-Root Functions
Find the domain of the function $y = \sqrt{2x} + 4$.

The domain of a function is the _____ of *x*-coordinates.
To be part of the domain, the values in the radicand must be greater than

or equal to _____.

What is the expression inside the square root? _____

Complete the inequality. $2x \geq$ ___

Solve the inequality.

$2x \geq$ ___

$\dfrac{2x}{\Box} \geq \dfrac{\Box}{\Box}$

$x \geq$ ___

The domain of the function is $x \geq$ ___.

Graphing Square-Root Functions
Graph $y = \sqrt{x} - 2$.

Complete the table to graph
the function $y = \sqrt{x}$.

x	0	1	4	9
y	0	___	___	___

Move the function to the right ___ units
to graph the function $y = \sqrt{x} - 2$.

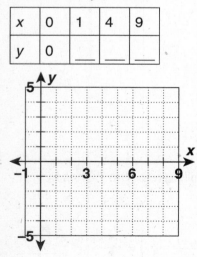

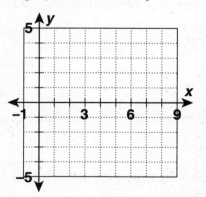

Holt Algebra 1

Name _____ Date _____ Class _____

Ready To Go On? Problem Solving Intervention
11-1 Square-Root Functions

A square-root function is a function in which the variable is included in the radicand.

On wet concrete, the function $y = \sqrt{12x}$ gives the speed in miles per hour when the length of the skid mark is x feet. Find the speed that the car was traveling if it left a skid mark that was 210 ft long. Round your answer to the nearest hundredth.

Understand the Problem

1. What does x represent in the function? _____

2. What does y represent? _____

3. What are you asked to find? _____

Make a Plan

4. How long was the skid mark? _____

5. For which variable do you substitute the value 210? ____

Solve

6. Substitute the given value for x into the function.

$y = \sqrt{12(\underline{\hspace{1cm}})}$

$y = \sqrt{\underline{\hspace{1.5cm}}}$

$y = \underline{\hspace{2cm}}$

7. To which place are you asked to round your answer? _____

8. Which number is in the thousandths place? ____

9. The speed of the car was _____ mi/h.

Look Back

10. To check your answer, substitute it in for y and solve for x.

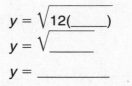

$$\underline{\hspace{1.5cm}} = \sqrt{12x}$$

$$(\underline{\hspace{1.5cm}})^2 = (\sqrt{12x})^2$$

$$\underline{\hspace{2cm}} = 12x$$

$$\frac{\boxed{}}{12} = \frac{12x}{12}$$

$$\underline{\hspace{1.5cm}} = x$$

11. Does your answer check? _____

Holt Algebra 1

Name _____ Date _____ Class _____

Find this vocabulary word in Lesson 11-2 and the Multilingual
Glossary.

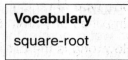

Vocabulary
square-root

Simplifying Square-Root Expressions

Simplify the expression $\sqrt{\dfrac{125}{5}}$.

Simplify the expression inside the radicand. $\quad \dfrac{125}{5} = \dfrac{\square \cdot \square \cdot \square}{5} = \underline{\quad}$

Find the square root of the simplified expression.

Which number multiplied by itself is 25? ___ $\qquad \sqrt{\square} = \underline{\quad}$

So $\sqrt{\dfrac{125}{5}} = \underline{\quad}$.

Using the Product Property of Square Roots

Simplify the expression $\sqrt{j^6 k^3}$. **All variables represent nonnegative numbers.**

The square root of $j^6 k^3$ is equal to the product of the _____ of j^6 and the

square root of ___.

$$\sqrt{j^6 k^3} = \sqrt{\underline{\quad}} \cdot \sqrt{k^3}$$

$(j^3)^{\underline{\ }} = j^6 \longrightarrow \sqrt{j^6} = j^{\underline{\ }} \qquad \Big| \qquad \sqrt{k^3} = \sqrt{k^{\underline{\ }}} \cdot \sqrt{k^1} \qquad \sqrt{k^2} = k^{\underline{\ }}$

$$\sqrt{j^6 k^3} = j^{\underline{\ }} k^{\underline{\ }} \sqrt{k}$$

Using the Quotient Property of Square Roots

Simplify the expression $\sqrt{\dfrac{9}{121z^2}}$. **All variables represent nonnegative numbers.**

The square root of $\dfrac{9}{121z^2}$ is equal to the quotient of the _____ of 9 and the

square root of _____.

$= \dfrac{\sqrt{9}}{\sqrt{\square}}$ Use the Quotient Property to rewrite the expression.

$= \dfrac{\square}{11\square}$ Find the square root of the numerator and the denominator.

Holt Algebra 1

Name _____ Date _____ Class _____

Ready to Go On? Problem Solving Intervention
11-2 Radical Expressions

One type of radical expression contains square roots. These expressions can be simplified or written as a number with decimal.

How long is the diagonal of a rectangular picture frame that is 18 in. wide and 20 in. long? Give the answer as a radical expression in simplest form. Then estimate the length to the nearest tenth of an inch.

Understand the Problem

1. What are you first asked to do? _____

2. What is the second part of the problem? _____

3. What is the final part of the problem? _____

Make a Plan

4. A rectangle can be divided into two _____ triangles.

5. Which formula can you use to find the length of a diagonal in a right triangle?

   _____

6. Fill in the given values in the diagram.

   ___ in. [diagram of rectangle with diagonal labeled x]

   ___ in.

Solve

Recall the Pythagorean Theorem, $a^2 + b^2 = c^2$, where a and b are the lengths of the legs of the triangle and c is the length of the hypotenuse.

7. What is the length of each leg? _____

8. What variable represents the length of the diagonal? ___

9. Substitute the values from Exercises 7 and 8 into the formula. $\underline{}^2 + \underline{}^2 = c^2$

10. Simplify the equation. $\underline{}^2 + \underline{}^2 = c^2$

    $\underline{} + 400 = c^2$

    $\underline{} = c^2$

    $\sqrt{\underline{}} = \sqrt{c^2}$

    $\sqrt{\underline{} \cdot 181} = c$

    $\underline{}\sqrt{181} = c$

11. Estimate the length to the nearest tenth of an inch.

    $\underline{}\sqrt{181} = c$

    $2 \cdot \underline{} = c$

    $\underline{} = c$

    The diagonal of the frame is _____ in.

Look Back

12. Substitute your answer in for c and check your answer.

    $a^2 + b^2 = c^2$

13. Does your answer check? _____

    $18^2 + 20^2 = \underline{}^2$

    $724 \approx \underline{}$

Holt Algebra 1

Ready To Go On? Skills Intervention

SECTION 11A *11-3 Adding and Subtracting Radical Expressions*

Find this vocabulary word in Lesson 11-3 and the Multilingual Glossary.

Vocabulary
like radicals

Adding and Subtracting Square-Root Expressions
Simplify each expression.

A. $15\sqrt{10} + 6\sqrt{10}$

What are the numbers inside each of the two radicals? _____

Are the radicals like or unlike radicals? _____

Use the Distributive Property to rewrite the expression.

$15\sqrt{10} + 6\sqrt{10}$

$= \sqrt{10}(\Box + \Box)$

$= \sqrt{10}(\Box)$ Combine like terms.

$= \Box\sqrt{10}$

B. $9\sqrt{z} - 5\sqrt{z}$

What are the numbers inside each of the two radicals? _____

Are the radicals like or unlike radicals? _____

Use the Distributive Property to rewrite the expression.

$9\sqrt{z} - 5\sqrt{z}$

$= \sqrt{z}(\Box - \Box)$

$= \sqrt{z}(\Box)$ Combine like terms.

$= \Box\sqrt{z}$

Simplifying Before Adding and Subtracting
Simplify the expression $\sqrt{96} - \sqrt{24}$.

Simplify $\sqrt{96}$.

What is the LARGEST square number that divides into 96 without a remainder? ___

Rewrite $\sqrt{96}$ as the square root of a product. $\sqrt{96} = \sqrt{\Box \cdot 6} = \sqrt{\Box} \cdot \sqrt{6} = \Box\sqrt{6}$

What is the LARGEST square number that divides into 24 without a remainder? ___

Rewrite $\sqrt{24}$ as the square root of a product. $\sqrt{24} = \sqrt{\Box \cdot 6} = \sqrt{\Box} \cdot \sqrt{6} = \Box\sqrt{6}$

$\sqrt{96} - \sqrt{24} = \Box\sqrt{6} - \Box\sqrt{6}$

Are the radicals like or unlike radicals? _____

Use the Distributive Property. $\Box\sqrt{6} - \Box\sqrt{6} = \sqrt{6}(\Box - \Box)$

Combine like terms. $\sqrt{6}(\Box - \Box) = \sqrt{6}(\Box) = \Box\sqrt{6}$

     Holt Algebra 1

SECTION 11A Ready To Go On? Skills Intervention
11-4 Multiplying and Dividing Radical Expressions

Multiplying Square Roots
Multiply. Write the product $\sqrt{6}\sqrt{12}$ in simplest form.

Rewrite the product as the square root of a product. $\sqrt{6}\sqrt{12} = \sqrt{6 \cdot \boxed{}} = \sqrt{\boxed{}}$

What is the LARGEST square number that divides evenly into 72? ___

Rewrite the number inside the radical. $\sqrt{\boxed{}} = \sqrt{\boxed{} \cdot 2}$

Simplify. $\qquad\qquad = \sqrt{\boxed{}} \cdot \sqrt{2}$

$\qquad\qquad\qquad = \boxed{}\sqrt{2}$

Multiplying Sums and Differences of Radicals
Multiply. Write the product $(4 + \sqrt{7})(5 - \sqrt{7})$ in simplest form.

Use FOIL to help you correctly use the Distributive Property.

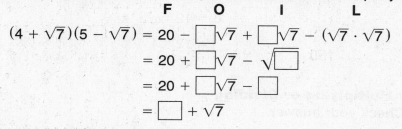

$\qquad\qquad$ **F** $\qquad$ **O** $\qquad\qquad$ **I** $\qquad\qquad$ **L**

$(4 + \sqrt{7})(5 - \sqrt{7}) = 20 - \boxed{}\sqrt{7} + \boxed{}\sqrt{7} - (\sqrt{7} \cdot \sqrt{7})$

$\qquad\qquad\qquad = 20 + \boxed{}\sqrt{7} - \sqrt{\boxed{}}$

$\qquad\qquad\qquad = 20 + \boxed{}\sqrt{7} - \boxed{}$

$\qquad\qquad\qquad = \boxed{} + \sqrt{7}$

Rationalizing the Denominator
Simplify the quotient $\dfrac{\sqrt{10m}}{\sqrt{32}}$. All variables represent nonnegative numbers.

Rewrite $\dfrac{\sqrt{10m}}{\sqrt{32}}$ with one radical. $\dfrac{\sqrt{10m}}{\sqrt{32}} = \sqrt{\dfrac{10m}{\boxed{}}}$

Simplify the fraction in the radical. $\qquad = \sqrt{\dfrac{2 \cdot \boxed{}m}{2 \cdot \boxed{}}} = \sqrt{\dfrac{\boxed{}m}{\boxed{}}}$

Rewrite the expression using the Quotient of Square Roots Property. $\qquad = \dfrac{\sqrt{\boxed{}m}}{\sqrt{\boxed{}}}$

Simplify the radical in the numerator and denominator. $\qquad = \dfrac{\sqrt{\boxed{}}m}{4}$

Holt Algebra 1

Ready To Go On? Skills Intervention

SECTION 11A *11-5 Solving Radical Equations*

Find these vocabulary words in Lesson 11-5 and the Multilingual Glossary.

Vocabulary
radical equation

Solving Radical Equations by Adding or Subtracting

Solve the equation $\sqrt{x} - 6 = 12$. Check your answer.

$\sqrt{x} - 6 = 12$

$+\boxed{} = +\boxed{}$ Add ___ to both sides.

$\sqrt{x} = \boxed{}$

$(\sqrt{x})^2 = (\boxed{})^2$ Square both sides.

$x = \boxed{}$ ⟶ Check your answer: $x = \boxed{}$

$\sqrt{x} - 6 = 12$

$\sqrt{\boxed{}} - 6 = 12$

$\boxed{} - 6 = 12$

$\boxed{} = 12$

Does your answer check? _____

Solving Radical Equations by Multiplying or Dividing

Solve the equation $-4\sqrt{x} = -8$. Check your answer.

$-4\sqrt{x} = -8$

$\dfrac{-4\sqrt{x}}{\boxed{}} = \dfrac{-8}{\boxed{}}$ Divide both sides by ____.

$\sqrt{x} = \boxed{}$

$(\sqrt{x})^2 = (\boxed{})^2$ Square both sides.

$x = \boxed{}$ ⟶ Check your answer: $x = \boxed{}$

$-4\sqrt{x} = -8$

$-4\sqrt{\boxed{}} = -8$

$-4(\boxed{}) = -8$

$(\boxed{}) = -8$

Does your answer check? _____

Holt Algebra 1

SECTION 11B Ready To Go On? Skills Intervention
11-6 Geometric Sequences

Find these vocabulary words in Lesson 11-6 and the Multilingual Glossary.

Vocabulary	
geometric sequence	common ratio

Extending Geometric Sequences

Find the next three terms in each geometric sequence.

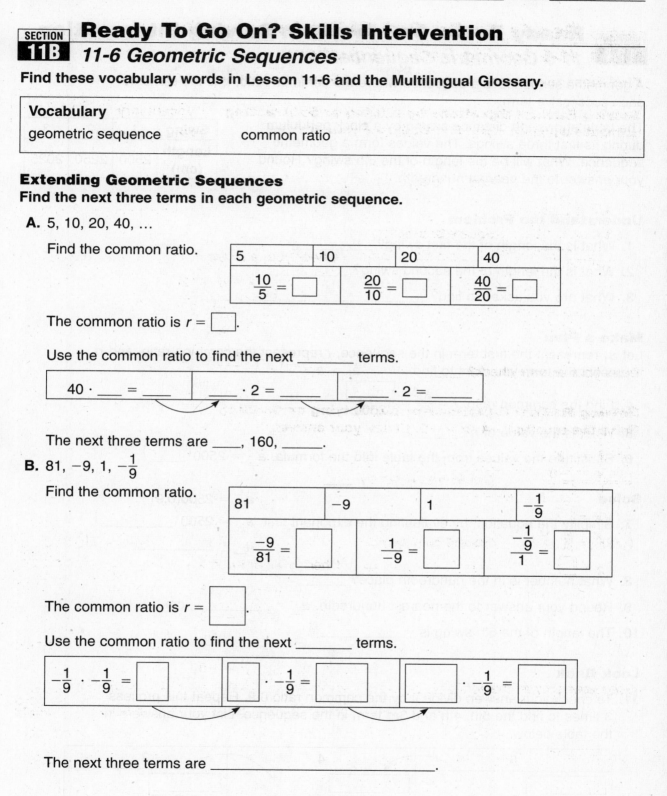

A. 5, 10, 20, 40, …

Find the common ratio.

5	10	20	40
$\frac{10}{5} = \square$	$\frac{20}{10} = \square$	$\frac{40}{20} = \square$	

The common ratio is $r = \square$.

Use the common ratio to find the next _____ terms.

$40 \cdot \underline{\quad} = \underline{\quad}$	$\underline{\quad} \cdot 2 = \underline{\quad}$	$\underline{\quad} \cdot 2 = \underline{\quad}$

The next three terms are ____, 160, _____.

B. 81, −9, 1, $-\frac{1}{9}$

Find the common ratio.

81	−9	1	$-\frac{1}{9}$
$\frac{-9}{81} = \square$	$\frac{1}{-9} = \square$	$\frac{-\frac{1}{9}}{1} = \square$	

The common ratio is $r = \square$.

Use the common ratio to find the next _____ terms.

$-\frac{1}{9} \cdot -\frac{1}{9} = \square$	$\square \cdot -\frac{1}{9} = \square$	$\square \cdot -\frac{1}{9} = \square$

The next three terms are _____.

Holt Algebra 1

SECTION 11B Ready To Go On? Problem Solving Intervention

11-6 Geometric Sequences

A geometric sequence is a sequence where the common ratio, r, is the same in each successive term.

The table shows the distance swung by a clock pendulum during its first three swings. The values form a geometric sequence. What will be the length of the 6th swing? Round your answer to the nearest hundredth.

Swing	1	2	3
Length (cm)	2500	2250	2025

Understand the Problem

1. What is the length of the first swing? _____

2. What is the length of the second swing? _____

3. What are you asked to find? _____

Make a Plan

Let a_1 represent the first term in the sequence, r represent the common ratio, and n represent the term you want to find. $a_n = a_1 r^{n-1}$

4. Find the common ratio: $r = \dfrac{a_2}{a_1} = \dfrac{\boxed{}}{2500} = $ _____

5. What is the value of n? _____

6. Substitute the values from the table into the formula. $a_{\underline{}} = 2500\left(\underline{}\right)^{\underline{}-1}$

Solve

$a_{\underline{}} = 2500(0.9)^{\underline{}}$

7. Simplify the equation, by evaluating the exponent first. $a_{\underline{}} = 2500\left(\underline{}\right)$

$a_{\underline{}} = $ _____

8. What number is in the hundredth place? _____

9. Round your answer to the nearest hundredth. $a_{\underline{}} = $ _____ cm

10. The length of the 6th swing is _____.

Look Back

11. To check your answer, divide it by the common ratio 0.9. Repeat this process 3 times to find the 5th, 4th and 3rd term in the sequence. List your answers in the table below.

5		4		3
$\dfrac{\boxed{}}{0.9} = $ _____		$\dfrac{\boxed{}}{0.9} = $ _____		$\dfrac{\boxed{}}{0.9} = $ _____

Does your result for the 3rd term match the value in the original table? _____

Holt Algebra 1

SECTION 11B — Ready To Go On? Skills Intervention
11-7 Exponential Functions

Find this vocabulary word in Lesson 11-7 and the
Multilingual Glossary.

Vocabulary

exponential function

Graphing $y = ab^x$ with $a > 0$ and $b > 1$.
Graph the exponential function $y = 2(3)^x$.

Complete the table to generate ordered pairs.

Plot the points and connect them.

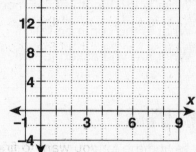

x	$y = 2(3)^x$	Ordered Pairs
-1	$y = 2(3)^{\square} = 2\left(\dfrac{\square}{\square}\right) = \square$	$\left(-1, \dfrac{}{\_\_}\right)$
0	$y = 2(3)^{\square} = 2(\square) = \_\_$	$(0, \_\_)$
1	$y = 2(3)^{\square} = 2(\square) = \_\_$	$(1, \_\_)$
2	$y = 2(3)^{\square} = 2(\square) = \_\_$	$(2, \_\_)$

Graphing $y = ab^x$ with $0 < b < 1$.

Graph the exponential function $y = -2\left(\dfrac{1}{2}\right)^x$.

Complete the table to generate ordered pairs.

Plot the points and connect them.

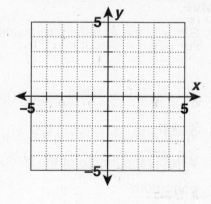

x	$y = -2\left(\dfrac{1}{2}\right)^x$	Ordered Pairs
-1	$y = -2\left(\dfrac{1}{2}\right)^{\square} = -2(\square) = \_\_$	$(-1, \_\_)$
0	$y = -2\left(\dfrac{1}{2}\right)^{\square} = -2(\square) = \_\_$	$(0, \_\_)$
1	$y = -2\left(\dfrac{1}{2}\right)^{\square} = -2\left(\dfrac{\square}{\square}\right) = \_\_$	$(1, \_\_)$
2	$y = -2\left(\dfrac{1}{2}\right)^{\square} = -2\left(\dfrac{\square}{\square}\right) = \_\_$	$\left(2, \dfrac{\square}{\square}\right)$

Holt Algebra 1

SECTION 11B Ready To Go On? Problem Solving Intervention
11-7 Exponential Functions

An exponential function is a function where the independent variable appears as an exponent.

The function $y = 10(1.1)^x$ gives the length, in inches, of a model airplane after being enlarged by 10% x times. What is the length of the airplane after it has been enlarged 5 times? Round your answer to the nearest hundredth.

Understand the Problem

1. What is the length of the model airplane before it is enlarged? _____

2. What is the common ratio? _____

3. What are you asked to find? _____

_____

Make a Plan

4. To find the length of the airplane after it has been enlarged 5 times, substitute

   ____ in for x.

5. Substitute the value for x into the function. $y = 10(1.1)^x$

   $y = 10(1.1)^{\underline{}}$

Solve

6. Simplify the equation, by evaluating the exponent first.

   $y = 10(1.1)^{\underline{}}$

   $y = 10(\underline{})$

   $y = \underline{}$

7. What number is in the thousandths place? _____

8. What is the length of the airplane after it has been enlarged 5 times to the nearest

   hundredth? _____ in.

Look Back

9. Use a graphing calculator to graph the function $y = 10(1.1)^x$.

   Use the TRACE feature to move the cursor to where the value for x is
   approximately 5. What is the approximate corresponding value for y? ____

10. Does this value for y correspond to your answer in Exercise 8? _____

Holt Algebra 1

Name _____ Date _____ Class _____

Ready To Go On? Skills Intervention
11-8 Exponential Growth and Decay

Find these vocabulary words in Lesson 11-8 and the Multilingual Glossary.

Vocabulary			
exponential growth	compound interest	exponential decay	half-life

Exponential Growth
Write a function to model each situation. Then find the value of the function after the given amount of time. Round to the nearest dollar.

A. Twenty thousand dollars is invested for 15 years at a rate of 1%.

An exponential growth function has the form $y = a(1 + r)^t$ where:

- a represents the _____ amount, or $_____.
- r represents the _____, or ____%.
- t represents the _____.

Substitute these values into the formula $y = a(1 + r)^t$.

$y = \boxed{}\left(1 + \boxed{}\right)^t$

Now, let $t =$ ____ years and solve for y.

$y = \boxed{}(1.01)^{\boxed{}}$

$y = 20{,}000\left(\boxed{}\right)$

$y = 23{,}219.38$

The value of the investment in 15 years will be $_____.

B. $6000 is invested at rate of 2.5% compounded semi-annually for 8 years.

The formula for compound interest is $A = P\left(1 + \frac{r}{n}\right)^{nt}$ where:

- A represents the _____ after t _____.
- P represents the _____ amount.
- r represents the annual interest _____.
- n represents the number of times the _____ is compounded per year.

What is the original amount? _____

What is the interest rate? _____

Semi-annual means ____ times per year.

Substitute these values into the formula.

Now, let $t =$ ____ years and solve for A.

$A = 6000\left(1 + \dfrac{\boxed{}}{\boxed{}}\right)^{\boxed{}t}$

$A = 6000\left(1 + \dfrac{0.025}{\boxed{}}\right)^{\boxed{}\boxed{}}$

$A = 6000(1.0125)^{\boxed{}}$

$A = 6000\left(\boxed{}\right)$

The amount of money in 8 years will be $_____.

$A = \boxed{}$

Holt Algebra 1

Name _____ Date _____ Class _____

SECTION	# Ready To Go On? Problem Solving Intervention
11B	*11-8 Exponential Growth and Decay*

Exponential growth and decay models many real-world situations like population, value, half-life, etc.

A certain isotope has a half-life of almost 2 years. About how much will be left from a 50-g sample after 20 years. Round your answer to the nearest thousandth.

Understand the Problem

1. How much of the isotope is present before it begins to decay? _____

2. What is the half-life of the isotope? _____

3. What are you asked to find? _____

Make a Plan

Let *A* represent the final amount, *P* represent the original amount, and *t* represent the number of half-lives in a given time period. $A = P(0.5)^t$

4. Find the value of *t*: $t = \dfrac{\text{time period}}{\text{half-life}} = \dfrac{\boxed{}}{2} = $ ___

5. What is the value of *P*? _____

6. Substitute known values into the formula. $A = \underline{}(0.5)^{\overline{}}$

Solve

7. Solve the equation for *A*, by evaluating the exponent first.

$$A = \underline{}(0.5)^{\overline{}}$$

$$A = 50(\underline{\hspace{3cm}})$$

$$A = \underline{\hspace{3cm}}$$

8. Which number is in the ten-thousandths place? _____

9. Round your answer to the nearest thousandth. $A = $ _____ g

10. How many grams of the isotope is left from a 50-g sample after 20 years? _____

Look Back

11. Substitute your answer from Exercise 10 for *A*   _____ $= P(0.5)^{10}$
    and solve for *P*.

    _____ $= P(\underline{\hspace{3cm}})$

    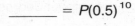 $= \dfrac{P(0.0009765625)}{(\underline{\hspace{2cm}})}$

12. Does your answer check? _____   _____ $= P$

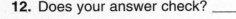

Holt Algebra 1

Name _____ Date _____ Class _____

Graphing Data to Choose a Model

Graph each data set. Which kind of model best describes the data?

A. $\{(-0.5, -5.5),(0, -4),(1, -1),(2, 2),(3, 5)\}$

Plot the coordinate points and connect them.

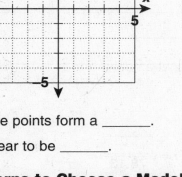

The coordinate points form a _____.

The data appear to be _____.

B. $\left\{\left(-2, -\frac{1}{9}\right),\left(-1, -\frac{1}{3}\right),(0, -1),(1, -3), (2, -9)\right\}$

Plot the coordinate points and connect them.

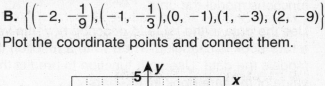

The coordinate points form a _____.

The data appear to be _____.

Using Patterns to Choose a Model

Look for a pattern in the data set $\left\{(-1, 9), (0, 3), (1, 1), \left(2, \frac{1}{3}\right), \left(3, \frac{1}{9}\right)\right\}$ **to determine which kind of model best describes the data.**

Complete the table and determine the pattern.

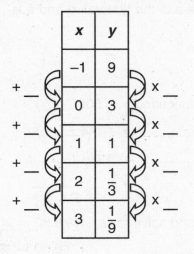

x	y
−1	9
0	3
1	1
2	$\frac{1}{3}$
3	$\frac{1}{9}$

For every constant change in the

_____, there is a constant

ratio of _____ in the *y*-coordinate.

Because there is a constant ratio,
the data appear to be

_____.

Holt Algebra 1

SECTION 11B Ready To Go On? Problem Solving Intervention
11-9 Linear, Quadratic, and Exponential Models

Different types of models can describe different situations. You must first look at the data and determine the pattern. It is possible that quadratic, linear, or exponential functions model the data.

Use the data in the table to describe how the value of a rare book is changing. Then write a function that models the data. Use your function to predict the value of the rare book in 16 years.

Value of a Rare Book				
Years	0	1	2	3
Value ($)	50	62.5	78.13	97.66

Understand the Problem

1. What are you first asked to do? _____

2. What is the second part of the problem? _____

3. What is the final part of the problem? _____

Make a Plan

4. Determine the common ratio.

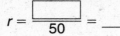

$r = \dfrac{\boxed{}}{50} = $ _____ $r = \dfrac{\boxed{}}{62.50} = $ _____ $r = \dfrac{\boxed{}}{78.13} = $ _____

5. Is there a common ratio? _____

6. The value of the book is increasing by _____% each year.

Solve

Recall the general form of an exponential function, where *a* is the first value and *b* is the common ratio. $y = ab^x$

7. What is the common ratio? _____

8. What is the value of the book in year 0? _____

9. Use the values from Exercises 7 and 8 to write the function. $y = 50(\underline{})^x$

10. Substitute 16 in for *x* and solve for *y*. $y = 50(\underline{})^{-}$

11. In 16 years, the value of the rare book will be _____. $y = 50(\underline{})$

$y \approx $ _____

Look Back

12. Substitute your answer for *y* into the original function and solve for *a*. $1776.50 = a(\underline{})^{-}$

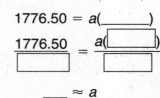

$1776.50 = a(\underline{})$

$\dfrac{1776.50}{\boxed{}} = \dfrac{a(\boxed{})}{\boxed{}}$

13. Does your answer check? _____

___ $\approx a$

Holt Algebra 1

Name _____ Date _____ Class _____

1-1 Variables and Expressions
Give two ways to write each algebraic expression in words.

1. $6 + z$ _____

2. $r - 4$ _____

3. $\frac{s}{5}$ _____

4. $9m$ _____

5. Jane bikes at a rate of 12 miles per hour. Write an expression for the amount she bikes in h hours.

_____

6. It takes 35 minutes for a pan of brownies to bake. Write an expression for the number of minutes left after m minutes have elapsed.

_____

Evaluate each expression for $x = 2$, $y = 10$, and $z = 3$.

7. $y \div x$ **8.** xy

_____   _____

9. $x + y$ **10.** $y - z$

_____   _____

1-2 Adding and Subtracting Real Numbers
Add or subtract.

11. $76 + (-19)$ **12.** $54 - 21$

_____   _____

13. $6 - \left(-2\frac{1}{2}\right)$ **14.** $x + (-12)$ for $x = -6$

_____   _____

15. Taylor's credit card balance shows a balance of $-\$50$. What will the balance be after Taylor makes a credit card payment of \$85?

_____

SECTION 1A

Ready to Go On? Quiz continued

1-3 Multiplying and Dividing Real Numbers
Find the value of each expression.

16. $-6(6)$ _____

17. $8 \div \dfrac{4}{9}$ _____

18. $5.6 \div 0$ _____

19. $-\dfrac{1}{4}x$ for $x = -\dfrac{1}{4}$ _____

20. Alex babysat for $8\dfrac{1}{2}$ hours. Alex charges $8.00 per hour. How much money did

   Alex earn babysitting? _____

1-4 Powers and Exponents
Simplify each expression.

21. $(-6)^2$

_____

22. -3^2

_____

23. $\left(-\dfrac{2}{5}\right)^3$

_____

24. $\left(-\dfrac{1}{3}\right)^5$

_____

25. A gigameter is a unit of length equal to 10 to the 9th power. Express this number in

   two ways. _____

1-5 Roots and Irrational Numbers
Find each square root.

26. $\sqrt{169}$ _____

27. $-\sqrt{81}$ _____

28. $\sqrt{196}$ _____

29. $\sqrt{\dfrac{4}{100}}$ _____

30. Tom is building a square kitchen table. The table will cover 39 square feet. Find
   the length of a side of the table to the nearest tenth of a foot.

   _____

Classify each real number. Write all classifications that apply.

31. $\dfrac{1}{9}$ _____

32. $\sqrt{15}$ _____

33. $\sqrt{900}$ _____

34. -9 _____

Holt Algebra 1

SECTION 1B Ready to Go On? Quiz

1-6 Properties of Real Numbers
Name the property that is illustrated in each equation.

1. $12 \cdot 26 = 26 \cdot 12$ _____

2. $3 + (2 + 11) = (3 + 2) + 11$ _____

3. $a(-7) = -7a$ _____

4. $ar + 25 = 25 + ar$ _____

Write each product using the Distributive Property. Then simplify.

5. $8(56)$ **6.** $6(26)$

_____   _____

7. $13(16)$ **8.** $4(102)$

_____   _____

Find a counterexample to show that each statement is false.

9. The set of odd numbers is closed under subtraction.

_____

10. The set of negative integers is closed under subtraction.

_____

1-7 Simplifying Expressions
Simplify each expression.

11. $-8 + 16 \div (-2)$ **12.** $28 - 7 + 5$

_____   _____

Holt Algebra 1

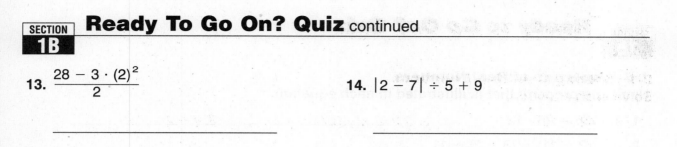

13. $\dfrac{28 - 3 \cdot (2)^2}{2}$

14. $|2 - 7| \div 5 + 9$

_____

_____

Answer the following question.

15. The formula for a baseball player's total number of bases is $Hits + D + 2T + 3H$. Use this expression and the information in the table to determine the player's total number of bases.

Batting Information	Number
Hits	16
Double (D)	0
Triple (T)	3
Home run (H)	1

_____

Simplify each expression by combining like terms.

16. $6s + 20s$

17. $28x + 3$

18. $-6.3d + 9.5d$

_____

_____

_____

19. $5b - 3b$

20. $7x + 3 - 2x$

21. $5t + 4 + 2t - 3$

_____

_____

_____

Use properties and operations to show that the first expression simplifies to the second expression.

22. $5x^2 + 6x - 9x^2 + x;\ -4x^2 + 7x$

$(-9x^2 + 5x^2) + (6x + x)$

23. $-3(4x + 3y + 5x - 2y);\ -27x - 3y$

$-3(4x + 5x) - 3(3y - 2y) = -3(9x) - 3(y)$

_____

_____

Holt Algebra 1

SECTION 2A Ready to Go On? Quiz

2-1 Solving One-Step Equations
Solve each equation.

1. $x - 42 = 16$

2. $2.3 = k - 0.7$

3. $j + 2 = -11$

_____

_____

_____

4. $52 = 4y$

5. $3.4 = \dfrac{n}{2}$

6. $\dfrac{2}{3} = g - \dfrac{1}{6}$

_____

_____

_____

7. At the beginning of the week, Joshua had \$356 in his savings account. At the end of the week, he had only \$123 in his savings account. Write and solve an equation to find the amount of money that Joshua spent during the week.

_____

8. There are 450 students who participate in extracurricular activities at school. This is $\dfrac{5}{8}$ of the total number of students enrolled in the school. Write and solve an equation to find the number of students enrolled in the school.

_____

2-2 Solving Two-Step Equations
Solve each equation.

9. $4r + 60 = 400$

10. $3.0 + 0.2g = 3.8$

11. $60 - 2j = 40$

_____

_____

_____

12. $\dfrac{x}{5} - 2 = 6$

13. $\dfrac{7}{8}x + 3 = 17$

14. $2 - \dfrac{1}{2}x = 3$

_____

_____

_____

15. A house painter charges each customer a \$50 estimation fee and then \$30 per hour. Write and solve an equation to find the number of hours the painter worked if she earned \$1250 at the job.

_____

16. Jan's charm bracelet weighs a total of 9.0 ounces with each charm having a weight of 1.2 ounces. Write and solve an equation to find the number of charms on her bracelet if the bracelet chain itself weighs 3.0 ounces.

_____

Holt Algebra 1

SECTION 2A

Ready to Go On? Quiz continued

2-3 Solving Multi-Step Equations

Solve each equation.

17. $\dfrac{5n - 3}{2} = 6$ 18. $8b - 4 + 2b = 16$ 19. $2(f - 7) = 10$

_____   _____   _____

20. $5d - 4 - 8d = 2$ 21. $\dfrac{3}{2}(x - 2) = 6$ 22. $2(1 + 3y) = 11$

_____   _____   _____

23. A small nursery displays 34 potted trees in four rows. The first row has 7 maple trees. The second and third rows each have the same number of dogwood trees. The fourth row has 11 willow trees. Write and solve an equation to determine the number of dogwood trees in each row.

_____

24. An ice cream shop sells a sundae with 1 topping for $2.75. A sundae with 2 or more toppings costs $2.00 plus $0.60 for each topping. Anna bought 2 sundaes and her bill was $6.55. One sundae had one topping. Write and solve an equation to find the number of toppings on the second sundae.

_____

2-4 Solving Equations with Variables on Both Sides

25. $6x - 5 = 4x + 7$ 26. $4(3x - 6) = 3(4x - 3)$

_____   _____

27. $4(2n - 5) = 7(2n + 4)$ 28. $6(k + 7) = -6(k + 7)$

_____   _____

29. On the first day of the month, one investment began with $1568 and started losing $16 each day. Another investment began with $854 and started earning $26 each day. Write and solve an equation to determine the number of days in which the two investments will have the same amount of money. What will that amount be?

_____

30. Twice June's age increased by one is three times her age decreased by 10. Write and solve an equation to find June's age.

_____

Holt Algebra 1

SECTION 2B

Ready to Go On? Quiz

2-5 Solving Proportions

1. Last month, the ratio of DVDs to VHS tapes sold at a video store was _____
8:3. Sixty VHS tapes were sold. How many DVDs were sold?

2. A florist designs an arrangement of roses to have a ratio of 1 red rose _____
to 3 white roses. If the arrangement has two dozen white roses, how
many red roses will it have?

Find the unit rate.

3. An 8-oz can of corn costs $0.96.

4. Brian can type 990 words in 30 minutes.

_____ _____

5. A potter makes 110 pots in 5 days.

6. A farmer harvests 180 bushels of apples
from an orchard of 9 trees.

_____ _____

Solve each proportion.

7. $\dfrac{-12}{x} = \dfrac{3}{2}$

8. $\dfrac{k}{9} = \dfrac{6}{12}$

_____ _____

9. $\dfrac{2}{6} = \dfrac{r+2}{11}$

10. $\dfrac{-5}{9} = \dfrac{10}{x+8}$

_____ _____

11. Find 25% of 60. _____

12. Find 160% of 12. _____

13. 27 is what percent of 60? _____

14. What percent of 125 is 400? _____

15. 12 is 75% of what number? _____

16. 160% of what number is 64? _____

17. A college savings fund has 30% of the money invested in stocks. If the stocks have
a value of $3000, what is the value of the college fund?

_____

18. An architectural drawing of a building has a scale of 1 in. = 2 ft. The length of a
wall in the drawing is 6.5 in. What is the length of the wall in the building?

_____

Holt Algebra 1

2-6 Solving Literal Equations for a Variable

19. Solve $6m + n = p - 7$ for p.

20. Solve $a + b = 4(c - 5)$ for c.

_____

_____

21. Solve $6k + 7n = 12$ for k.

22. Solve $I = V/R$ for V.

_____

_____

23. A simple microscope can produce an enlarged image of an object. The formula $m = \dfrac{i}{o}$ relates the magnification of the microscope, m, to the length of the image, i, and the length of the object, o.

  a. Solve $m = \dfrac{i}{o}$ for i. _____

  b. A student views a 0.03-mm strand of algae under a microscope that has a magnification of 50. The image of the strand will have what length?

  _____

2-7 Solving Absolute-Value Equations
Solve each equation.

24. $|m| = 3$

25. $11 = |q|$

26. $|2y| = 8$

_____

_____

_____

27. $|2n + 1| = 7$

28. $|z| + 7 = 5$

29. $2|q| + 1 = 3$

_____

_____

30. A hose clamp has a diameter of $2\frac{1}{2}$ inches. The screw can be used to increase or decrease the diameter of the clamp by $\frac{1}{8}$ of an inch. Write and solve an absolute-value equation to find the minimum and maximum diameter of the clamp.

$2\frac{1}{2}$ in.

_____

_____

Holt Algebra 1

Name _____ Date _____ Class _____

SECTION 3A

Ready to Go On? Quiz

3-1 Graphing and Writing Inequalities

Describe the solutions of each inequality in words.

1. $-3 < x$

2. $t - 3 \leq 8$

_____

_____

3. $4w \geq 12$

4. $5 > 6 - x$

_____

_____

Graph each inequality.

5. $x > -4$

6. $m \leq 2\frac{1}{2}$

7. $g < \sqrt{8 + 8}$

8. $h \geq 3^2$

Write the inequality shown by each graph.

9. _____

10. _____

11. _____

Write an inequality for each situation and graph the solutions.

12. You must spend at least 50 dollars to use a coupon. _____

13. The speed limit is less than 55 miles per hour. _____

14. To qualify, earnings cannot be more than $200. _____

Holt Algebra 1

SECTION 3A **Ready to Go On? Quiz** continued

3-2 Solving Inequalities by Adding and Subtracting
Solve each inequality and graph the solutions.

15. $k + 6 \leq 9$

16. $5 > p - 2$

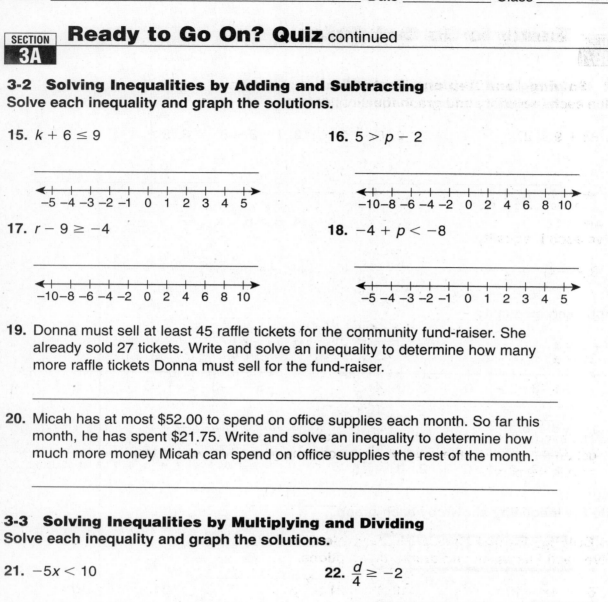

17. $r - 9 \geq -4$

18. $-4 + p < -8$

19. Donna must sell at least 45 raffle tickets for the community fund-raiser. She already sold 27 tickets. Write and solve an inequality to determine how many more raffle tickets Donna must sell for the fund-raiser.

_____

20. Micah has at most $52.00 to spend on office supplies each month. So far this month, he has spent $21.75. Write and solve an inequality to determine how much more money Micah can spend on office supplies the rest of the month.

_____

3-3 Solving Inequalities by Multiplying and Dividing
Solve each inequality and graph the solutions.

21. $-5x < 10$

22. $\dfrac{d}{4} \geq -2$

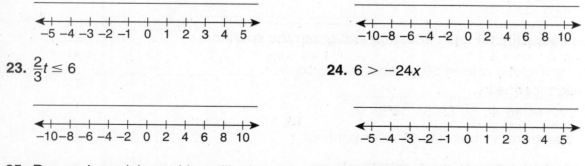

23. $\dfrac{2}{3}t \leq 6$

24. $6 > -24x$

25. Romans' new ink cartridge will print up to 250 pages. Roman's printing a 15-page booklet to hand out at a presentation. What are the possible number of booklet's Roman can print?

_____

Holt Algebra 1

Ready to Go On? Quiz

SECTION 3B

3-4 Solving Two-Step and Multi-Step Inequalities

Solve each inequality and graph the solutions.

1. $3x + 9 < 27$

$-2\ -1\ 0\ 1\ 2\ 3\ 4\ 5\ 6\ 7$

2. $8x - 5 > 11$

$-4\ -3\ -2\ -1\ 0\ 1\ 2\ 3\ 4\ 5$

3. $8 \geq 1 - 7t$

$-4\ -3\ -2\ -1\ 0\ 1\ 2\ 3\ 4\ 5$

Solve each inequality.

4. $3(x - 4) > -2$

5. $\frac{1}{2}a + \frac{1}{3} > \frac{3}{4}$

6. $3^2 - x > 3(4 - 6)$

7. $18y + 9 - 7y \leq 42$

8. The average of Lynn's two test scores must be at least 93 to make an A. Lynn got an 88 on her first test. What scores can she get on her second test to make an A in the class?

_____

3-5 Solving Inequalities with Variables on Both Sides

Solve each inequality and graph the solutions.

9. $6x < 4x + 10$

$-2\ -1\ 0\ 1\ 2\ 3\ 4\ 5\ 6\ 7$

10. $7y - 21 > 4y$

$0\ 1\ 2\ 3\ 4\ 5\ 6\ 7\ 8\ 9$

11. $h - 5 \geq 2h + 4$

$-10\ -9\ -8\ -7\ -6\ -5\ -4\ -3\ -2\ -1$

Solve each inequality.

12. $3(x - 4) > 2(x + 6)$

13. $3(4 - y) \geq y$

14. $6(t + 4) < 6t - 24$

15. $-4(8 + y) < 5(1 + y)$

Holt Algebra 1

SECTION 3B **Ready to Go On? Quiz** continued

16. Catherine has $57 in the bank and deposits $12 per month. Nicholas has $120 in the bank and deposits $9 per month. For how many months will Nicholas have the larger balance than Catherine?

_____

3-6 Solving Compound Inequalities
Solve each compound inequality and graph the solutions.

17. $-1 < x + 3 \leq 7$

18. $m - 3 < -4$ OR $m + 3 > 5$

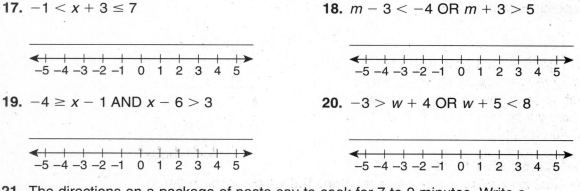

19. $-4 \geq x - 1$ AND $x - 6 > 3$

20. $-3 > w + 4$ OR $w + 5 < 8$

21. The directions on a package of pasta say to cook for 7 to 9 minutes. Write a compound inequality to show the acceptable cooking times for this pasta.

_____

3-7 Solving Absolute-Value Inequalities
Solve each inequality and graph the solutions.

22. $|x| + 1 < 4$

23. $|x| - 1 > 3$

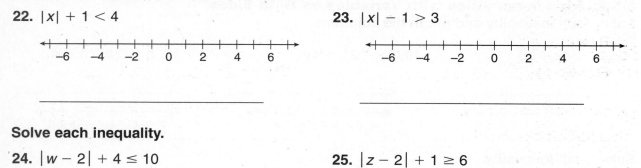

Solve each inequality.

24. $|w - 2| + 4 \leq 10$

25. $|z - 2| + 1 \geq 6$

26. The density, d, of a 100-kg plastic block is listed as 1.70 g/cm^3. The manufacturer states that the actual density of the block may vary by as much as 0.03 g/cm^3. Write and solve an absolute-value inequality for the range of possible densities of the block.

_____

Holt Algebra 1

SECTION 4A Ready To Go On? Quiz

4-1 Graphing Relationships
Choose the graph that best represents each situation.

1. Your distance from the ground as you ride a Ferris wheel for three minutes.

    _____

2. The height of a yo-yo during a competition.

    _____

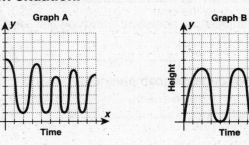

3. Julius goes to a carnival with $10. Each ride ticket costs $2. Sketch a graph to show his remaining amount of money if he purchases 1, 2, 3, 4, or 5 ride tickets.

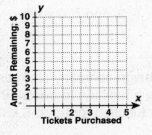

4-2 Relations and Functions
Give the domain and range of each relation. Tell whether the relation is a function. Explain.

4.
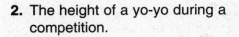

Domain: _____

Range: _____

Explain: _____

_____

_____

5.

x	−3	−3	0	3	3
y	4	4	4	4	4

Domain: _____

Range: _____

Explain: _____

_____

_____

4-3 Writing and Graphing Functions
Determine a relationship between the x- and y-values. Write an equation.

6.

x	1	2	3	4
y	−2	−1	0	1

_____

7.

x	1	2	3	4
y	−4	−8	−12	−16

_____

Holt Algebra 1

SECTION 4A **Ready to Go On? Quiz** continued

Identify the dependent and independent variables. Write a rule in function notation for each situation.

8. An administrative assistant can type 65 words per minute.

_____

9. An appliance repair company charges a $45 service fee plus $25 per hour.

_____

Evaluate each function for the given input values.

10. For $f(x) = 4x - 3$, find $f(x)$ when $x = 3$.   11. For $g(x) = x^3 - x$, find $g(x)$ when $x = -3$.

_____   _____

12. A graphics design company charges an initial $25 set up fee and $12 per t-shirt printed. Write a function to describe the situation. Find a reasonable domain and range for the function for up to 6 t-shirts.

_____

Graph each equation. Then tell whether the equation represents a function.

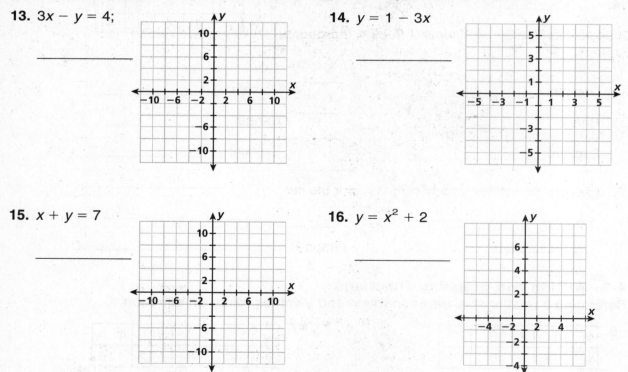

13. $3x - y = 4$;

_____

14. $y = 1 - 3x$

_____

15. $x + y = 7$

_____

16. $y = x^2 + 2$

_____

Holt Algebra 1

SECTION 4B Ready to Go On? Quiz

4-4 Scatter Plots and Trend Lines

The table shows the number of hits and
runs scored in a softball game.

hits	4	8	8	10	10	14	14
runs	1	5	7	7	9	10	12

1. Graph a scatter plot using the given data.

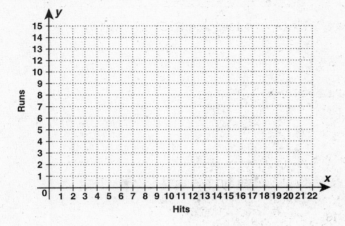

2. Describe the correlation illustrated by the scatter plot. _____

3. Predict the number of runs out of 17 hits. _____

Choose the scatter plot below that best represents the described relationship. Explain.

4. age of a car and value of the car _____

_____

5. age of a car and miles per gallon _____

_____

6. age of a car and the annual cost to repair the car _____

_____

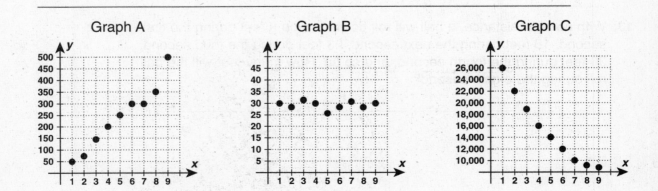

Graph A   Graph B   Graph C

Holt Algebra 1

SECTION
4B

Ready to Go On? Quiz continued

7. The scatter plot shows the estimated annual tax returns for the years 2004 to 2010. Based on this relationship, predict the number of tax returns in 2013.

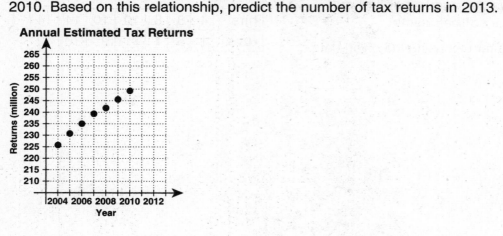

Annual Estimated Tax Returns

_____

4-5 Arithmetic Sequences

Determine whether each sequence appears to be an arithmetic sequence. If so, find the common difference and the next three terms.

8. 21, 13, 5, −3, …

_____

9. 4, 8, 16, 32, …

_____

10. −6.5, −4, −1.5, 1, …

_____

Find the indicated term of the arithmetic sequence.

11. 25th term: 9, 2, −5, −12, …   12. 16th term: $a_1 = 8$; $d = 3$

_____   _____

13. With no air resistance, a ball will roll down a ramp 9 feet during the first second, 16 feet during the next second, 23 feet during the third second, 30 feet during the fourth second, and so on. How many feet will the ball roll during the eighth second?

_____

Holt Algebra 1

SECTION 5A **Ready To Go On? Quiz**

5-1 Linear Equations and Functions
Graph each linear equation. Then tell whether it represents a function.

1. $x + y = 6$ **2.** $y = 1 + 2x$ **3.** $x - 2 = 0$

_____   _____   _____

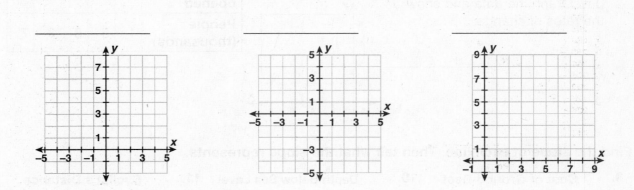

5-2 Using Intercepts

4. A water balloon that holds 2 gallons of water has a leak and is losing water at a rate of $\frac{1}{2}$ gallon per minute. The function $f(x) = 2 - \frac{1}{2}x$ gives the amount of water in the pool after x minutes. Graph the function and find its intercepts. What does each intercept represent?

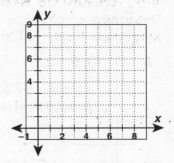

_____

_____

_____

_____

Use intercepts to graph the line describe by each equation.

5. $4x - 3y = 12$ **6.** $-2y + 8x = -16$ **7.** $y = -4x + 5$

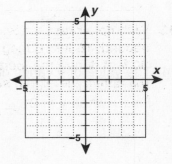

Holt Algebra 1

Ready to Go On? Quiz continued

5-3 Slope

8. The chart gives the number of people in an amusement park at various times throughout the day. Graph the data and show the rates of change.

_____

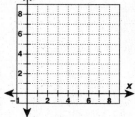

Amusement Park Attendance					
Hours after the park has opened	0	2	4	6	8
People (thousands)	1	5	8	8	7

Find the slope of each line. Then tell what the slope represents.

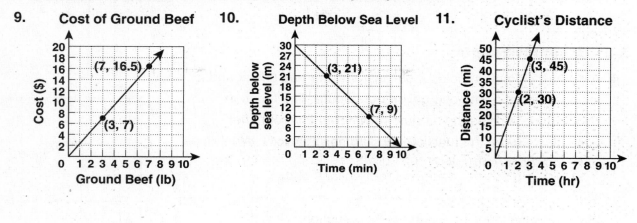

9. Cost of Ground Beef   10. Depth Below Sea Level   11. Cyclist's Distance

_____   _____   _____

5-4 Direct Variation

Tell whether each relationship is a direct variation. If so, identify the constant of variation.

12.

x	4	8	16	28
y	1	2	4	7

13.

x	−8	−4	−2	0
y	16	20	22	24

_____   _____

14. The value of y varies directly with x, and $y = 28$ when $x = 8$.

Find x when $y = 21$. _____

Holt Algebra 1

SECTION 5B   Ready to Go On? Quiz

5-5   Slope-Intercept Form

Graph each line given the slope and *y*-intercept.

1. slope $= \frac{1}{3}$; *y*-intercept $= 1$ **2.** slope $= -2$; *y*-intercept $= 4$ **3.** slope $= 1$; *y*-intercept $= -4$

Write each equation in slope-intercept form, and then graph.

4. $4x + y = 6$ **5.** $3x - 12y = 24$ **6.** $5x + y = 5x - 4$

7. A painter charges a flat fee of \$35 and then \$25 for every gallon of paint used. The graph shows the total cost per gallon as a function of the number of gallons of paint used.

a. Write an equation to represent the situation.

_____

b. Identify the slope and *y*-intercept and describe the meaning of each.

_____

_____

Cost of Painter

5-6   Point-Slope Form

Graph the line with the given slope that contains the given point.

8. slope $= 4$; $(0, 2)$ **9.** slope $= -\frac{2}{5}$; $(-2, 4)$ **10.** slope $= 1$; $(-4, -2)$

Holt Algebra 1

SECTION 5B **Ready to Go On? Quiz** continued

5-6 Point-Slope Form continued
Write an equation in slope-intercept form for the line through the two points.

11. (2, 2) and (5, 11)   **12.** (−6, −7) and (2, 9)   **13.** (−1, 2) and (−3, 10)

_____   _____   _____

14. (4, 2) and (11, −5)   **15.** (−2, −8) and (6, 32)   **16.** (−3, 7) and (5, −9)

_____   _____   _____

5-7 Slopes of Parallel and Perpendicular Lines
Identify which lines are parallel.

17. $y = -3x$; $y = 3x + 2$;
$y = 3x$; $y - 4 = 3(x + 6)$

18. $y = \frac{1}{4}x - 3$; $y = -\frac{1}{4}x + 5$;
$y = -4x$; $y + 3 = -\frac{1}{4}(x + 6)$

_____   _____

Identify which lines are perpendicular.

19. $y = -6x - 2$; $y = \frac{1}{6}x$;
$y = 4x - 3$; $x = -6$

20. $y = -\frac{2}{3}x$; $y = \frac{2}{3}x - 1$;
$y = \frac{3}{2}x$; $y = 3$; $x = 2$

_____   _____

21. Write an equation in slope-intercept form for the line that passes through (5, 6) and is parallel to the line described by $4x - 5y = 20$.

22. Write an equation in slope-intercept form for the line that passes through (10, 3) and is perpendicular to the line described by $y = -\frac{5}{2}x - 3$.

_____   _____

23. Write an equation in slope-intercept form for the line that passes through (4, 6) and is parallel to the line described by $y = \frac{1}{2}x + 2$.

24. Write an equation in slope-intercept form for the line that passes through (6, 5) and is perpendicular to the line described by $2x + 3y = 7$.

_____   _____

Holt Algebra 1

SECTION 6A Ready To Go On? Quiz

6-1 Solving Systems by Graphing

Tell whether the ordered pair is a solution of the given system.

1. $(-1, 4)$; $\begin{cases} y = -3x + 1 \\ y = x + 5 \end{cases}$

2. $(1, 5)$; $\begin{cases} x - 3y = 2 \\ 2x - 5y = 5 \end{cases}$

3. $(8, -2)$; $\begin{cases} y = -\frac{1}{4}x \\ y + 3x = 22 \end{cases}$

_____ _____ _____

Solve each system by graphing.

4. $\begin{cases} y = x + 4 \\ y = \frac{3}{4}x + 2 \end{cases}$

5. $\begin{cases} y = -2x - 3 \\ 3x - y = 3 \end{cases}$

6. $\begin{cases} \frac{1}{3}x + y = 5 \\ 4x - 2y = 4 \end{cases}$

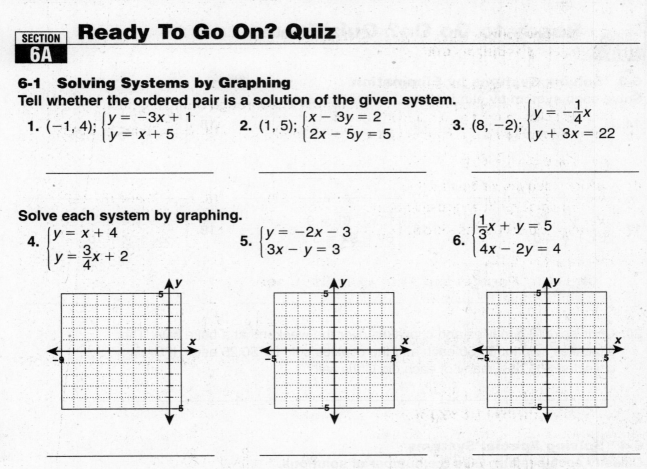

_____ _____ _____

7. Bill and Steve both owe their mother money. Bill owes his mother $300 and plans to pay her $25 every week. Steve owes his mother $550 and plans to pay her $75 every week. After how many weeks will they both owe their mother the same amount of money? What amount will that be?

_____

6-2 Solving Systems by Substitution

Solve each system by substitution.

8. $\begin{cases} y = x - 2 \\ 4x + y = 8 \end{cases}$

9. $\begin{cases} -4x + 2y = -6 \\ 3x + y = 2 \end{cases}$

10. $\begin{cases} -y = x \\ y = 3x + 4 \end{cases}$

_____ _____ _____

11. $\begin{cases} y = x + 10 \\ -2x - 10y = -52 \end{cases}$

12. $\begin{cases} y = -x \\ -y = 4x + 9 \end{cases}$

13. $\begin{cases} y = 6x - 3 \\ y = x + 5 \end{cases}$

_____ _____ _____

Holt Algebra 1

SECTION 6A **Ready to Go On? Quiz** continued

6-3 Solving Systems by Elimination
Solve each system by elimination.

14. $\begin{cases} x + 2y = 20 \\ 3x - 2y = -12 \end{cases}$

15. $\begin{cases} x + y = 5 \\ 3x + y = -11 \end{cases}$

16. $\begin{cases} 4x + 3y = 19 \\ -3x + 4y = -8 \end{cases}$

_____ _____ _____

17. $\begin{cases} x - y = 12 \\ 2x + y = 0 \end{cases}$

18. $\begin{cases} 12x - 6y = 9 \\ 6y - 9x = 3 \end{cases}$

19. $\begin{cases} -x - y = 8 \\ -2x - y = 10 \end{cases}$

_____ _____ _____

20. Chris sold 180 cookies and cupcakes over the weekend at a bake sale. The cupcakes sold for $0.50 each and the cookies sold for $0.25 each. If Chris collected $66 how many of each did Chris sell?

_____

6-4 Solving Special Systems
Classify each system. Give the number of solutions.

21. $\begin{cases} 2y = 1 - \frac{1}{2}x \\ x = 2 - 4y \end{cases}$

22. $\begin{cases} y = -3x + 1 \\ 3x + y = -1 \end{cases}$

23. $\begin{cases} 4x - 3y = 12 \\ y = 3(x - 4) \end{cases}$

_____ _____ _____

_____ _____ _____

6-5 Applying Systems of Equations
Solve each problem.

24. The sum of the digits of a two-digit number is 9. When the digits are reversed, the new number is 27 more than the original number. What is the original number?

_____

25. The sum of the digits of a two-digit number is 11. When the digits are reversed, the new number is 9 less than the original number. What is the original number?

_____

Holt Algebra 1

SECTION
6B

Ready To Go On? Quiz

6-6 Solving Linear Inequalities

Tell whether the ordered pair is a solution of the inequality.

1. $(4, -3)$; $y < -3x + 2$ **2.** $(5, 18)$; $y \geq 4x - 6$ **3.** $(2, -4)$; $y \leq 5x - 12$

_____   _____   _____

Graph the solutions of each linear inequality.

4. $y \geq 5x - 4$ **5.** $4x - y < 3$ **6.** $3x + 4y < 12$

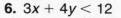

7. Barbara has no more than $144 to buy jewelry. Earrings cost
$12 each and necklaces cost $24 each. How many of each
can she buy? Write a linear inequality to describe the situation.
Graph the linear inequality and give three possible combinations
of earrings and necklaces Barbara can buy.

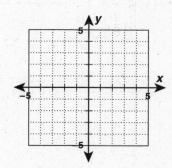

_____

_____

_____

Write an inequality to represent each graph.

8. _____   **9.** _____   **10.** _____

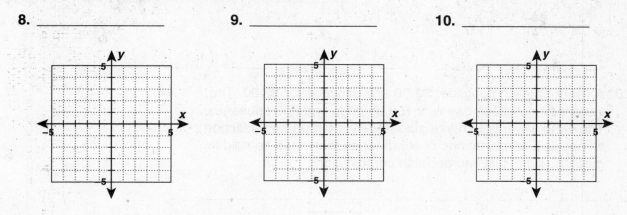

Holt Algebra 1

SECTION 6B

Ready to Go On? Quiz continued

6-7 Solving Systems of Linear Inequalities

Tell whether the ordered pair is a solution of the given system.

11. $(-1, -4);$ $\begin{cases} y < -3x \\ y > x - 4 \end{cases}$

12. $(3, 2);$ $\begin{cases} y \leq x + 2 \\ y \geq -3x - 2 \end{cases}$

13. $(0, 0);$ $\begin{cases} y \geq 2x \\ 2x + y < -4 \end{cases}$

_____ _____ _____

Graph each system of linear inequalities. Give two ordered pairs that are solutions and two that are not solutions.

14. $\begin{cases} y > 3 \\ y < x + 1 \end{cases}$

15. $\begin{cases} x + y \leq 4 \\ 3x - y \geq -3 \end{cases}$

16. $\begin{cases} 3x - 2y < 6 \\ 2x + 3y \geq -6 \end{cases}$

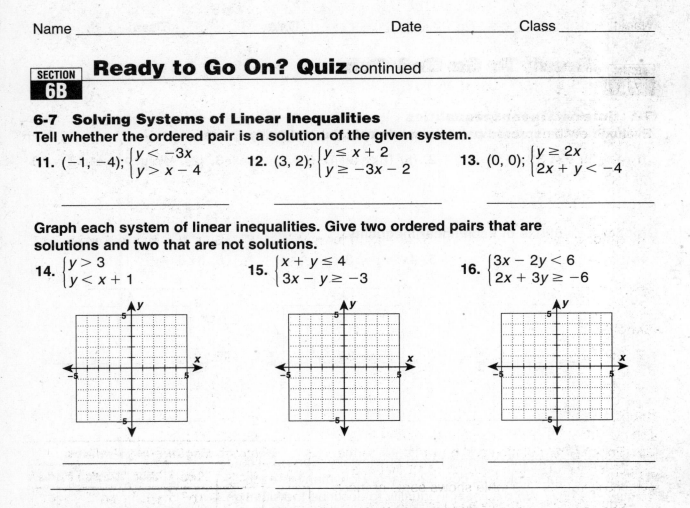

_____ _____ _____

_____ _____ _____

Graph each system of linear inequalities and describe the solutions.

17. $\begin{cases} y \geq x + 2 \\ y \geq x - 3 \end{cases}$

18. $\begin{cases} y > -3x - 2 \\ y < -3x + 3 \end{cases}$

19. $\begin{cases} y > -2x + 4 \\ y < -2x - 1 \end{cases}$

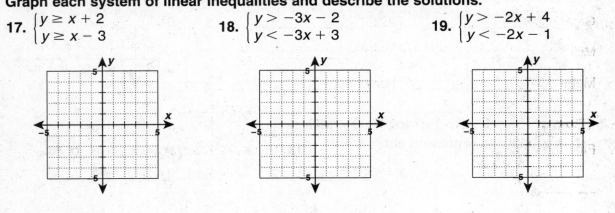

_____ _____ _____

20. A vendor sells hotdogs for $2.00 and sausage for $3.00. The vendor begins each day with 150 hotdogs and 200 sausages. The vendor wants to make at least $600. Graph and describe all possible combinations of sandwiches that could be sold to meet the goal. List two possible combinations.

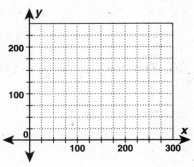

_____

Holt Algebra 1

SECTION 7A Ready To Go On? Quiz

7-1 Integer Exponents

Evaluate each expression for the given value(s) of the variable(s).

1. a^{-4} for $a = 3$

2. w^{-6} for $w = -5$

3. $w^{-2}y$ for $w = 5$ and $y = -3$

_____   _____   _____

4. a^0 for $a = 12$

5. $(6 - w)^{-8}$ for $w = 7$

6. $a^0 b^{-3}$ for $a = 5$ and $b = 10$

_____   _____   _____

Simplify.

7. $6w^{-4}$

8. $\dfrac{y^7}{w^{-3}}$

9. $3x^{-2}y^0$

10. $\dfrac{w^{-6}}{b^{-4}}$

_____   _____   _____   _____

11. Engineering notation can be written in terms of a base unit, with a power of 10 that is a multiple of 3. The table shows some of these equivalences. Simplify each expression.

Selected Engineering Prefixes					
Giga	Mega	Kilo	Milli	Micro	Nano
10^9	10^6	10^3	10^{-3}	10^{-6}	10^{-9}

Giga _____   Kilo _____

Milli _____   Micro _____

Mega _____   Nano _____

7-2 Powers of 10 and Scientific Notation

12. Find the value of 10^5.

13. Write 0.00000004 as a power of 10.

_____   _____

14. Write 1,000,000,000,000 as a power of 10.

15. Find the value of 15.7×10^5.

_____   _____

16. The wavelength of red light is 0.0000007 m. Write this length in scientific notation.

_____

Holt Algebra 1

SECTION 7A

Ready to Go On? Quiz continued

7-3 Multiplication Properties of Exponents
Simplify.

17. $3^5 \cdot 3^2$ **18.** $5^4 \cdot 5^{-2}$ **19.** $(2x^5)^3$ **20.** $(-6w^6)^2$

_____   _____   _____   _____

21. The closest star to Earth is Proxima Centauri, which is 4.3 light-years away (one light-year equals 5.88×10^{12} miles). How far, in miles, is Proxima Centauri from Earth? Write your answer in scientific notation and standard form.

_____

7-4 Division Properties of Exponents
Simplify.

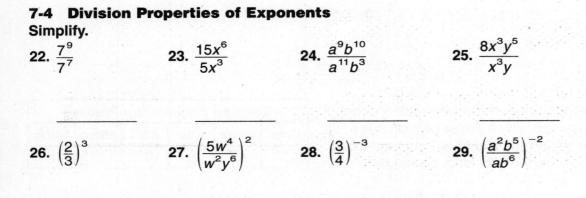

22. $\dfrac{7^9}{7^7}$ **23.** $\dfrac{15x^6}{5x^3}$ **24.** $\dfrac{a^9 b^{10}}{a^{11} b^3}$ **25.** $\dfrac{8x^3 y^5}{x^3 y}$

_____   _____   _____   _____

26. $\left(\dfrac{2}{3}\right)^3$ **27.** $\left(\dfrac{5w^4}{w^2 y^6}\right)^2$ **28.** $\left(\dfrac{3}{4}\right)^{-3}$ **29.** $\left(\dfrac{a^2 b^5}{ab^6}\right)^{-2}$

_____   _____   _____   _____

Simplify each quotient and write the answers in scientific notation.

30. $(9 \times 10^{10}) \div (3 \times 10^4)$ **31.** $(4.5 \times 10^6) \div (9 \times 10^9)$ **32.** $(2 \times 10^5) \div (5 \times 10^5)$

_____   _____   _____

7-5 Fractional Exponents
Simplify each expression. All variables represent nonnegative numbers.

33. $36^{\frac{1}{2}}$ **34.** $27^{\frac{1}{3}}$ **35.** $1^{\frac{2}{3}}$ **36.** $16^{\frac{3}{2}}$

_____   _____   _____   _____

37. $\sqrt{x^4 y^2}$ **38.** $\sqrt[3]{q^6}$ **39.** $\sqrt[3]{k^{15}}$ **40.** $\sqrt[3]{r^3 s^9}$

_____   _____   _____   _____

Holt Algebra 1

Name _____ Date _____ Class _____

7-6   Polynomials

Write each polynomial in standard form and give the leading coefficient.

1. $7x^2 + 4x^5 - 2r$ **2.** $y^3 + 3 - 8y^2 + 4y$ **3.** $-8w^4 - 3w + w^5$

_____   _____   _____

4. $3 + y + 5y^2$ **5.** $9 + 4x^4$ **6.** $-2a^2 + 9 + a^8 + 2a$

_____   _____   _____

Classify each polynomial according to its degree and number of terms.

7. $3a^2 + 4a - a^4 + 3a^3$ **8.** $4x^2 + 8 - 3x$ **9.** $3x^3 + 5x^2 - 1$

_____   _____   _____

10. $7 - 5b^4 + 2b + 5b^2$ **11.** $7w^2$ **12.** $3a^4 - 6a^8 + 2a + 9$

_____   _____   _____

13. The function $P(x) = x^3 - 3x^2 + 12$ gives the profit on a product. What is the

profit on 800 units? _____

7-7   Adding and Subtracting Polynomials

Add or subtract.

14. $(12x^4 + 5x^3) + (6x^3 + 7x)$ **15.** $(4x^2 - 3) + (10x^2 + 5x - 7)$

_____   _____

16. $(13d^6 - 4d^2) + (3d^4 + 2)$ **17.** $(7y^3 + 5y^2) - (3y^2 + 4y)$

_____   _____

18. $(8w^2 - 4w) - (6w^2 + 6w)$ **19.** $(a^2 - 11) - (-6a^3 + 3a)$

_____   _____

20. The measures of the sides of a triangle are shown as
polynomials. Write a simplified polynomial to represent

the perimeter of the triangle. _____

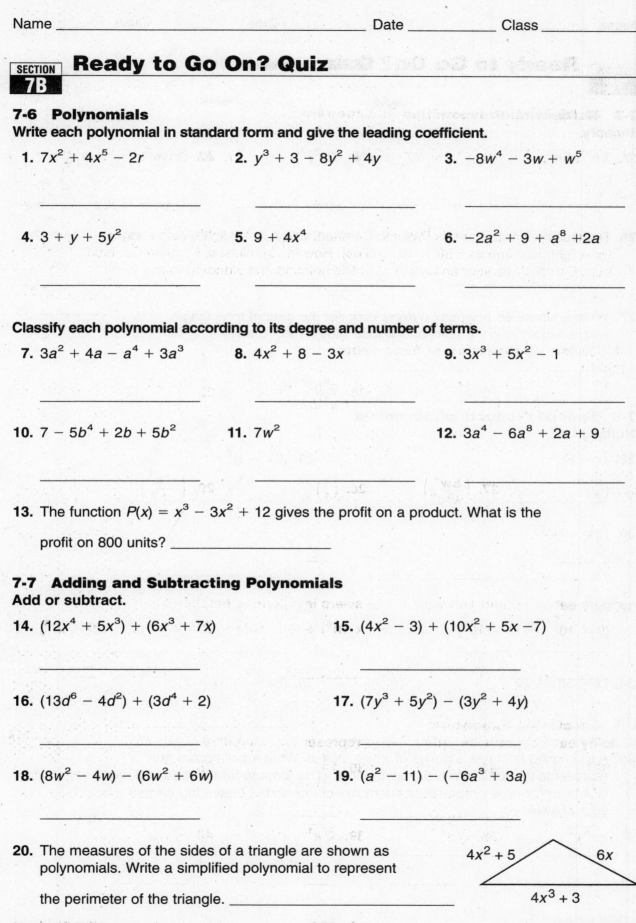

$4x^2 + 5$ $6x$

$4x^3 + 3$

Holt Algebra 1

Ready to Go On? Quiz continued

7-8 Multiplying Polynomials
Multiply.

21. $4h^3 \cdot 6h^6$

22. $(x^9 y^5)(-7x^2 y^4)$

23. $3mn(6m^2 + 4m^3 n)$

_____ _____ _____

24. $(4w + 3)^2$

25. $(3x^3 + 2y)(5x + y)$

26. $(a^2 + 4)(3a^2 - 4a - 7)$

_____ _____ _____

27. Write a simplified polynomial expression for the area of a rectangle whose length is $x + 8$ units and whose width is $x - 5$ units.

_____

7-9 Special Products of Binomials
Multiply.

28. $(x + 8)^2$

29. $(2x + 3)^2$

_____ _____

30. $(3x + 7y)^2$

31. $(a - 5)^2$

_____ _____

32. $(x - y)^2$

33. $(4x - 3)^2$

_____ _____

34. $(x - 3)(x + 3)$

35. $(6x - 7)(6x + 7)$

_____ _____

36. A swimming pool has a radius of $x - 4$ inches. Write a polynomial that represents the area of the swimming pool. (The formula for the area of a circle is $A = \pi r^2$, where r represents the radius of the circle.) Leave the symbol π in your answer.

_____

Holt Algebra 1

SECTION 8A

Ready To Go On? Quiz

8-1 Factors and Greatest Common Factors
Write the prime factorization of each number.

1. 84

2. 60

3. 150

_____   _____   _____

4. 66

5. 72

6. 156

_____   _____   _____

Find the GCF of each pair of monomials.

7. $6x^4$ and $9x^2$

8. $25x^3$ and $20x^4$

_____   _____

9. -18 and $27c^5$

10. $5a$ and $7c$

_____   _____

11. Nichole is designing a quilt. She has cut out 60 red squares and 48 green squares. She plans for the quilt to have the same number of colored squares in each row, but, green and red squares will not be in the same row. How many rows will the quilt have if Nichole puts the greatest number of squares in each row?   _____

8-2 Factoring by GCF
Factor each polynomial. Check your answer.

12. $30x^2 + 12x$

13. $2a^2 - 10a^3$

_____   _____

14. $6x^4 - 15x^3 - 9x^2$

15. $4x^2 + 12x + 16$

_____   _____

16. The surface area of a cylinder can be found using the expression $2\pi r^2 + 2\pi rh$, where r represents the radius of the cylinder and h represents the height.

Factor this expression. _____

Holt Algebra 1

Ready To Go On? Quiz continued

8-2 Factoring by GCF continued

Factor each polynomial by grouping. Check your answer.

17. $x^3 - 3x^2 + 2x - 6$

18. $5x^3 + 10x^2 + x + 2$

19. $2r^3 - 8r^2 - 3r + 12$

_____ _____ _____

20. $3s^3 - 12s^2 - s + 4$

21. $4y^3 + 16y^2 - 2y - 8$

22. $8b^3 + 16b^2 - 2b - 4$

_____ _____ _____

8-3 Factoring $x^2 + bx + c$

Factor each trinomial. Check your answer.

23. $a^2 + 12a + 35$

24. $x^2 - 3x - 10$

25. $x^2 - 8x + 7$

_____ _____ _____

26. $x^2 + 13x - 30$

27. $c^2 - 13c + 36$

28. $y^2 - 12y + 32$

_____ _____ _____

29. Simplify and factor the polynomial $n(n + 7) + 12$. Show that the original polynomial and the factored form describe the same sequence of numbers for $n = 0, 1, 2, 3,$ and 4.

_____

8-4 Factoring $ax^2 + bx + c$

Factor each trinomial. Check your answer.

30. $2a^2 + 5a + 2$

31. $6x^2 + 11x + 4$

32. $3x^2 - x - 10$

_____ _____ _____

33. $4x^2 - 14x + 12$

34. $6c^2 - 12c - 18$

35. $12y^2 - y - 20$

_____ _____ _____

36. The area of a rectangle is $(10x^2 + 21x + 9)$ cm^2. The length is $(5x + 3)$ cm. What is the width of the rectangle?

_____

Holt Algebra 1

SECTION 8B

Ready To Go On? Quiz

8-5 Factoring Special Products

Determine whether each trinomial is a perfect square. If so, factor it. If not, explain why.

1. $a^2 + 6a + 9$

2. $16x^2 - 40x + 25$

3. $w^2 - 12w + 4$

_____   _____   _____

4. $5y^2 - 14y + 16$

5. $x^2 + 4x + 4$

6. $25h^2 - 70h + 49$

_____   _____   _____

7. An architect is designing rectangular windows with an area of $(x^2 + 22x + 121)$ ft². The dimensions of the windows are of the form $ax + b$, where a and b are whole numbers. Find an expression for the perimeter of the windows. Find the perimeter of a window when $x = 3$ ft.

_____

Determine whether each trinomial is the difference of two squares. If so, factor it. If not, explain why.

8. $r^2 - 144$

9. $4a^2 - 30$

10. $1 - 25a^4$

_____   _____   _____

11. $36k^2 - 9k^6$

12. $49a^2 + 64$

13. $w^4 - a^2$

_____   _____   _____

14. The area of a square is $(49x^2 - 28x + 4)$ in².

   a. What is the length of a side of the square? _____

   b. What is the perimeter of the square? _____

   c. What are the length of a side, the perimeter, and the area of the square

   when $x = 4$ in.? _____

8-6 Choosing a Factoring Method

Tell whether each expression is completely factored. If not, factor it.

15. $7x^2 + 35x + 7 = 7(x^2 + 5x + 1)$

16. $16x^3 - 24x^2 = 8x(2x^2 - 3x)$

_____   _____

Holt Algebra 1

SECTION 8B **Ready To Go On? Quiz** continued

8-6 Choosing a Factoring Method continued

17. $4x^5 - 16x = 4x(x^4 - 4)$ **18.** $3a^2 - 42a + 147 = 3(a^2 - 14a + 49)$

_____   _____

19. $8y^3 - 8y^2 - 12y + 12 = 4(2y^2 - 3)(y - 1)$ **20.** $3y^2 + 17y + 10 = (3y + 2)(y + 5)$

_____   _____

Factor each polynomial completely. Check your answer.

21. $4x^3 - 24x^2 + 36x$ **22.** $3x^2y - 12xy^2$ **23.** $3a^2 + a + 1$

_____   _____   _____

24. $12x^3 - 3x$ **25.** $4x^2 + 12x - 112$ **26.** $x^5 - 16x$

_____   _____   _____

Write an expression for each situation. Then factor your expression.

27. The difference of the square of a pipe's length and 49.

_____

28. The square of Catherine's age plus 18 times Catherine's age plus 81.

_____

29. Three times the square of a truck's speed minus three times the trucks speed plus 18.

_____

30. Four times the square of cherries on a tree minus 11 times the number of cherries minus 21.

_____

31. Write an expression for the area of the shaded region. Then factor the expression.

_____

SECTION 9A

Ready To Go On? Quiz

9-1 Quadratic Equations and Functions

Without graphing, tell whether each point is on the graph of the given equation.

1. $y - 4x^2 = -5$; (2, 11) **2.** $2x^2 + y = 3x + 6$; (3, −3) **3.** $4x^2 + 8x = y$; (2, −1)

_____ _____ _____

4. $f(x) = x^2 + 6x - 1$; (1, 6) **5.** $3x^2 + 5x = y + 2$; (−2, 1) **6.** $y = x^2 - 9x + 3$; (−3, 39)

_____ _____ _____

Tell whether the graph of each quadratic function opens upward or downward and whether the parabola has a maximum or a minimum.

7. $y = -2x^2 - 3x + 7$ **8.** $y = 3x^2 + 2x + 5$ **9.** $f(x) = 4x - 0.25x^2$

_____ _____ _____

10. Graph the function $y = \frac{1}{4}x^2 - 4$ and give the domain and range.

11. Graph the function $y = x^2 - 2x + 3$ and give the domain and range.

_____ _____

9-2 Characteristics of Quadratic Functions

Find the zeros of each function from its graph. Then find its axis of symmetry.

12.

13.

14.

_____ _____ _____

Holt Algebra 1

9-2 Characteristics of Quadratic Functions, continued

Find the vertex of each parabola.

15. $y = x^2 - 4x + 2$ **16.** $y = 4 - 6x - 3x^2$ **17.** $y = x^2 + 4x + 2$

_____   _____   _____

18. $y = x^2 - 1 + 2x$ **19.** $y = 0.5x^2 - 1$ **20.** $y = 2x^2 + 8x - 13$

_____   _____   _____

21. The height in feet of an arched bridge can be modeled by
$y = -0.05x^2 + 2x$, where x is the distance in feet from one
end of the bridge. How tall is the bridge?   _____

9-3 Graphing Quadratic Functions
Graph each quadratic function.

22. $y = x^2 + 4x + 7$ **23.** $y = x^2 - 6x - 7$ **24.** $y = x^2 - 2x - 6$

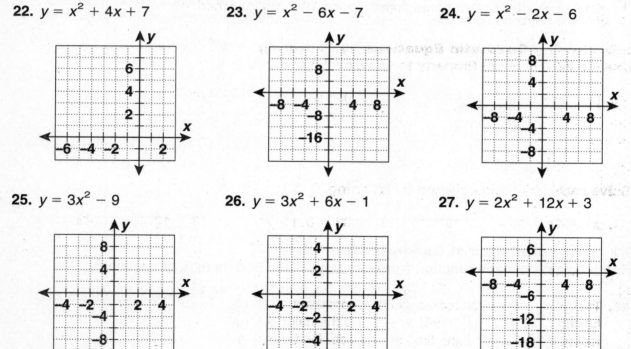

25. $y = 3x^2 - 9$ **26.** $y = 3x^2 + 6x - 1$ **27.** $y = 2x^2 + 12x + 3$

Holt Algebra 1

SECTION 9B

Ready To Go On? Quiz

9-4 Solving Quadratic Equations by Graphing

Solve each equation by graphing the related function.

1. $x^2 - 16 = 0$

2. $x^2 + 4x - 5 = 0$

3. $3x^2 + 3x = 18$

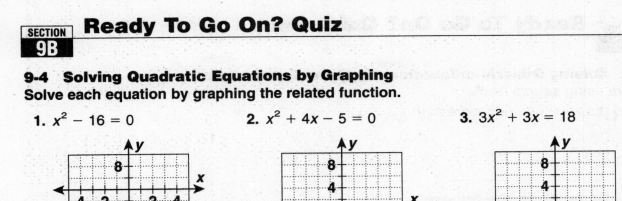

_____   _____   _____

4. The height of a rocket fired from a platform 80 feet above the ground can be approximated by $h = -16t^2 + 64t + 80$, where h is the height in feet and t is the time in seconds. Find the time it takes the rocket to reach the ground after it is launched. _____

9-5 Solving Quadratic Equations by Factoring

Use the Zero Product Property to solve each equation.

5. $(x + 2)(x + 7) = 0$ 6. $(x - 4)(x - 5) = 0$ 7. $x(x + 3) = 28$ 8. $(x + 6)(x - 7) = 30$

_____   _____   _____   _____

Solve each quadratic equation by factoring.

9. $x^2 - 4x - 45 = 0$ 10. $x^2 - 12x + 32 = 0$ 11. $x^2 + x = 12$ 12. $-8x - 48 = -x^2$

_____   _____   _____   _____

13. The height of a small rocket can be approximated by the function $h(t) = -16t^2 + 96t$, where h is the height of the rocket in feet and t is the time in seconds. Find the time it takes the rocket to return to the ground. _____

Holt Algebra 1

Ready To Go On? Quiz continued

9-6 Solving Quadratic Equations by Using Square Roots
Solve using square roots.

14. $4x^2 = 64$

15. $64x^2 - 81 = 0$

16. $-22 = x^2 - 58$

_____

_____

_____

9-7 Completing the Square
Complete the square for each expression.

17. $x^2 - 14x + \Box$

18. $x^2 + 6x + \Box$

19. $x^2 + 3x + \Box$

_____

_____

_____

Solve by completing the square.

20. $x^2 + 12x = 13$

21. $x^2 + 13 = 8x$

22. $x^2 - 4x = 2$

_____

_____

_____

23. The length of a rectangle is 4 feet more than the width. The area of the rectangle is 32 square feet. Find the length and width. Round your answer to the nearest tenth of a foot.

_____

x

$x + 4$

9-8 The Quadratic Formula
Solve using the Quadratic Formula. Round your answer to the nearest hundredth.

24. $3x^2 + 4x - 4 = 0$

25. $2x^2 + 6 = -x$

26. $4x^2 + 8x = 3$

_____

_____

_____

9-9 The Discriminant
Find the number of solutions and the number of *x*-intercepts of each equation.

28. $3x^2 + 12x = -13$

29. $x^2 + 16 = 8x$

30. $x^2 - 4x = 2$

_____

_____

_____

_____

_____

_____

Holt Algebra 1

SECTION 10A

Ready To Go On? Quiz

10-1 Inverse Variation

Tell whether each relationship represents an inverse variation. Explain.

1.

x	2	3	4
y	12	8	6

2.

x	5	7	9
y	−10	14	18

_____

3. $xy = \frac{1}{2}$ **4.** $y = x + 3$ **5.** $x = \frac{2}{y}$ **6.** $y = 2x$

_____ _____   _____ _____

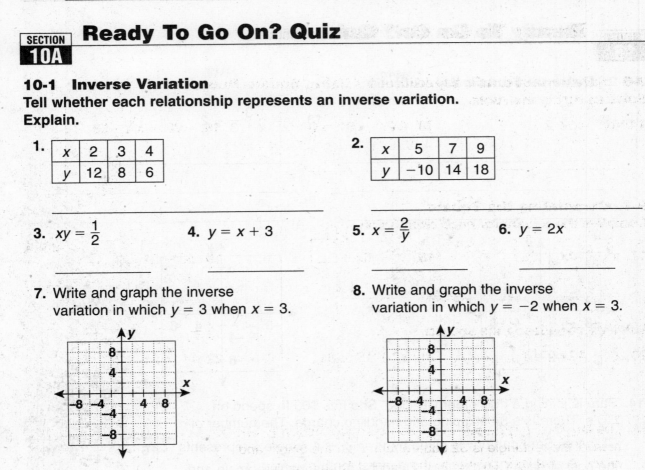

7. Write and graph the inverse variation in which $y = 3$ when $x = 3$.

8. Write and graph the inverse variation in which $y = -2$ when $x = 3$.

_____

9. The cost of campaign buttons for the student government elections varies inversely to the number of buttons ordered. Fifty buttons cost $0.90 each. How

many buttons can be purchased if they cost $0.75 each? _____

10-2 Rational Functions

Identify the excluded values and the vertical and horizontal asymptotes for each rational function. Then graph each function.

10. $y = \frac{1}{x}$ _____

11. $y = \frac{2}{x + 1}$ _____

_____   _____

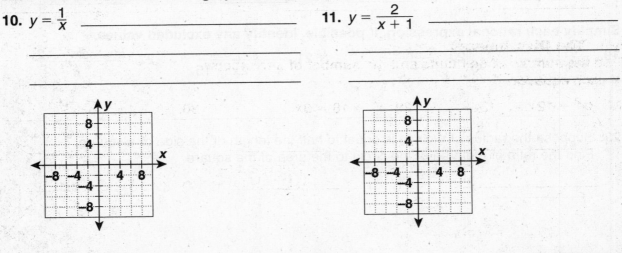

Holt Algebra 1

10-2 Rational Functions, continued

12. $y = \dfrac{5}{x - 2}$

13. $y = \dfrac{3}{x + 3} + 2$

_____

_____

_____

_____

_____

_____

14. Sara is joining a mail order CD club. She has $60 to spend on CD's. There is a $4 shipping and handling charge. The number of CD's that Sara can buy is given by $y = \dfrac{60}{x} - 4$, where x represents the cost of each CD in dollars. Describe a reasonable domain and range and graph the function.

_____

10-3 Simplifying Rational Expressions
Find any excluded values of each rational expression.

15. $\dfrac{2t}{t + 1}$

16. $\dfrac{t - 3}{t + 4}$

17. $\dfrac{6}{t^2 + 1}$

18. $\dfrac{3}{t^2 - 1}$

_____

Simplify each rational expression, if possible. Identify any excluded values.

19. $\dfrac{4n}{12n^3}$

20. $\dfrac{n^2 + 3n}{6n}$

21. $\dfrac{x - 3}{x^2 + 2x - 15}$

22. $\dfrac{x^2 + 4x - 12}{x^2 - x - 2}$

_____

23. Suppose the radius of a circle is equal to half the length of the side of a square. Find the ratio of the area of the circle to the area of the square.

_____

Holt Algebra 1

SECTION 10B Ready To Go On? Quiz

10-4 Multiplying and Dividing Rational Expressions
Multiply. Simplify your answer.

1. $\dfrac{m-3}{m+2} \cdot (2m^2 + 4m)$

2. $\dfrac{3}{x+3} \cdot (x^2 + 6x + 9)$

_____

_____

3. $\dfrac{12x^4 y^3}{x^2 y} \cdot \dfrac{7xy}{3xy^2} \cdot \dfrac{9x^4}{28x^3 y^2}$

4. $\dfrac{3(a^3 - a)}{a-1} \cdot \dfrac{1}{a+1}$

_____

_____

5. $\dfrac{x^2 + x - 2}{x^2 + 3x - 4} \cdot \dfrac{x+3}{x+2}$

6. $\dfrac{z^2 - z - 6}{z^2 - 2z - 8} \cdot \dfrac{z^2 + 7z + 12}{z^2 - 9}$

_____

_____

Divide. Simplify your answer.

7. $4b^5 \div \dfrac{b^3}{2}$

8. $\dfrac{z^2 - 4}{4z^2} \div \dfrac{z^2 - 3z + 2}{z^2 - z}$

9. $\dfrac{x^2 + 2x - 8}{x^2 + x - 6} \div \dfrac{x+4}{x-3}$

_____

_____

10-5 Adding and Subtracting Rational Expressions
Add or subtract. Simplify your answer.

10. $\dfrac{7}{3x} + \dfrac{8}{3x}$

11. $\dfrac{2}{3y} - \dfrac{6}{3y}$

_____

_____

12. $\dfrac{x^2 + 5x}{x-6} - \dfrac{3x + 48}{x-6}$

13. $\dfrac{3m}{5m} + \dfrac{1}{m^2}$

_____

_____

14. $\dfrac{5}{x-3} - \dfrac{x-4}{x^2 - x - 6}$

15. $\dfrac{5a-2}{a^2 + a - 20} - \dfrac{3}{a+5} + \dfrac{a}{a-4}$

_____

_____

Holt Algebra 1

SECTION 10B **Ready To Go On? Quiz** continued

10-6 Dividing Polynomials
Divide.

16. $(20n^2 - 10n) \div 5n$ **17.** $(12p^4 + 8p^3 - 24p^2) \div (-4p^2)$ **18.** $(x^2 - 8x + 15) \div (x - 3)$

_____   _____   _____

Divide using long division.

19. $(x^2 - 5x - 36) \div (x + 4)$ **20.** $(m^2 + 22m + 121) \div (m + 11)$ **21.** $(3y^2 - 7y + 9) \div (y + 1)$

_____   _____   _____

10-7 Solving Rational Equations
Solve. Identify any extraneous solutions.

22. $\dfrac{3}{x + 1} = \dfrac{6}{x}$

23. $\dfrac{2}{x^2} = \dfrac{1}{6x}$

24. $\dfrac{2x}{x + 3} - \dfrac{x}{x + 7} = \dfrac{x^2 - 11}{x^2 + 10x + 21}$

25. $\dfrac{2}{x + 3} + \dfrac{1}{x} = \dfrac{4}{3x}$

26. $\dfrac{4x - 1}{x + 2} = x$

27. $\dfrac{2}{x + 3} + \dfrac{3}{8} = \dfrac{5}{4x + 12}$

10-8 Applying Rational Equations
Solve. Check your answer.

28. A greenhouse technician must prepare a solution that is 20% fertilizer. She has 60 milliliters of a solution that is 50% fertilizer. What volume of water must she add to make a solution that is 20% fertilizer?

_____

29. You have a lawn-care business. You are looking to add a partner to help you mow lawns. There is a lawn that takes you 30 minutes to mow. The person you are considering to hire can mow it in 45 minutes. How long will it take the two of you to mow the lawn working together?

_____

Holt Algebra 1

Name _____ Date _____ Class _____

11-1 Square-Root Functions

1. On hot blacktop, the function $y = \sqrt{15x}$ gives the speed in
miles per hour when the length of a skid mark is x feet. Find
the speed that a car was traveling if it left a skid mark that
was 300 ft long. Round your answer to the nearest hundredth. _____

Find the domain of each square-root function.

2. $y = \sqrt{2x} - 5$ **3.** $y = \sqrt{x - 7}$ **4.** $y = \sqrt{3x - 12}$

_____   _____   _____

Graph each square-root function.

5. $y = \sqrt{x - 4}$ **6.** $y = \sqrt{x} + 2$ **7.** $y = \sqrt{5 + 2x}$

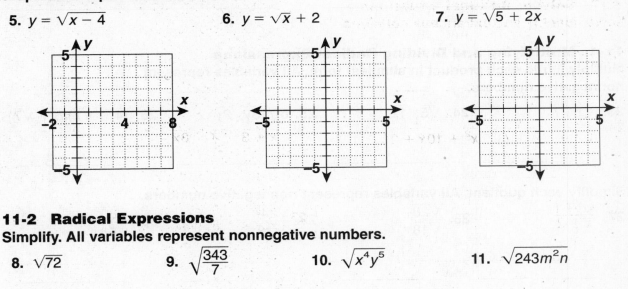

11-2 Radical Expressions
Simplify. All variables represent nonnegative numbers.

8. $\sqrt{72}$ **9.** $\sqrt{\dfrac{343}{7}}$ **10.** $\sqrt{x^4 y^5}$ **11.** $\sqrt{243m^2 n}$

_____ _____ _____ _____

12. $\sqrt{\dfrac{24}{49}}$ **13.** $\sqrt{\dfrac{192}{144}}$ **14.** $\sqrt{\dfrac{9x^2}{25}}$ **15.** $\sqrt{\dfrac{98x^{10}}{64x^6}}$

_____ _____ _____ _____

16. How long is the diagonal of a rectangular parking lot that is
100 m long and 180 m wide? Give the answer as a radical
expression in simplest form. Then estimate the length to the
nearest tenth of a meter. _____

Holt Algebra 1

SECTION 11A

Ready To Go On? Quiz continued

11-3 Adding and Subtracting Radical Expressions
Simplify each expression.

17. $15\sqrt{11} - 7\sqrt{11}$

_____

18. $4\sqrt{y} + 4\sqrt{y}$

_____

19. $\sqrt{180} + \sqrt{45}$

_____

20. $3\sqrt{63} + \sqrt{28}$

_____

21. $8\sqrt{5} - 2\sqrt{9}$

_____

22. $\sqrt{192y} + \sqrt{12y} - \sqrt{300y}$

_____

11-4 Multiplying and Dividing Radical Expressions
Multiply. Write each product in simplest form. All variables represent nonnegative numbers.

23. $\sqrt{5}\sqrt{7}$

_____

24. $\sqrt{5}\sqrt{12}$

_____

25. $6\sqrt{18y}\sqrt{2y}$

_____

26. $(4 - \sqrt{7})(6 + \sqrt{7})$

_____

Simplify each quotient. All variables represent nonnegative numbers.

27. $\dfrac{\sqrt{21}}{\sqrt{5}}$

_____

28. $\dfrac{\sqrt{28}}{\sqrt{18}}$

_____

29. $\dfrac{\sqrt{24k}}{\sqrt{18}}$

_____

30. $\dfrac{\sqrt{80}}{\sqrt{5h}}$

_____

11-5 Solving Radical Equations
Solve each equation. Check your answer.

31. $\sqrt{x} - 3 = 15$

_____

32. $-5\sqrt{x} = -25$

_____

33. $\dfrac{7\sqrt{x}}{3} = 14$

_____

34. $\sqrt{6x - 3} - \sqrt{57 + x} = 0$

_____

35. $\sqrt{15 + 2x} = x$

_____

36. $\sqrt{3x} + 18 = 10$

_____

Holt Algebra 1

SECTION 11B Ready To Go On? Quiz

11-6 Geometric Sequences
Find the next three terms in each geometric sequence.

1. 3, 12, 48, 192, ...   **2.** −512, 64, −8, 1...   **3.** −2, 10, −50, 250...

_____   _____   _____

4. The first term of a geometric sequence is 4 and the common ratio

is 2. What is the 8th term of the sequence? _____

5. The table shows the height of a bouncing basketball during its
first three bounces. The values form a geometric sequence.
What will be the height of the 8th bounce?

Bounce	Height (in.)
1	108
2	54
3	27

_____

11-7 Exponential Functions

6. The function $y = 18(0.8)^x$ gives the length, in inches, of a photograph after
being reduced by 20% x times. What is the length of the photograph after it has
been reduced 8 times? Round your answer to the nearest hundredth.

_____

Graph each exponential function.

7. $y = 4^x$ **8.** $y = 3(3)^x$ **9.** $y = -3(2)^x$ **10.** $y = -(0.75)^x$

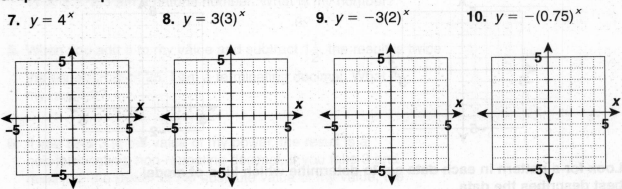

11. The function $y = 600(0.4)^x$ gives the amount of an aspirin, in milligrams,
present in a patient's system x hours after taking a 600-milligram dose. In how
many hours will there be less than 100 mg of the drug in a patient's system?

_____

Holt Algebra 1

Ready to Go On? Enrichment

SECTION 1B

Order of Operations
Simplify each expression.

1. $\dfrac{\sqrt{\dfrac{6 + 16 \cdot 2^3 - 12 + 22}{2(25 - 16) - 14}}}{3^3 \div 9 + 3}$ _____

2. $\dfrac{\left|-200 - (-450) - 850\right| \times 2}{2^5 + 2^3} - \left[5(-16 - 4) + \dfrac{18 + 2}{2^2}\right]$ _____

3. $\dfrac{(3^2 + 5 \cdot 4^2 - 12 \cdot 5^2 + 20) + 20(10) + 1}{2 + 3}$ _____

4. $\dfrac{\dfrac{9 - 6 \cdot 2 - 4 \cdot 6}{-3}}{\sqrt{\dfrac{2^3 \cdot 2^2 \cdot 2^1}{(\sqrt{169} - 5) \cdot (5 + 3)}}}$ _____

5. $16 \cdot \dfrac{\sqrt{150 - 120 - 45 + 40}}{\sqrt{225} - \left|\dfrac{150}{-2}\right| + 6 \cdot 10}$ _____

6. $\left|\dfrac{\sqrt{4^2 \cdot 4^2 \cdot 4^2} - 120 \cdot \dfrac{2}{5}}{-2}\right|$ _____

Holt Algebra 1

Ready to Go On? Enrichment

Diophantine Equations

Diophantus (about 200-284) is known to some as the 'father of algebra'. He studied primarily the solutions of algebraic equations and the theory of numbers.

One type of equation he studied has the form $ax + by = c$ where a, b, and c are all integers and the solutions to the equation (x, y) are also integers. These types of equations are now known as Diophantine Equations. They can be quite difficult to solve and many times the only way to solve them is by guessing and checking.

Solve each Diophantine Equation. Find at least one pair of positive integers for x and y that make the equation true.

1. $3x + 4y = 12$

   a. Solve the equation for y. _____

   b. What number must x be divisible by?

   Why? _____

   c. Find at least one solution. _____

2. $-2x + 3y = -9$

   a. Solve the equation for y. _____

   b. What number must x be divisible by?

   Why? _____

   c. Find at least one solution. _____

3. $x - 2y = 10$

4. $-4x + y = 15$

5. $8x - 19y = 100$

6. $3x + 7y = 35$

7. $-5x + 11y = 30$

8. $3x + 4y = 32$

9. $7x - y = 14$

10. $-3x + 5y = 9$

Holt Algebra 1

Ready to Go On? Enrichment

Proportions in Paint

Thousands of different paint colors are possible because *colorants*, or dyes, are used in different proportions. For example, one type of beige requires 2 parts black, 1 part maroon, and 15 parts deep gold. The ratio describing this situation is shown below.

$$\text{black:maroon:deep gold} = 2{:}1{:}15$$

Suppose 5 ounces of black colorant are used to make the beige. Then how many ounces of maroon and deep gold colorant need to be used?

Step 1   Find the amount of maroon colorant.

$\dfrac{\text{black} \rightarrow 2}{\text{maroon} \rightarrow 1}$	Write a ratio comparing black to maroon.
$2/1 = 5/x$	Write a proportion. Let x be the ounces of maroon.
$2(x) = 1(5)$	Use cross products.
$2x = 5$	Simplify.
$2x/2 = 5/2$	Divide both sides by 2.
$x = 2.5$	So, 2.5 ounces of maroon colorant are used.

Step 2   Find the amount of deep gold colorant.

$\dfrac{\text{maroon} \rightarrow 1}{\text{deep gold} \rightarrow 15}$	Write a ratio comparing maroon to deep gold.
$1/15 = 2.5/y$	Write a proportion. Let y be the ounces of deep gold.
$1(y) = 15(2.5)$	Use cross products.
$y = 37.5$	So, 37.5 ounces of deep gold colorant are used.

1. An almond color is made by using 4 parts of new green, 3 parts of maroon, and 12 parts of deep gold.

   a) Write a ratio comparing the amounts of new green, maroon, and deep gold. _____

   b) If 14 ounces of new green colorant are used, how much maroon and deep gold colorants are needed? _____

2. Periwinkle is made by mixing thalo green, thalo blue, and magenta in the ratio 16:20:35. If 15 ounces of thalo blue colorant are used, how much thalo green and magenta colorants need to be used?

   _____

3. Navy blue is made by using the following colorants: 55 parts black, 14 parts blue, and 50 parts magenta. If 180 grams of magenta colorant are used, how much black and blue colorants are needed?

   _____

Holt Algebra 1

Ready to Go On? Enrichment

Triangle Inequalities

The Triangle Inequality Theorem states that "For any triangle, the sum of the lengths of any two sides is greater than the length of the third side". This inequality defines the existence of a triangle. There is a theorem in geometry that determines whether a given triangle is a right triangle, obtuse triangle, or acute triangle.

A right triangle has exactly one 90 degree angle.

An obtuse triangle has exactly one angle greater than 90 degrees.

An acute triangle has no angle with a measure greater than or equal to 90 degrees.

In a triangle with sides a, b, and c with c being the longest side:

If $c^2 > a^2 + b^2$, the triangle is obtuse.

If $c^2 = a^2 + b^2$, the triangle is a right triangle.

If $c^2 < a^2 + b^2$, the triangle is acute.

Determine whether the triangles, with these given side lengths, are acute, right, or obtuse.

1. 2, 3, 4   **2.** 3, 4, 5

_____   _____

3. 6, 6, 7   **4.** 7, 20, 24

_____   _____

5.   **6.**

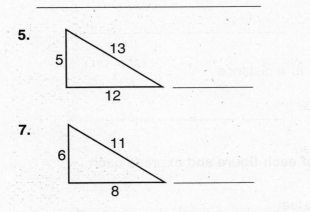   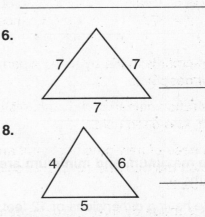

7.

8.

9. The longest side of an acute triangle measures 12 inches. One of the shorter sides is 7 inches. Express the length of the third side as an inequality.

_____

10. The two shorter sides of an obtuse triangle measure 5 cm and 10 cm. Express the length of the third side as an inequality.

_____

Holt Algebra 1

Name _____ Date _____ Class _____

SECTION 3B Ready to Go On? Enrichment

The Greatest Possible Error

Measurements made with a ruler are not precise. The greatest possible error in a measurement is one-half of the unit of measure. For example, if you measure a line segment to be 4.7 cm, the greatest possible error is one-half of 0.1 cm, or 0.05 cm.

The minimum length of this line segment is (4.7 − 0.05) or 4.65 and the maximum length is (4.7 + 0.05) or 4.75. Written as an inequality it can be represented as $4.65 \le \ell < 4.75$, where ℓ is the length.

Find the greatest possible error for each of the following.

1. a line segment, ℓ, 3.2 m long

2. an object, b, weighing 1.5 g

3. a pitcher, p containing 2.75 L

4. a distance, d of 1.75 miles

Determine the inequality representing Exercises 1 to 4.

5. a line segment

6. an object

7. a pitcher

8. a distance

Determine the maximum and minimum areas of each figure and express each as an inequality.

9. A rectangle having dimensions of 12 feet by 8 feet

10. A square having a side length of 10.34 cm

Holt Algebra 1

Ready to Go On? Enrichment

Profit-Loss-Revenue

An important concept in business is the ability to make a profit. Profit is equal to the amount of sales minus the cost of production. If the sales are greater than the cost, the business makes a profit. If the sales are less than the cost, the business is losing money.

Use the information below to answer each question.

A manufacturer of compact-disc players sells them to a retailer for $45 each. It costs the manufacturer $200 plus $25 each to produce the compact-disc player.

1. Write a function, s, to represent the total amount of sales of

   compact-disc players, n. _____

2. Write a function, c, to represent the total cost of producing the

   compact-disc players, n. _____

3. Graph the functions s and c on the same coordinate grid.

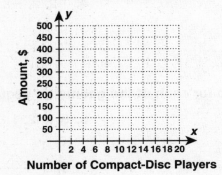

Number of Compact-Disc Players

4. For what dollar amount is the sales and the cost equal? _____

5. For what value of n is the sales and the cost equal? _____

6. Write an inequality that represents the value(s) of n for which the cost is more than the sales.

   _____

7. Write an inequality that represents the value(s) of n for which the manufacturer makes a profit.

   _____

Holt Algebra 1

SECTION 4B	**Ready to Go On? Enrichment**

Geometric Sequences

A geometric sequence is a sequence in which each term is a product of the previous term and a common ratio, r. For example, 2, 4, 8, 16, … is a geometric sequence. The common ratio, r is 2. Each term is the product of the previous term and 2.

The common ratio can be determined by finding the quotient of two consecutive terms. In the sequence 1, −4, 16, −64, … the common ratio is −4 because $\frac{-4}{1} = \frac{16}{-4} = \frac{-64}{16}$.

A geometric sequence has the general form $a_n = a_1 \cdot r^{n-1}$, where n is the term number, and a_1 is the first term in the sequence.

Determine whether each of the following is a geometric sequence.

1. $\frac{1}{3}$, 1, 3, 9, …

2. 2, 4, 6, 8, …

3. 1, 1, 2, 3, …

4. −2, 2, −2, 2, …

Determine the common ratio for each of the geometric sequences.

5. 5, 15, 45, 135, …

6. 8, 4, 2, 1, …

7. −2, 4, −8, 16, …

8. $\frac{1}{5}$, 1, 5, 25, …

Write the general form of the geometric sequence.

9. 5, 10, 20, 40, …

10. −1, −3, −9, −27, …

11. 100, 10, 1, $\frac{1}{10}$, …

12. 12, 6, 3, $\frac{3}{2}$, …

Holt Algebra 1

Ready To Go On? Enrichment

SECTION 5A

Onto Functions

A relation is a function if for every number in the domain, there is one and only one number in the range. Another way to describe a function is to determine if it is onto. A function is onto if and only if all the numbers of the range are paired with all of the numbers in the domain.

For example, the function in Table 1 is described as onto because each number in the range has a number from the domain assigned to it.

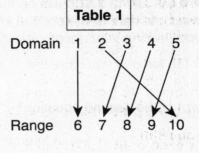

The function in the Table 2 is not onto because the number 7 in the range does not have a number in the domain assigned to it.

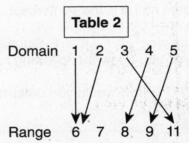

Determine if each function can be described as onto.

1. _____

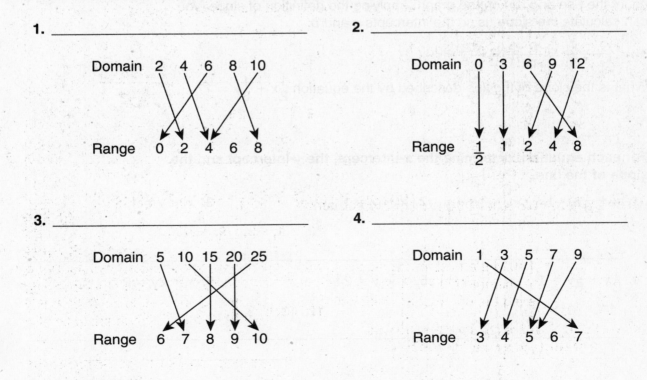

2. _____

3. _____

4. _____

Holt Algebra 1

Ready to Go On? Enrichment

Intercept–Intercept Form

Look at the graph of the equation $\frac{1}{2}x + \frac{1}{3}y = 1$ and $\frac{1}{-4}x + \frac{1}{5}y = 1$ shown on the right. The y-intercept for the first equation is 3, so you know that the point (0, 3) lies on the line. Another point containing 0 also lies on the line; it is the point (2, 0). The x-coordinate of the point at which the line crosses the x-axis is called the x-intercept.

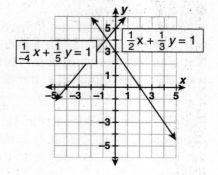

You can see that for the second equation, the y-intercept is 5.

What is the x-intercept of the second equation? _____

An equation in the form $\frac{1}{a}x + \frac{1}{b}y = 1$ is in intercept-intercept form. In this form, a is the x-intercept and b is the y-intercept.

Look back at the equation $\frac{1}{-4}x + \frac{1}{5}y = 1$. Since it is in intercept-intercept form, you know the following relationships.

$\frac{1}{a} = \frac{1}{-4} \qquad \frac{1}{b} = \frac{1}{5}$ How would you determine a and b?

$a = -4 \qquad b = 5$ _____

You can use the intercept-intercept for to determine the slope of the line. Recall that slope equals rise over run. You can use the two intercepts to count the rise and run on the graph. Applying the definition of slope, you can calculate the slope using the intercepts a and b.

$$m = \frac{y_2 - y_1}{x_2 - x_1} = \frac{0-b}{a - 0} = -\frac{b}{a}$$

What is the slope of the line described by the equation $\frac{1}{2}x + \frac{1}{3}y = 1$?

$m =$

_____

For each equation, determine the x-intercept, the y-intercept and the slope of the line.

1. $x + \frac{1}{6}y = 1$ 2. $x - y = 1$ 3. $x + y = 1$

_____   _____   _____

4. $\frac{1}{2}x + \frac{1}{6}y = 1$ 5. $x + y = 2$ 6. $x - 2y = 2$

_____   _____   _____

182   **Holt Algebra 1**

SECTION 6A Ready to Go On? Enrichment

Using a Matrix to Represent a System of Equations

A matrix is a rectangular array of numbers enclosed in a single set of brackets. If each equation in a system of equations is written in standard form, you can represent the system with a matrix equation. The matrix equation is made up of three matrices; one for the coefficients on the variables x and y, one for the variables x and y, and one for the constants.

For example, the system of equations $\begin{cases} 3x - y = 6 \\ x + y = -2 \end{cases}$ is represented by the matrix

equation $\begin{bmatrix} 3 & -1 \\ 1 & 1 \end{bmatrix} \begin{bmatrix} x \\ y \end{bmatrix} = \begin{bmatrix} 6 \\ -2 \end{bmatrix}$.

Determine which system of equations represents the correct matrix equation.

1. _____ $\begin{cases} x + y = 8 \\ x - y = 2 \end{cases}$
     a. $\begin{bmatrix} 3 & -1 \\ 6 & 2 \end{bmatrix} \begin{bmatrix} x \\ y \end{bmatrix} = \begin{bmatrix} 4 \\ -8 \end{bmatrix}$

2. _____ $\begin{cases} 3x - y = 4 \\ 6x + 2y = -8 \end{cases}$
     b. $\begin{bmatrix} 1 & -1 \\ 2 & 3 \end{bmatrix} \begin{bmatrix} x \\ y \end{bmatrix} = \begin{bmatrix} 2 \\ 9 \end{bmatrix}$

3. _____ $\begin{cases} x - y = 2 \\ 2x + 3y = 9 \end{cases}$
     c. $\begin{bmatrix} -5 & 8 \\ 10 & 3 \end{bmatrix} \begin{bmatrix} x \\ y \end{bmatrix} = \begin{bmatrix} 21 \\ 15 \end{bmatrix}$

4. _____ $\begin{cases} -5x + 8y = 21 \\ 10x + 3y = 15 \end{cases}$
     d. $\begin{bmatrix} 1 & 1 \\ 1 & -1 \end{bmatrix} \begin{bmatrix} x \\ y \end{bmatrix} = \begin{bmatrix} 8 \\ 2 \end{bmatrix}$

Create a matrix equation for each system of equations.

5. $\begin{cases} x - 5y = 0 \\ 2x - 3y = 7 \end{cases}$
     6. $\begin{cases} 4x + 3y = 19 \\ 3x - 4y = 8 \end{cases}$
     7. $\begin{cases} 5x + 3y = 12 \\ 4x - 5y = 17 \end{cases}$

_____   _____   _____

8. $\begin{cases} x + y = 7 \\ x - y = 9 \end{cases}$
     9. $\begin{cases} 12x - 9y = 114 \\ 12x + 7y = 82 \end{cases}$
     10. $\begin{cases} 2x - 3y = -4 \\ x + 3y = 7 \end{cases}$

_____   _____   _____

11. $\begin{cases} \frac{1}{2}x + y = 12 \\ x + \frac{1}{5}y = 10 \end{cases}$
     12. $\begin{cases} \frac{2}{3}x + \frac{1}{3}y = -9 \\ \frac{1}{4}x + \frac{3}{4}y = 16 \end{cases}$
     13. $\begin{cases} 1.2x - 1.6y = 2.4 \\ -0.8x + 0.2y = -1.2 \end{cases}$

_____   _____   _____

Holt Algebra 1

SECTION 6B Ready to Go On? Enrichment

Describing Geometric Regions with a System of Inequalities

Describe the shaded region of the graph by writing a system of inequalities consisting of three different linear inequalities. To write this system, follow these steps:

1. Determine the slope and *y*-intercept of each line.

2. Write inequalities in slope-intercept form.

3. If the line is solid use either $\leq$ or $\geq$. If the line is dashed, use either $<$ or $>$.

4. If the shaded region is "above" the line use the symbol $>$, and if the shaded region is "below" the line, use the symbol $<$.

For example, the system of inequalities that describes the region below is $\begin{cases} x \geq -2 \\ y \geq -4 \\ y \leq \dfrac{-3}{2}x - 1 \end{cases}$

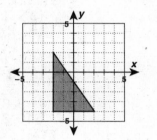

Write a system of inequalities that describes each region.

1.

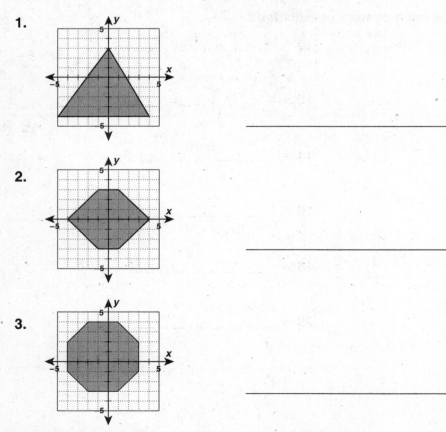

_____

2.

_____

3.

_____

Holt Algebra 1

SECTION
7A

Ready To Go On? Enrichment

Digits

Using the digits 1, 2, 3 and 4 and addition, subtraction, multiplication, division, parentheses, and exponents, write an expression equivalent to the numbers 1 to 20.

- You must use all four digits in each expression.

- You may use any of the operations but each symbol may be used only once in each expression.

An example has been done for you. There may be more than one correct expression for a given number.

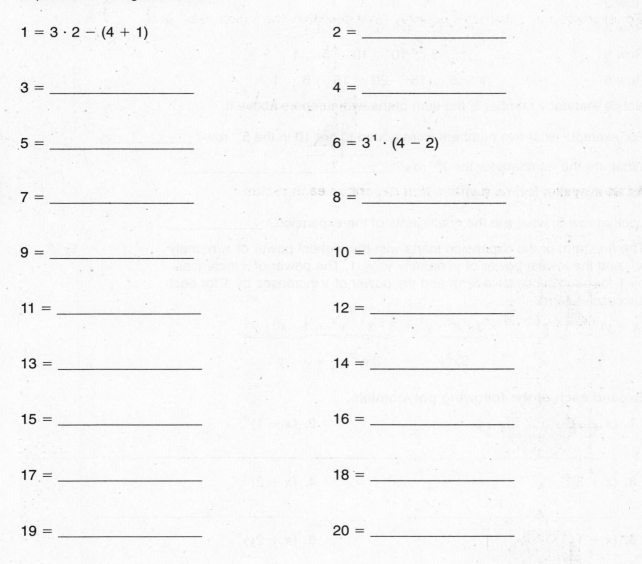

$1 = 3 \cdot 2 - (4 + 1)$ $2 = $ _____

$3 = $ _____ $4 = $ _____

$5 = $ _____ $6 = 3^1 \cdot (4 - 2)$

$7 = $ _____ $8 = $ _____

$9 = $ _____ $10 = $ _____

$11 = $ _____ $12 = $ _____

$13 = $ _____ $14 = $ _____

$15 = $ _____ $16 = $ _____

$17 = $ _____ $18 = $ _____

$19 = $ _____ $20 = $ _____

Holt Algebra 1

Ready to Go On? Enrichment

Pascal's Triangle

Pascal's Triangle is a geometric arrangement of numbers. These numbers represent the binomial coefficients. That is, they represent the coefficients of the terms of the expansion of $(x + y)^n$. The first seven rows of Pascal's Triangle look like this.

Row 0   1

Row 1   1 1

Row 2   1 2 1

Row 3   1 3 3 1

Row 4   1 4 6 4 1

Row 5   1 5 10 10 5 1

Row 6   1 6 15 20 15 6 1

Notice that each number is the sum of the two numbers above it.

For example what two numbers were added to get 10 in the 5th row? _____

What are the numbers for the 7th row? _____

As an example, find $(x + y)^3$.

Look at row 3, what are the coefficients of the expansion? _____

The first term of the expansion starts with the highest power of x, namely x^3, and the lowest power of y, namely $y^0 = 1$. The power of x increases by 1 for each successive term and the power of y increases by 1 for each successive term.

$(x + y)^3 = \underline{1 \cdot x^3 \cdot y^0} + \underline{3 \cdot x^2 \cdot y^1} + \underline{3 \cdot x^1 \cdot y^2} + \underline{1 \cdot x^0 \cdot y^3}$

$\qquad = \qquad x^3 \qquad + \quad 3x^2y \quad + \quad 3xy^2 \quad + \quad y^3$

Expand each of the following polynomials.

1. $(x + y)^4$

    _____

2. $(x + 1)^5$

    _____

3. $(x + 3)^4$

    _____

4. $(x + 2)^3$

    _____

5. $(x + 1)^9$

    _____

6. $(x + 2y)^5$

    _____

Holt Algebra 1

Name _____ Date _____ Class _____

Ready To Go On? Enrichment

Sum and Differences of Cubes

While it is possible to factor the sum and differences of two squares, it is also possible to factor the sum and differences of two cubes.

The sum of two cubes can be factored in the following way:

$$a^3 + b^3 = (a + b)(a^2 - ab + b^2)$$

The differences of two cubes can be factored in the following way:

$$a^3 - b^3 = (a - b)(a^2 + ab + b^2)$$

Factor each of the following.

1. $r^3 - s^3$

_____

2. $x^3 + y^3$

_____

3. $x^3 + 8$

_____

4. $n^3 - 64$

_____

5. $8y^3 + 27$

_____

6. $pq^3 - 64p$

_____

Express each of the following as the sum or difference of two cubes.

7. $(m - 1)(m^2 + m + 1)$

_____

8. $(2 + 3t)(4 - 6t + 9t^2)$

_____

9. $(b - 64)(b^2 + 4b + 16)$

_____

10. $(x + 7)(x^2 - 7x + 49)$

_____

11. $(2y - 1)(4y^2 + 2y + 1)$

_____

12. $(3 + 2t)(9 - 6t + 4t^2)$

_____

13. $(s + 10)(s^2 - 10s + 100)$

_____

14. $2(x - 4)(x^2 + 4x + 16)$

_____

Holt Algebra 1

Ready To Go On? Enrichment

Fourth Degree Trinomials
Sometimes it is possible to write a trinomial of the fourth degree, $a^4 + a^2b^2 + b^4$, as a difference of two squares and then factor.

Example: Factor $4a^4 - 21a^2b^2 + 9b^4$.

Step I Find the square roots of the first and last terms.

$$\sqrt{4a^4} = 2a^2 \qquad\qquad \sqrt{9b^4} = 3b^2$$

Step II Find twice the product of the square roots from the terms in Step 1.

$$2(2a^2)(3b^2) = 12a^2b^2$$

Step III Split the middle term of the trinomial into two parts. One part is either the answer from the Step II or its opposite. The other part should be the opposite of a perfect square.

$$-21a^2b^2 = -12a^2b^2 - 9a^2b^2$$

Step IV Rewrite the trinomial as the difference of two squares and then factor.

$$4a^4 - 21a^2b^2 + 9b^4 = (4a^4 - 12a^2b^2 + 9b^4) - 9a^2b^2$$
$$= (2a^2 - 3b^2)^2 - 9a^2b^2$$
$$= [(2a^2 - 3b^2) - 3ab][(2a^2 - 3b^2) - 3ab]$$
$$= (2a^2 + 3ab - 3b^2)(2a^2 - 3ab - 3b^2)$$

Factor each trinomial.

1. $16d^4 + 7d^2 + 1$

_____

2. $p^4 + p^2 + 1$

_____

3. $4x^4 - 13x^2 + 1$

_____

4. $4x^4 - 9x^2y^2 + 16y^4$

_____

5. $9r^4 + 26r^2s^2 + 25s^4$

_____

6. $4a^4 - 5a^2c^2 + 25c^4$

_____

Holt Algebra 1

SECTION 9A

Ready To Go On? Enrichment

Graphing Cubic Equations

Just as quadratic equations can be graphed, equations to the third power can also be graphed. To determine the general form of a cubic equation graph the equation $y = x^3$.

Complete the table and plot your points on the graph.

x	$y = x^3$
−2	$(-2)^3 = -8$
−1	$(-1)^3 = -1$
0	$(0)^3 = 0$
1	$(1)^3 = $ _____
2	$(2)^3 = $ _____

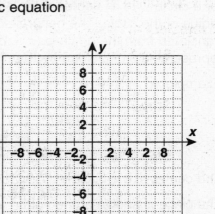

Complete the table and then graph the cubic equations.

1. $y = \frac{1}{3}x^3$

x	y
−3	_____
−1	_____
0	_____
1	
3	

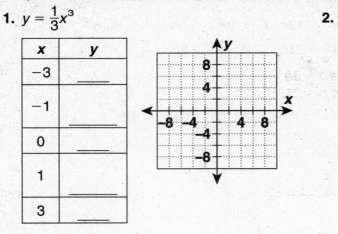

2. $y = -x^3$

x	y
−2	_____
−1	_____
0	_____
1	_____
2	_____

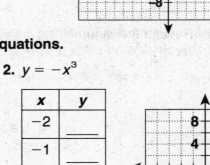

3. $y = x^3 + 2$

x	y
−3	_____
−1	_____
0	_____
1	_____
3	_____

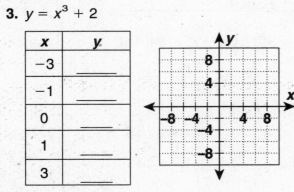

4. $y = x^3 - 2$

x	y
−3	_____
−1	_____
0	_____
1	_____
3	_____

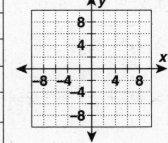

Holt Algebra 1

SECTION 9B Ready To Go On? Enrichment

Graphing Circles by Completing the Square

Completing the square can be used to graph circles. The general equation
for a circle with its center at the origin is $x^2 + y^2 = r^2$, where r is the
radius of the circle. The general equation of a circle with its center
translated from the origin is $(x - h)^2 + (y - k)^2 = r^2$. An equation
representing a circle can be transformed into the sum of two squares.

Example: $x^2 - 14x + y^2 + 6y + 49 = 0$

$(x^2 - 14x + \underline{\quad}) + (y^2 + 6y + \underline{\quad}) = -49$

$(x^2 - 14x + \mathbf{49}) + (y^2 + 6y + \mathbf{9}) = -49 + \mathbf{49} + \mathbf{9}$

$(x - 7)^2 + (y + 3)^2 = 9$

$(x - 7)^2 + (y + 3)^2 = 3^2$

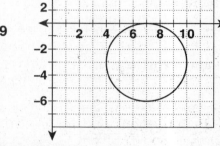

The center of the circle is $(7, -3)$ and the radius is 3.

The circle is shown at the right.

**Complete the square on the following equations. Identify the center
and radius of the circle and then graph.**

1. $x^2 - 8x + y^2 + 2y + 13 = 0$

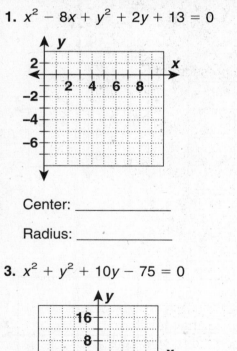

Center: _____

Radius: _____

2. $x^2 + 6x + y^2 + 4y + 12 = 0$

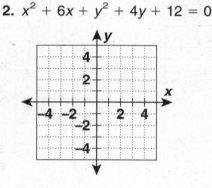

Center: _____

Radius: _____

3. $x^2 + y^2 + 10y - 75 = 0$

Center: _____

Radius: _____

4. $x^2 - 8x + y^2 - 84 = 0$

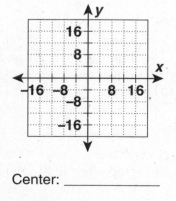

Center: _____

Radius: _____

Holt Algebra 1

Ready To Go On? Enrichment

SECTION
10A

Other Types of Variation

Two types of variation have been discussed thus far. Direct variation is an equation

of the form $y = kx$ while inverse variation is an equation of the form $y = \frac{k}{x}$ or $xy = k$.

Two important laws from Chemistry arise from the idea of variation. Boyle's Law states that the volume of a gas at a given temperature varies inversely with applied

pressure. Mathematically, this inverse variation can be expressed as $V = \frac{k}{P}$, where

V is the volume, P is the applied pressure, and k is a constant. Charles' Law states that the volume of a gas at a given pressure varies directly with temperature. Mathematically, this direct variation can be stated $V = kT$, where V is the volume, T is the temperature, and k is a constant.

Combining the two laws results in what is called a joint variation: The volume of a gas varies directly with the temperature and inversely with pressure.

Answer each question.

1. Write the mathematical statement for the joint variation of the two gas laws.

_____

2. a. If the volume of a sample of gas is 3.241 L under a pressure of 0.20 atm at a temperature of 300 Kelvin, find k.

_____

    b. If the pressure was adjusted to 0.50 atm and the temperature was changed to 320 Kelvin, determine the volume of the sample of gas.

_____

    c. If the temperature of the sample was held constant at 320 Kelvin, what would the pressure need to be adjusted to in order to return the volume to 2 L?

_____

3. a. Suppose a 5 L sample of gas under went the following changes: the pressure was changed from 0.1 atm to 0.07 atm, and the temperature was changed from 400 Kelvin to 320 Kelvin. Determine the volume of the sample of gas.

_____

    b. Holding the pressure constant at 0.07 atm, what change in temperature would return the gas to a volume of 5 L?

_____

Holt Algebra 1

Name _____ Date _____ Class _____

Synthetic Division

Synthetic division is a shortcut that can be used when dividing a polynomial by a binomial. In order for synthetic division to work, the divisor must be in the form of $x - c$, that is, a variable minus a constant.

Example: $(x^3 + 6x^2 - x - 30) \div (x - 2)$. Divide.

The value of c is 2.

Write the coefficients of the dividend and the value for c in the upper left corner.

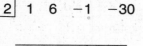
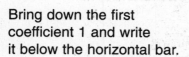

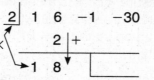

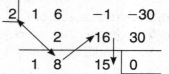

Bring down the first coefficient 1 and write it below the horizontal bar.

Multiply 2 by 1 to get 2. Write the product under the next coefficient and add.

Repeat the steps (multiply, write the product under the next coefficient and add) with the remaining numbers.

The quotient is $x^2 + 8x + 15$.

Use synthetic division to find each quotient.

1. $(4x^2 + 19x - 5) \div (x + 5)$

_____

2. $(3y^2 - 5y - 12) \div (y - 3)$

_____

3. $(4a^3 - 3a^2 + 2a - 3) \div (a - 1)$

_____

4. $(5w^3 - 6w^2 + 3w + 14) \div (w + 1)$

_____

5. $(y^3 + 1) \div (y - 1)$ (*Hint*: There are missing terms, fill in the missing terms with 0.)

_____

6. $(2y^5 - 5y^4 - 3y^2 - 6y - 23) \div (y - 3)$

_____

Holt Algebra 1

SECTION 11A Ready To Go On? Enrichment

Derive the Distance Formula from the Pythagorean Theorem

The Pythagorean Theorem, $a^2 + b^2 = c^2$, can be used to find the length of the hypotenuse of a right triangle given the length of the two legs. The figure below shows that a right triangle can be created between any two points.

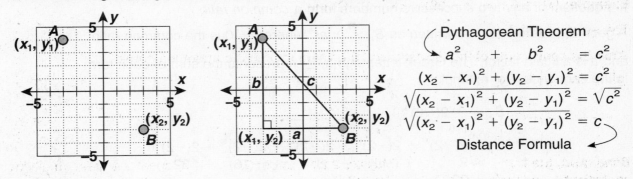

Pythagorean Theorem

$$a^2 + b^2 = c^2$$
$$(x_2 - x_1)^2 + (y_2 - y_1)^2 = c^2$$
$$\sqrt{(x_2 - x_1)^2 + (y_2 - y_1)^2} = \sqrt{c^2}$$
$$\sqrt{(x_2 - x_1)^2 + (y_2 - y_1)^2} = c$$

Distance Formula

The distance between $A(-3, 4)$ and $B(3, -3)$ can be determined by using the distance formula.

$$d = \sqrt{(x_2 - x_1)^2 + (y_2 - y_1)^2}$$
$$d = \sqrt{(3 - (-3))^2 + (-3 - 4)^2}$$
$$d = \sqrt{(6)^2 + (-7)^2}$$
$$d = \sqrt{36 + 49}$$
$$d = \sqrt{85}$$
$$d \approx 9.22$$

So $\overline{AB}$ is 9.22 units long.

Find the distance between the two points. Round your answer to the nearest hundredth.

1. $A(1, 2)$ and $B(4, 6)$

2. $C(-5, 0)$ and $D(5, 0)$

3. $E(-2, -2)$ and $F(2, 2)$

_____

4. $G(-5, 4)$ and $H(-8, -3)$

5. $J(6, -1)$ and $K(3, -6)$

6. $L(0, 10)$ and $M(-3, 5)$

_____

7. $N(-2, 1)$ and $P(1, -2)$

8. $Q(10, 3)$ and $R(8, -1)$

9. $S(-9, 7)$ and $T(-7, 5)$

_____

Holt Algebra 1

Name _____ Date _____ Class _____

Ready To Go On? Enrichment

Geometric Series

A series is the sum of a sequence of terms. In other words, a series is a list of numbers with addition operations between them. Series can be finite, meaning that there is an end, or infinite. A geometric series is a sequence of numbers such that the quotient of any two successive numbers form a *common ratio*.

A geometric series can be written as $S_n = \sum\limits_{k=0}^{n} ar^k$ where $r \neq 0$ is the common ratio and a is a scale factor. The Greek letter sigma, $\sum$, represents the sum of each term in the sequence. For example:

$$S_4 = \sum_{k=0}^{4} 2(-2)^k$$
$$= 2(-2)^0 + 2(-2)^1 + 2(-2)^2 + 2(-2)^3 + 2(-2)^4$$
$$= 2 \quad\ + (-4) \ + \ 8 \quad\ + (-16) \ + \ 32$$
$$= 22$$

Find the value of each geometric series.

1. $S_3 = \sum\limits_{k=0}^{3} 3(-3)^k$

_____

2. $S_4 = \sum\limits_{k=0}^{4} 2\left(\dfrac{1}{2}\right)^k$

_____

3. $S_4 = \sum\limits_{k=0}^{4} 4\left(-\dfrac{1}{2}\right)^k$

_____

4. $S_3 = \sum\limits_{k=0}^{3} \dfrac{1}{2}(4)^k$

_____

5. $S_3 = \sum\limits_{k=0}^{3} -1\left(-\dfrac{1}{3}\right)^k$

_____

6. $S_4 = \sum\limits_{k=0}^{4} 9\left(\dfrac{2}{3}\right)^k$

_____

7. $S_5 = \sum\limits_{k=0}^{5} 4(-1)^k$

_____

8. $S_4 = \sum\limits_{k=0}^{4} \dfrac{1}{3}(-3)^k$

_____

Holt Algebra 1

Ready to Go On? Skills Intervention
1-1 Variables and Expressions

Find these vocabulary words in Lesson 1-1 and the Multilingual Glossary.

Vocabulary

variable	constant	numerical expression
algebraic expression		evaluate

Translating from Algebra to Words
Give two ways to write each algebraic expression in words.

A. $8 + k$

Identify the constant in the expression. __8__

Identify the variable in the expression. __k__

Name two words that mean the same thing as the + symbol. __Add__ __Sum__

Write the expression $8 + k$ in words: the __sum__ of 8 and k OR k added to __8__.

B. $\frac{c}{4}$

What operation does the fraction bar indicate? __Division__

Identify the divisor in the expression. __4__ Identify the dividend. __c__

When you find the answer to a division problem you find the __quotient__.

Write the expression $\frac{c}{4}$ in words: c __divided__ by 4 OR the quotient of __c__ and __4__.

Evaluating Algebraic Expressions
Evaluate each expression for $x = 6$, $y = 5$, and $z = 2$.

A. xy

What operation is indicated by the expression? __Multiplication__

What value should you substitute for x? __6__ for y? __5__

Rewrite the expression using the substituted values. (__6__)(__5__) Simplify. __30__

B. $x - z$

What operation is indicated by the − symbol? __Subtraction__

What value should you substitute for x? __6__ for z? __2__

Rewrite the expression using the substituted values. __6__ − __2__ Simplify. __4__

1 **Holt Algebra 1**

Ready to Go On? Problem Solving Intervention
1-1 Variables and Expressions

An algebraic expression contains variables, constants, and operations. A variable is a letter or symbol used in an expression to represent a value that can change, like x, and a constant is a value that does not change, like 3.

A swimmer is competing in a 50-lap race. Write an expression for the number of laps left after the swimmer has completed c laps.

Understand the Problem

1. How many laps is the race? __50__

2. What variable represents the number of laps? __c__

3. What are you being asked to do?
   Write an expression for the number of laps left after the swimmer has completed c laps.

Make a Plan

4. The phrase *number of laps left* corresponds to which operation symbol? __−__

5. Identify the constant in the problem. __50__

6. Identify the variable in the problem. __c__

Solve

7. What value should be written first in the expression, the constant or the variable? Why?
   The constant, 50, because you are trying to determine the number of laps left after c laps.

8. Write an expression for the number of laps left after the swimmer has completed c laps. __50__ − __c__

Look Back

9. Think of a simpler problem: The race is 50 laps. If you swim 20 laps, how many laps will be left? __30__

10. Now use your expression to determine the following: If the swimmer has completed 20 laps, how many laps left does he have left to swim? __50__ − 20 = __30__
    Is the number of laps left to swim more or less than 50 laps? __Less__

11. Does your expression represent the situation? Explain.
    Yes, when I substituted a value for c, the expression results in a reasonable number of laps left to swim.

2 **Holt Algebra 1**

Ready to Go On? Skills Intervention
1-2 Adding and Subtracting Real Numbers

Find these vocabulary words in Lesson 1-2 and the Multilingual Glossary.

Vocabulary

absolute value	opposites	additive inverse

Adding Real Numbers
Add.

A. $52 + (-13)$

When you add two numbers with different signs, find the difference of their __absolute values__ and use the sign of the number with the __greater__ absolute value.

What is the absolute value of 52? __52__ What is the absolute value of −13? __13__

Find the difference of the absolute values of 52 and 13. __39__

What is the sign on the number that has the greatest absolute value? __Positive__

What is $52 + (-13)$? __39__

B. $x + (-10)$ for $x = -12$

When you add two numbers with the same sign, __add__ their absolute values and use the __sign__ of the numbers.

What value should you substitute for x? __−12__

Rewrite the expression using the substituted value. __−12 + (−10)__

What is the absolute value of −12? __12__ What is the absolute value of −10? __10__

Find the sum of the absolute values of −12 and −10. __22__

What is the sign on the numbers? __Negative__ What is $-12 + (-10)$? __−22__

Subtracting Real Numbers
Subtract 40 − 57.

To subtract a number, __add__ its opposite. What is the opposite of −57? __57__

Rewrite the expression using the opposite, or additive inverse, of −57. __40 + (−57)__

When the signs of the numbers are different, find the __difference__ of their absolute values.

What is 57 − 40? __17__

What is the sign on the number that has the greatest absolute value? __Negative__

So, what is 40 − 57? __−17__

3 **Holt Algebra 1**

Ready to Go On? Problem Solving Intervention
1-2 Adding and Subtracting Real Numbers

To add or subtract numbers with the same sign, add the numbers and use the sign of the numbers. To add or subtract numbers with different signs, subtract the smaller number from the larger and use the sign of the larger number.

The outdoor temperature is currently −6°F. By midnight the temperature is predicted to increase 14°F. If the prediction is accurate, what will be the outdoor temperature at midnight?

Understand the Problem

1. What is the current temperature? __−6°F__

2. What is the predicted temperature increase? __14°F__

3. Should the predicted midnight temperature be less than or more than −6°F? __More than__

Make a Plan

4. Plot −6°F and 14°F on a number line.
   −8° −6° −4° −2° 0° 2° 4° 6° 8° 10° 12° 14° 16°

5. What number is larger, −6 or 14? __14__

6. What is the sign of the larger number? __Positive__

7. Since the current temperature is predicted to increase, do you need to add or subtract the two temperatures to find the midnight temperature? __Add__

Solve

8. Find the sum. −6°F + 14°F = ? Remember: to add numbers with different signs, subtract the smaller number from the larger and use the sign of the larger number.
   __14__ − 6 = __8__ ; So −6°F + 14°F = __8°F__

9. Is the sum positive or negative? How do you know?
   Positive; The sign of the large number, 14, is positive.

Look Back

10. Use the number line in Exercise 4 to help you check your answer. Plot your answer from Exercise 8 on the number line in Exercise 4.

11. How many degrees does the temperature have to increase to go from −6°F to 0°F? __6°__ How many degrees does the temperature have to increase to go from 0°F to the point you just plotted? __8°__
    Add these two values __6__ + __8__ = __14__ ; If the sum is 14, your answer checks.

4 **Holt Algebra 1**

195

Holt Algebra 1

Ready to Go On? Skills Intervention
1-3 Multiplying and Dividing Real Numbers

Find these vocabulary words in Lesson 1-3 and the Multilingual Glossary.

Vocabulary	
reciprocal	multiplicative inverse

Multiplying and Dividing Signed Numbers
Find the value of the expression 5(−8).

If two numbers have the same sign, their product or quotient is __positive__.

If two numbers have different signs, their product or quotient is __negative__.

Are the signs in the expression 5(−8) the same or different? __Different__

So, what is the product of 5(−8)? __−40__

If the expression were changed to −5(−8), is the product positive or negative? __Positive__

Dividing by Fractions
Divide $-14 \div \frac{7}{9}$.

Two numbers are reciprocals if their product is __1__.

If you switch the numerator and the __denominator__ of a fraction, you get the reciprocal of that number. What is the reciprocal of $\frac{7}{9}$? $\boxed{\frac{9}{7}}$

$-14 \div \frac{7}{9}$

$= -14 \cdot \frac{9}{7}$ Multiply by the reciprocal.

$= \frac{-126}{7}$ Multiply the numerator. Multiply the denominator.

$= -18$ Simplify. The signs are different, so the quotient is __negative__.

Multiplying and Dividing with Zero
Divide $80.2 \div 0$.

The product of any number and 0 is __0__.

The quotient of 0 and any nonzero number is __0__.

Can you divide a number by zero? __No__

$80.2 \div 0$ is the same as $\frac{80.2}{0}$

So division by zero is __undefined__.

   5   Holt Algebra 1

Ready to Go On? Problem Solving Intervention
1-3 Multiplying and Dividing Real Numbers

The product or quotient of two numbers with the same sign is positive. The product or quotient of two numbers with different signs is negative.

The airplane Paul is traveling on averages 520 miles per hour. If the plane has been in the air for $3\frac{1}{2}$ hours, how far has the plane traveled?

Understand the Problem

1. What is the average rate of the plane? __520 miles per hour__

2. How long has the plane been in the air? __$3\frac{1}{2}$ hours__

3. What are you trying to determine? __The distance the plane has traveled.__

4. What should be the units of your final answer? __Miles__

5. Should your answer be more than or less than 520? How do you know?
__More than; The rate is for one hour and since the plane is traveling more than one hour, the distance will be more than 520 miles.__

Make a Plan

6. To find distance, do you multiply or divide the rate and time? __Multiply__

7. Write the decimal equivalent of $3\frac{1}{2}$ hours. __3.5 hours__

8. Let d represent the distance traveled. Write an equation to represent the situation.

Rate of the plane	Time the plane has been in the air	=	Distance Traveled
520	· 3.5	=	d

Solve

9. Multiply. $\frac{520 \cdot 3.5}{1820} = d$ How far has the plane traveled? __1820 miles__

10. Is the product positive or negative? __Positive__ How do you know? __The product of two numbers with the same sign is positive.__

Look Back

11. To check a multiplication problem, you can divide the __product__ by either of the two factors.

12. Use division to check your answer. Substitute the value for d from Exercise 9.
$\frac{d}{520} = \frac{1820}{520} = 3.5$; If the quotient is 3.5, your answer checks.

   6   Holt Algebra 1

Ready to Go On? Skills Intervention
1-4 Powers and Exponents

Find these vocabulary words in Lesson 1-4 and the Multilingual Glossary.

Vocabulary		
power	base	exponent

Evaluating Powers
Simplify each expression.

A. $(-4)^4$

What is the base in the expression? __−4__

What is the exponent in the expression? __4__

The exponent tells how many times the base is used as a factor.

Rewrite the expression using −4 as a factor __4__ times.

$(-4) \times (-4) \times (-4) \times (-4)$

Is the product positive or negative? __Positive__

$(-4) \times (-4) \times (-4) \times (-4) = $ __256__   So, $(-4)^4 = $ __256__.

B. -6^2

What is the exponent in the expression? __2__

Keeping in mind that the negative sign is *not* in parenthesis, what is the base in the expression? __6__

Rewrite the expression as $-1 \times 6 \times$ __6__. Is the product positive or negative? __Negative__

$-1 \times 6 \times$ __6__ $= $ __−36__   Simplify.

C. $\left(-\frac{1}{3}\right)^3$

What is the base in the expression? __$-\frac{1}{3}$__

What is the exponent in the expression? __3__

Is the negative sign part of the base? __Yes__ Why? __It is within the parenthesis.__

Use $\left(-\frac{1}{3}\right)$ as a factor __3__ times. $\left(-\frac{1}{3}\right) \cdot \left(-\frac{1}{3}\right) \cdot \left(-\frac{1}{3}\right) = $ __$-\frac{1}{27}$__

Writing Powers
Write 125 as a power given the base of 5.

Check to see how many factors of 5's it takes to get a product of 125.

$5 \times 5 = $ __25__; Does this equal 125? __No__

$5 \times 5 \times 5 = $ __125__; Does this equal 125? __Yes__ Write the power: $5^{\boxed{3}}$

   7   Holt Algebra 1

Ready To Go On? Skills Intervention
1-5 Roots and Irrational Numbers

Find these vocabulary words in Lesson 1-5 and the Multilingual Glossary.

Vocabulary			
square root	perfect square	cube roots	natural numbers
whole numbers	integers	rational numbers	
terminating decimal	repeating decimal	irrational numbers	

Find Roots
Find each root.

A. $\sqrt{64}$

A number multiplied by __itself__ to form a product is called a square root of that product.

What symbol is used to represent positive square roots? __$\sqrt{}$__

What number multiplied by itself equals 64? $8 \cdot$ __8__ $= 64$

Complete: $\sqrt{64} = \sqrt{8 \cdot \boxed{8}} = $ __8__

B. $-\sqrt{625}$

What symbol is used to represent negative square roots? __$-\sqrt{}$__

What number multiplied by itself equals 625? $25 \cdot$ __25__ $= 625$

What is the opposite of this value? __−25__

Complete: $-\sqrt{625} = -\sqrt{25 \cdot \boxed{25}} = $ __−25__

C. $\sqrt{\frac{49}{81}}$

Complete: $\sqrt{49} = \sqrt{7 \cdot \boxed{7}} = $ __7__   Complete: $\sqrt{81} = \sqrt{9 \cdot \boxed{9}} = $ __9__

You can rewrite $\sqrt{\frac{49}{81}}$ as $\frac{\sqrt{49}}{\sqrt{81}}$. So, $\frac{\sqrt{49}}{\sqrt{81}} = \frac{\sqrt{7 \cdot 7}}{\sqrt{9 \cdot 9}} = \boxed{\frac{7}{9}}$

Classifying Real Numbers

A. $\sqrt{18}$

$\sqrt{18} = 4.242640687$

Since this number is not a perfect square, it is __irrational__.

B. $\frac{9}{11}$

$\frac{9}{11} = 0.8181\overline{81}$

Since this number can be written as a repeating decimal it is a __rational number__.

   8   Holt Algebra 1

---

   196   Holt Algebra 1

Ready to Go On? Problem Solving Intervention
1-5 Roots and Irrational Numbers

You can use square roots of perfect squares to help estimate the square roots of other numbers.

Angie is installing a window in the shape of a square. The window will cover 150 square feet. Find the length of a side of the square window to the nearest tenth of a foot.

Understand the Problem

1. What is the area of the window? __150 square feet__

2. What is the shape of the window? __Square__

3. What are you trying to determine? __The length of a side of the square window to the nearest tenth of a foot.__

Make a Plan

4. What do you know to be true about the side lengths of a square? __They have the same measure.__

5. If you know the area of the square how can you determine the length of the side of a square? $A = s^2$ $\sqrt{A} = $ __s__

6. Is the area of the window a perfect square? __No__ So, estimate to find the side length.

7. Find the two perfect squares that surround 150.

144		150		169
$\sqrt{144} = $ __12__ $12^2 = $ __144__				$\sqrt{169} = 13$ $13^2 = 169$

Solve

8. Find $\sqrt{144}$. __12__   Find $\sqrt{169}$. __13__

9. So the square root of 150 is between __12__ and __13__.

10. Guess 12.3: $12.3^2 = $ __151.29__ This value is too __high__. So $\sqrt{150}$ is __less__ than 12.3.

11. Guess 12.2: $12.2^2 = $ __148.84__ This value is too __low__. So $\sqrt{150}$ is __more__ than 12.2.

12. Because 150 is closer to __148.84__ than 151.29, $\sqrt{150}$ is closer to __$\sqrt{144}$__ than __$\sqrt{169}$__.

13. What is the length of the side of the window to the nearest tenth of a foot? __12.2 ft__

Look Back

14. Substitute the value from Exercise 13 into the area formula from Exercise 5.

$A = s^2 = $ __12.2__$^2 = $ __148.84__ Is your answer reasonable? __Yes__

9

Ready to Go On? Skills Intervention
1-6 Properties of Real Numbers

Identifying Properties
Name the property that is illustrated in each equation.

A. $5 \cdot c = c \cdot 5$

Write the order of multiplication on the left side of the equation. __$5 \cdot c$__

Write the order of multiplication on the right side of the equation. __$c \cdot 5$__

Because you can multiply real numbers in any order, the equation illustrates the __Commutative Property of Multiplication__

B. $5 + (j + 3) = (5 + j) + 3$

Write the grouping of the expression on the left side of the equation. __$5 + (j + 3)$__

Write the grouping of the expression on the right side of the equation. __$(5 + j) + 3$__

Because grouping does not change the sum of real numbers, the equation illustrates the

__Associative Property of Addition__

Using the Distributive Property with Mental Math
Write the product using the Distributive Property. Then simplify.

4(197)

Break the larger factor into a sum or difference that contains a multiple of 10.

$4(197) = 4($__200__ $-$ __3__$)$ Round 197 to 200.

$\quad = $ __4__$(200) - $__4__$(3)$ Use the Distributive Property.

$\quad = $ __800__ $-$ __12__   Mentally multiply the products.

$\quad = $ __788__   Mentally subtract the second product from the first.

The product of 4(197) is __788__.

Finding Counterexamples to Statements About Closure
Find a counterexample to show that the statement is false.

The set of odd numbers is closed under addition.

$a + b = $ __1__ $+$ __3__   Find two odd numbers, a and b, such that the sum is not an odd number. Try $a = 1$ and $b = 3$.

$\quad = $ __4__   Since 4 is not an odd number, this is a counterexample.

The statement is false.

10

Ready to Go On? Skills Intervention
1-7 Simplifying Expressions

Find these vocabulary words in Lesson 1-7 and the Multilingual Glossary.

Vocabulary

order of operations	terms	like terms	coefficient

Simplifying Numerical Expressions
Simplify the expression.

$(8^2 - 1) + 3 \times 2$

$\quad (8^2 - 1) + 3 \times 2$ What is the grouping symbol in the expression? __( )__

$\quad ($ __64__ $- 1) + 3 \times 2$ Evaluate the powers within the parentheses.

$\quad$ __63__ $+ 3 \times 2$ Subtract within the parentheses.

$\quad 63 + $ __6__   Multiply.

$\quad$ __69__   Add.

Combining Like Terms
Simplify the expression by combining like terms.

$7y + 9y$ $7y$ and $9y$ are like terms.

__16__y Add the coefficients.

Simplifying Algebraic Expressions
Use properties and operations to show that the first expression simplifies to the second expression.

$5(x + 2) - 3x + 1, 2x + 11$

Statements	Reasons
1. $5(x + 2) - 3x + 1$	
2. __5__$x + $ __5__$(2) - 3x + 1$	Distributive Property
3. $5x + $ __10__ $- 3x + 1$	Multiply.
4. $5x - $ __3__$x + $ __10__ $+ 1$	Commutative Property of Addition
5. $(5x - 3x) + (10 + 1)$	__Associative Property of Addition__
6. __$2x + 11$__	Combine like terms.

11

Ready to Go On? Problem Solving Intervention
1-7 Simplifying Expressions

Order of operations:
- First, perform operations within grouping symbols;
- then, evaluate powers;
- then, perform multiplication and division from left to right;
- finally, perform addition and subtraction from left to right.

To find the area of the square that is not covered by the circle, you can use the expression $s^2 - \pi\left(\dfrac{d}{2}\right)^2$. If the side length of the square, s, is 12 m and the diameter of the circle, d, is 12 m, find the non-shaded area, to the nearest square meter. Use 3.14 for π.

Understand the Problem

1. What is the expression you are to evaluate? __$s^2 - \pi\left(\dfrac{d}{2}\right)^2$__

2. What are you trying to determine? __The non-shaded area, to the nearest square meter__

Make a Plan

3. What value will you substitute for s? __12__ for d? __12__ for π? __3.14__

4. Is there more than one operation symbol in the expression? __Yes__ If so, what will you need to do to evaluate the expression correctly? __Follow the order of operations__

Solve

5. Substitute the values from Exercise 3 for the variables and evaluate.

$s^2 - \pi\left(\dfrac{d}{2}\right)^2$

$12^2 - 3.14\left(\dfrac{\boxed{12}}{2}\right)^2$ Substitute values for the variables.

$12^2 - 3.14\left(\boxed{6}\right)^2$ Perform the operation within the parenthesis.

$144 - 3.14\left(\boxed{36}\right)$ Evaluate the powers.

$144 - $ __113.04__   Multiply.

__30.96__   Subtract.

6. What is the non-shaded area, to the nearest square meter? __31 square meters__

Look Back

7. Use the drawing to find the area of the square. $A = s^2 = 12^2 = $ __144__

What is the area of the circle? $A = \pi r^2 = \pi(6)^2 = $ __113.04__

Subtract these two values and determine if your answer is correct.

$A_{square} - A_{circle} = $ __144__ $-$ __113.04__ $= $ __30.96__

12

Ready to Go On? Skills Intervention
2-1 Solving One-Step Equations

Find these vocabulary words in Lesson 2-1 and the Multilingual Glossary.

Vocabulary		
equation	solution of an equation	solution set

Solving Equations by Using Addition or Subtraction
Solve each equation.

A. $d + 8 = 17$

$d + 8 = 17$ Since 8 is **added** to d, to **undo** this addition,

$\underline{-8 \quad -8}$ **subtract** 8 from both sides.

$d \quad = \quad 9$ The solution set is { 9 }.

B. $q - 0.3 = 13.2$

$q - 0.3 = 13.2$ Since 0.3 is **subtracted** from q, to **undo** this subtraction,

$\underline{+0.3 \quad +0.3}$ **add** 0.3 to both sides.

$q \quad = \quad 13.5$ The solution set is { 13.5 }.

Solving Equations by Using Multiplication or Division
Solve each equation.

A. $3y = 39$

$3y = 39$ Since y is multiplied by 3, to **undo** this multiplication,

$\frac{3y}{3} = \frac{39}{3}$ **divide** both sides by 3.

$y = 13$ The solution set is { 13 }.

B. $-6 = \frac{w}{4}$

$-6 = \frac{w}{4}$ Since w is divided by 4, to **undo** this division,

$(4)(-6) = (4)\left(\frac{w}{4}\right)$ **multiply** both sides by 4.

$-24 = w$ The solution set is { -24 }.

Ready to Go On? Problem Solving Intervention
2-1 Solving One-Step Equations

To find the solution to an equation, isolate the variable. To isolate the variable, use inverse, or opposite, operations to undo operations on the variable.

When Jeremy began his 9th grade year in school he was 5 ft 4 in. tall. When he was measured for his graduation gown at the end of his 12th grade year, he was 6 ft 3 in. tall. Write and solve an equation to find how many inches Jeremy grew over 4 years.

Understand the Problem

1. How tall was Jeremy at the beginning of his 9th grade year? $\underline{5 \text{ ft } 4 \text{ in.}}$
2. How tall was Jeremy at the end of his 12th grade year? $\underline{6 \text{ ft } 3 \text{ in.}}$

Make a Plan

3. What do you need to determine? $\underline{\text{How many inches Jeremy grew in 4 years.}}$
4. How many total inches is 5 ft 4 in.? $\underline{64 \text{ in.}}$
5. How many total inches is 6 ft 3 in.? $\underline{75 \text{ in.}}$
6. Let h represent the number of inches Jeremy grew in 4 years. Write an equation to represent this situation.

Height in Grade 9	+	The number of inches Jeremy grew	=	Height in Grade 12
64	+	h	=	75

Solve

7. Solve the equation by isolating h.

$\boxed{64} + h = 75$

$\underline{-\boxed{64} \qquad -\boxed{64}}$ Isolate h.

$h = \boxed{11}$

8. The number of inches that Jeremy grew in 4 years is $\underline{11 \text{ in.}}$

Look Back

9. Substitute the solution for h into the equation you wrote in Exercise 6.

Height in Grade 9	+	The number of inches Jeremy grew	=	Height in Grade 12
64	+	11	=	75

10. Does your solution make the equation true? $\underline{\text{Yes}}$

Ready to Go On? Skills Intervention
2-2 Solving Two-Step Equations

Solving Two-Step Equations
Solve the equation. $5r + 15 = 155$ $5r + 15 = 155$

To isolate the variable r, subtract 15 from both sides. $\underline{-15 \quad -15}$

Since r is multiplied by 5, then **divide** both sides of the $5r = \boxed{140}$

equation by 5. $\frac{5r}{5} = \frac{\boxed{140}}{\boxed{5}}$

What is the value of r? $\underline{28}$ $r = \boxed{28}$

Check: Substitute the value for r back into the original equation. $5 \cdot \boxed{28} + 15 = 155$

Does your answer check? $\underline{\text{Yes}}$ $\boxed{155} = 155$

Solving Two-Step Equations That Contain Fractions
Solve the equation. $\frac{5}{8}n + 6 = 7$ $\frac{5}{8}n + 6 = 7$

To isolate the variable n, subtract 6 from both sides. $\underline{-6 \quad -6}$

Since n is multiplied by $\frac{5}{8}$, multiply both sides of the $\frac{5}{8}n = \boxed{1}$

equation by the reciprocal, $\frac{8}{5}$. $\left(\frac{8}{5}\right) \cdot \left(\frac{5}{8}n\right) = \boxed{1} \cdot \frac{8}{5}$

What is the value of n? $\underline{\frac{8}{5}}$ $n = \frac{\boxed{8}}{\boxed{5}}$

To check your answer, substitute the value for n back into the original equation. Does your answer check? $\underline{\text{Yes}}$ $\frac{5}{8} \cdot \frac{\boxed{8}}{\boxed{5}} + 6 = 7$

$\boxed{7} = 7$

Solving Two-Step Equations That Contain Fractions
Solve the equation. $\frac{1}{3}y - \frac{1}{2} = \frac{7}{2}$

To simplify, multiply both sides by 6, $6 \cdot \left[\boxed{\frac{1}{3}y} - \boxed{\frac{1}{2}}\right] = 6 \cdot \boxed{\frac{7}{2}}$

the LCD of the fractions. Distribute the LCD on the left.

Simplify. $2y - 3 = 21$

To isolate y, add 3 to both sides. $\underline{+3 \quad +3}$

Since y is multiplied by 2, divide both sides by 2. $2y = \boxed{24}$

$\frac{2y}{2} = \frac{\boxed{24}}{\boxed{2}}$

What is the solution set? $y = \boxed{12}$

To check your answer, substitute the value for y back into the original equation.

$\frac{1}{3}\left(\boxed{3}\right) - \frac{1}{2} = \frac{7}{2}$ Does your answer check? $\underline{\text{Yes}}$

Ready to Go On? Problem Solving Intervention
2-2 Solving Two-Step Equations

Equations that contain more than one operation require more than one step to solve. Use inverse operations and work backward to undo each operation one step at a time.

A fitness club offers membership for a joining fee of $99 and a monthly fee of $35. If Jenna has spent a total of $1009, how many months has Jenna been a member of the fitness club?

Understand the Problem

1. How much is the joining fee for the fitness club? $\underline{\$99}$
2. How much does the fitness club cost each month? $\underline{\$35}$
3. How much total has Jenna spent on the fitness club? $\underline{\$1009}$

Make a Plan

4. What do you need to determine? $\underline{\text{The number of months Jenna has been a member.}}$
5. Let m represent the number of months that Jenna has been a member. Write an equation to represent this situation.

Joining fee	+	Monthly fee	·	Number of months Jenna has been a member	=	Total amount spent
99	+	35	·	m	=	1009

Solve

6. Solve the equation by isolating m.

$99 + \boxed{35} m = 1009$

$\underline{-99 \qquad\qquad -\boxed{99}}$

$\boxed{35} m = \boxed{910}$

$\frac{\boxed{35m}}{\boxed{35}} = \frac{\boxed{910}}{\boxed{35}}$

$m = \boxed{26}$

7. Jenna has been a member of the fitness club for $\underline{26}$ months.

Look Back

8. Substitute the solution for m into the equation you wrote in Exercise 5.

Joining fee	+	Monthly fee	·	Number of months Jenna has been a member	=	Total amount spent
99	+	35	·	26	=	1009

9. Does your solution make the equation true? $\underline{\text{Yes}}$

Solving Multi-Step Equations
Solve.

$\frac{3m-5}{2}=11$

$\frac{3m-5}{2}=11$

$2\left(\frac{3m-5}{2}\right)=2(11)$ Since $3m-5$ is **divided** by 2, to undo this division, __multiply__ both sides by 2.

$3m-5=22$

$\underline{+5\;\;+5}$ Since 5 is **subtracted** from $3m$, to undo this subtraction, __add__ 5 to both sides.

$3m=27$

$\frac{3m}{3}=\frac{27}{3}$ Since m is **multiplied** by 3, to undo this multiplication, __divide__ both sides by 3

$m=9$ The solution set is [__9__].

Simplify Before Solving Equations
Solve.

$\frac{3c}{5}-4-\frac{2c}{5}=11$

$\frac{3c}{5}-4-\frac{2c}{5}=11$

$\frac{3c}{5}-\frac{2c}{5}-4=11$ Use the Commutative Property of Addition.

$\frac{c}{5}-4=11$ Combine __like__ terms.

$\frac{c}{5}-4=11$ Since 4 is **subtracted** from $\frac{c}{5}$, to undo this subtraction,

$\underline{+4\;\;+4}$ __add__ 4 to each side.

$\frac{c}{5}=15$ Since c is divided by 5, to undo this division,

$5\left(\frac{c}{5}\right)=5\,(15)$ __multiply__ each side by 5.

$c=75$ The solution set is [__75__].

Multi-step equations require multiple steps to solve. Use inverse operations and work backward to undo each operation one step at a time.

Jenna uses a coupon to buy pizzas for a party. The coupon states that if a customer pays $12.00 for two pizzas, each additional pizza costs $5.00. If Jenna paid $32.00 for the pizzas, how many pizzas did she buy?

Understand the Problem

1. How much is the total bill? __$32__

2. How much do the first two pizzas cost? __$12__

3. How much does each additional pizza cost? __$5__

Make a Plan

4. What do you need to determine? __the number of pizzas Jenna bought__

5. Let p represent the number of pizzas Jenna bought. What expression represents the number of pizzas that cost $5 each? __$p-2$__

6. Write an equation to represent the cost of the pizzas Jenna bought.

Cost of first two pizzas	+	Cost of each additional pizza	Number of additional pizzas	=	Total cost
12	+	5	$(p-2)$		32

Solve

7. Solve the equation by isolating p.

$12+5(p-2)=32$

$\underline{-12}\qquad\qquad=\underline{-12}$

$\frac{5(p-2)}{5}=\frac{20}{5}$

$p-2=4$

$\underline{+2}\;\;\underline{+2}$

$p=6$

8. How many pizzas did Jenna buy? __6__

Check

9. Substitute the solution p into the equation you wrote in Exercise 6.

$12+5(\boxed{6}-2)=32$

$12+\boxed{20}=32$

10. Does your solution make the equation true? __Yes__

Find these vocabulary words in Lesson 2-4 and the Multilingual Glossary.

Vocabulary	
identity	contradiction

Simplifying Each Side Before Solving Equations
Solve the equation. $4(k-3)=3(3k+6)$

Use the __Distributive__ Property to simplify this equation before you solve it.

$4(k-3)=3(3k+6)$

$4k-\boxed{12}=\boxed{9}k+18$ To collect the variables on the **right** side, subtract __$4k$__ from both sides.

$\underline{-4k}\qquad\underline{-4k}$

$\boxed{-12}=\boxed{5}k+18$ To collect the constants on the **left** side, subtract __18__ from both sides.

$\underline{-18}\qquad\;\;\underline{-18}$

$\boxed{-30}=5k$

$\frac{\boxed{-30}}{5}=\frac{5k}{5}$ To isolate the variable, __divide__ both sides by 5.

$\boxed{-6}=k$ What is the value of k? __-6__

Infinitely Many Solutions or No Solutions
Solve the equation. $5(2x-3)=2(5x-4)$

Use the __Distributive__ Property to simplify this equation before you solve it.

$5(2x-3)=2(5x-4)$

$10x-\boxed{15}=\boxed{10}x-8$ To collect the variables on the **right** side, subtract __$10x$__ from both sides.

$\underline{-10x}\qquad\;\;\underline{-10x}$

$\boxed{-15}=-8$ Complete the resulting equation.

Is the resulting equation a true statement or a false statement? __False__

What is the other name for a false statement given in the lesson? __Contradiction__

How many values make this equation true? __There is no solution.__

To solve equations with variables on both sides, begin by collecting the variable terms on one side of the equation.

One electrician charges his customers a $60 service fee plus $35 per hour. Another electrician charges her customers $65 per hour. How many hours must the electricians work in order for the total cost of an electrician to be the same? What is the total cost?

Understand the Problem

1. Describe how much the first electrician charges. __$60 service fee plus $35 per hour__

2. Describe how much the second electrician charges. __$65 per hour__

Make a Plan

3. What do you need to determine? __The number of hours the electricians have to work in order for their total cost to be equal.__

4. Let h represent the number of hours that the electricians must work. Write an equation to represent the situation.

Service fee for electrician #1	+	Hourly rate	Number of hours electrician #1 works	=	Hourly rate	Number of hours electrician #2 works
60	+	35	h	=	65	h

Solve

5. On which side should you collect the variable terms? __Right side__

6. Solve the equation by isolating h.

$60+\boxed{35}h=\boxed{65}h$

$\underline{-\boxed{35}h}\quad\underline{-\boxed{35}h}$

$60=\boxed{30}h$

$\frac{60}{\boxed{30}}=\frac{\boxed{30}h}{\boxed{30}}$

$\boxed{2}=h$

7. The number of hours that the electricians need to work for the total cost to be the same is __2__ hours.

8. What is the total cost for either of the electricians to work for this number of hours? __$130__

Look Back

9. Substitute the solution for h into the equation you wrote in Exercise 4.

Service fee for electrician #1	+	Hourly rate	Number of hours electrician #1 works	=	Hourly rate	Number of hours electrician #2 works
60	+	35	· 2	=	65	· 2

10. Does your solution make the equation true? __Yes__

Ready To Go On? Skills Intervention
2-5 Solving Proportions

Find these vocabulary words in Lesson 2-5 and the Multilingual Glossary.

Vocabulary

ratio	proportion	cross products	scale	scale drawing
rate	unit rate	scale model	conversion	factor

Solving Proportions
Solve each proportion.

A. $\frac{-22}{m} = \frac{11}{4}$

Complete the equation using cross products: $\quad 4 \cdot \boxed{-22} = \boxed{11} \cdot m$

Multiply. $\qquad \boxed{-88} = 11m$

To isolate m, __divide__ both sides by __11__. $\quad \frac{\boxed{-88}}{11} = \frac{11m}{11}$

What is the value of m? __−8__ $\qquad \boxed{-8} = m$

To check your answer, substitute the solution in for m.

$\frac{-22}{m} = \frac{11}{4} \rightarrow \frac{-22}{\boxed{-8}} = \frac{11}{4}$

Are the ratios equivalent? __Yes__

B. Find 20% of 60.

Use a proportion. $\qquad \frac{part}{whole} \quad \frac{percent}{100}$

Let x represent the part. $\qquad \frac{x}{\boxed{60}} = \frac{\boxed{20}}{100}$

Find the cross products. $\qquad \boxed{100}\,x = \boxed{1200}$

Since x is multiplied by 100, to undo the multiplication, divide both sides by __100__. $\quad \frac{100x}{\boxed{100}} = \frac{1200}{\boxed{100}}$

$x = \boxed{12}$

20% of 60 is $\boxed{12}$

Ready to Go On? Problem Solving Intervention
2-5 Solving Proportions

A comparison of two quantities by division is a ratio. Two ratios that are equivalent is a proportion.

The ratio of cats to dogs in the local animal shelter is 3:5. There are 60 dogs in the animal shelter. How many cats are in the animal shelter?

Understand the Problem

1. What is the ratio of cats to dogs? $\frac{3}{5}$ or 3:5 or 3 to 5

2. How many dogs are in the shelter? __60__

Make a Plan

3. What do you need to determine? __The number of cats in the animal shelter__

4. Complete the proportion: ratio of cats to dogs = $\frac{\text{number of cats}}{\boxed{\text{number of dogs}}}$

5. If c represents the number of cats in the shelter, complete the proportion to find the number of cats: $\frac{3}{5} = \frac{c}{\boxed{60}}$

Solve

6. To solve the proportion, multiply both sides by __60__.

7. Solve the equation for c. $\qquad$ 8. The number of cats in the shelter is __36__.

$\frac{3}{5} = \frac{c}{60}$

$(\boxed{60}) \cdot \frac{3}{5} = \frac{c}{60} \cdot (\boxed{60})$

$\boxed{36} = c$

Look Back

9. To check your solution, simplify the ratio of c to the number of dogs in the shelter.

$\frac{c}{60} = \frac{\boxed{36}}{60} = \frac{\boxed{3}}{5}$

10. Is this the same as the ratio of cats to dogs, 3:5? __Yes__

Ready To Go On? Skills Intervention
2-6 Solving Literal Equations for a Variable

Find these vocabulary words in Lesson 2-6 and the Multilingual Glossary.

Vocabulary

formula	literal equation

Solving Literal Equations for a Variable

A. Solve $7u + v = w - 6$ for w.

Which side of the equation is w located? __Right side__

What constant is on the same side of the equation as w? __6__

Which operation is between the w and the constant? __Subtraction__

To isolate w, __add__ 6 to both sides of the equation.

Complete: $7u + v + \boxed{6} = w - 6 + \boxed{6}$

$7u + v + \boxed{6} = w$

B. Solve $j + k = 4(m - 10)$ for m.

Which side of the equation is m located? __Right side__

What property do you use to simplify the equation first? __Distributive Property__

What is the resulting equation? $j + k = \boxed{4}\,m - \boxed{40}$

What constant is on the same side of the equation as $4m$? __40__

Which operation is between the $4m$ and the constant? __Subtraction__

To isolate $4m$, add __40__ to both sides of the equation.

Complete to find the resulting equation.

$j + k = \boxed{4}\,m - \boxed{40}$
$\underline{+\boxed{40} \qquad\qquad +\boxed{40}}$
$j + k + \boxed{40} = 4m$

$\frac{j + k + \boxed{40}}{4} = \frac{4m}{4}$

$\frac{j + k + \boxed{40}}{4} = m$

Ready to Go On? Problem Solving Intervention
2-6 Solving Literal Equations for a Variable

Rearrange a formula to isolate any variable by using inverse operations. Formulas are also called literal equations. Solve a literal equation by isolating one of the variables.

The formula for the circumference of a circle is $C = 2\pi r$, where C is the circumference, r is the radius of the circle, and π is the constant 3.14. Solve the equation for r. If the circumference of a circle is 62.8 in., what is the radius of the circle?

Understand the Problem

1. Which variable do you need to find? __r or radius__

2. What is the circumference of the given circle? __62.8 in.__ What is π? __3.14__

Make a Plan

3. To undo the multiplication between the 2 and r, __divide__ both sides by __2__.
$\quad C = 2\pi r$
$\quad \frac{C}{2} = \frac{2\pi r}{2} \rightarrow \frac{C}{2} = \pi r$

4. To undo the multiplication between the π and r, __divide__ both sides by __π__.
$\quad \frac{C}{2\pi} = \frac{\pi r}{\boxed{\pi}}$

5. What is the formula for the radius of a circle, r? $\frac{C}{\boxed{2\pi}} = r$

Solve

6. What value do you substitute in for C? __62.8__ and π? __3.14__

7. Simplify the equation and solve for r. $\quad \frac{\boxed{62.8}}{2 \cdot \boxed{3.14}} = r$

8. The radius of the circle is __10 in.__ $\qquad \boxed{10} = r$

Look Back

9. To check your solution, substitute the values into the original formula, $C = 2\pi r$.

$\quad C = 2 \cdot \pi \cdot r$
$\boxed{62.8} = 2 \cdot \boxed{3.14} \cdot \boxed{10}$
$\boxed{62.8} = \boxed{62.8}$

10. Does your solution make the equation true? __Yes__

Ready to Go On? Skills Intervention
2-7 Solving Absolute-Value Equations

Solving Absolute-Value Equations
Solve each equation.

A. $|x| = 6$

Think: What numbers are __6__ units from 0?

Case 1	Case 2	Rewrite the equation as two cases.
$x = \boxed{-6}$	$x = \boxed{6}$	

The solutions are -6 and 6. You can write the solution set as $\{-6, 6\}$.

B. $\dfrac{|x-3|}{2} = 4$

$\boxed{2}\left(\dfrac{|x-3|}{2}\right) = \boxed{2}(4)$ Since $|x-3|$ is divided by 2, to **undo the division, multiply** both sides by __2__.

$|x-3| = 8$ Think: What numbers are __8__ units from 0?

Case 1	Case 2
$x - 3 = \boxed{-8}$	$x - 3 = \boxed{8}$
$+\boxed{3} \; +\boxed{3}$	$+\boxed{3} \; +\boxed{3}$
$x = \boxed{-5}$	$x = \boxed{11}$

Rewrite the equation as two cases. Since 3 is **subtracted** from x, to **undo the subtraction, add** __3__ to both sides.

The solutions are -5 and 11. The solution set is $\{-5, 11\}$.

25   **Holt Algebra 1**

Ready to Go On? Problem-Solving Intervention
2-7 Solving Absolute-Value Equations

To solve absolute value equations, perform inverse operations to isolate the absolute value expression on one side of the equation. Then consider two cases.

At a flour-manufacturing plant, a machine fills sacks with 160 ounces of flour. If a sack is more than 2 ounces heavier or lighter than the desired weight, a second machine removes it from the manufacturing line. What are the weights of the heaviest and lightest sacks that the machine will *not* remove from the line?

Understand the Problem

1. What is the desired weight of a sack of flour? __160 oz__

2. By how much may the weight of a sack of flour vary? __± 2 oz__

Make a Plan

3. What do you need to determine? __two numbers that are 2 away from 160__

4. How can you write these two numbers using an absolute value equation?

$|x - 160| = 2$

Solve

5. Solve the equation by writing it as two cases.

Case 1	Case 2
$x - 160 = -2$	$x - 160 = 2$
$+160 \; +160$	$+160 \; +160$
$x = 158$	$x = 162$

6. What is the solution set to the equation you wrote in Exercise 4? $\{158, 162\}$

7. What is the minimum weight of the sack that the machine will allow? __158 oz__

8. What is the maximum weight of the sack that the machine will allow? __162 oz__

Check

9. Substitute each value in the solution set of x into the equation you wrote in Exercise 4.

$\left|\,\boxed{158} - 160\,\right| = 2$ $\left|\,\boxed{162} - 160\,\right| = 2$

$\left|\,\boxed{-2}\,\right| = 2$ $\left|\,\boxed{2}\,\right| = 2$

$\boxed{2} = 2$ $\boxed{2} = 2$

26   **Holt Algebra 1**

Ready To Go On? Skills Intervention
3-1 Graphing and Writing Inequalities

Find these vocabulary words in Lesson 3-1 and the Multilingual Glossary.

Vocabulary	
inequality	solution of an inequality

Graphing Inequalities

A. $b \le 7\frac{1}{2}$

What does the $\le$ symbol indicate? __Less than or equal to__

Is $7\frac{1}{2}$ included in the solution set? __Yes__

Should the circle drawn at $7\frac{1}{2}$ be solid or empty? __Solid__

In which direction should the arrow point? __Left__

Graph the inequality.

B. $r > -3$

What does the $>$ symbol indicate? __Greater than__

Is -3 included in the solution set? __No__

So, a(n) __open__ circle should be used and the arrow should point to the __right__.

Graph the inequality.

Writing an Inequality from a Graph

A.

Which direction does the arrow point? __Right__

What does the solid circle mean? __-2 is included in solution set__

Which symbol should be used? __$\ge$__

Write the inequality. __$x \ge -2$__

B.

Which direction does the arrow point? __Left__

What does the empty circle mean? __3.5 is not included in solution set__

Which symbol should be used? __$<$__

Write the inequality. __$x < 3.5$__

27   **Holt Algebra 1**

Ready To Go On? Skills Intervention
3-2 Solving Inequalities by Adding and Subtracting

Find this word in Lesson 3-2 and the Multilingual Glossary.

Vocabulary
equivalent inequality

Using Addition and Subtraction to Solve Inequalities
Solve each inequality and graph the solutions.

A. $y + 4 \le 9$

Step 1: Solve for y.

$y + 4 \le 9$ To isolate y, __subtract__ 4 from both sides of the inequality.

$-\underline{4} \; -\underline{4}$

$y \le 5$ Find the value of y.

Step 2: Graph the solution.

A(n) __solid__ circle should be used and the arrow should point to the __left__.

B. $x - 9 \ge -7$

Step 1: Solve for x.

$x - 9 \ge -7$ Isolate x by __adding__ 9 to both sides of the inequality.

$+\underline{9} \; +\underline{9}$

$x \ge 2$

Step 2: Graph the solution.

A(n) __solid__ circle should be used and the arrow should point to the __right__.

C. $5 > p - 4$

Step 1: Solve for p.

$5 > p - 4$ Isolate p by __adding__ 4 to both sides of the inequality.

$+\underline{4} \; +\underline{4}$

$9 > p$

Step 2: Graph the solution.

Another way to write this inequality is $p < $ __9__.

A(n) __empty__ circle should be used and the arrow should point to the __left__.

28   **Holt Algebra 1**

Holt Algebra 1

Ready to Go On? Problem Solving Intervention
3-2 Solving Inequalities by Adding and Subtracting

Solving one-step inequalities is much like solving one-step equations.

Kendra receives a weekly allowance of $15.00. She has already spent $11.50 on a movie ticket and a bag of popcorn. Write and solve an inequality to determine how much money Kendra can spend the rest of the week.

Understand the Problem

1. How much allowance does Kendra receive? **$15.00 per week**

2. How much has Kendra spent so far this week? **$11.50**

Make a Plan

3. What do you need to determine?
   The amount of money Kendra can spend the rest of the week.

4. What inequality symbol represents *less than or equal to*? **$\leq$**

Solve

5. Let *s* represent the amount of money Kendra can spend the rest of the week. Write an inequality to represent the situation.

The amount left to spend	+	$11.50	is less than or equal to	$15.00
s	+	$11.50	$\leq$	$15.00

6. Solve for *s* by subtracting 11.50 from both sides of the inequality. $s \leq$ **3.50**

7. The amount of money Kendra can spend the rest of the week is at most **$3.50**.

8. What is the least amount of money that Kendra can spend? **$0**

Look Back

9. Graph your solution on the number line. −5 −4 −3 −2 −1 0 1 2 3 4 5

10. Choose a number that is included in your solution. **Sample answer: $s = 2$**

11. Substitute this number for *s* into the inequality you wrote in Exercise 5. **$2 + 11.50 \leq 15.00$**

12. Does the number you chose in Exercise 10, make the inequality true or false? **True**

13. Does your solution make sense? **Yes**

29
Holt Algebra 1

Ready To Go On? Skills Intervention
3-3 Solving Inequalities by Multiplying and Dividing

Multiplying or Dividing by a Positive Number

Solve $\frac{2}{5}y \leq -4$. Then graph the solutions.

The variable, *y*, is being multiplied by $\frac{2}{5}$, so you need to multiply by the reciprocal of $\frac{2}{5}$ on both sides of the inequality.

Step 1: Solve for *y*.

$\frac{2}{5}y \leq -4$

$\frac{5}{2} \cdot \frac{2}{5}y \leq -4 \cdot \frac{5}{2}$ Isolate *y* by **multiplying** both sides of the inequality by $\frac{5}{2}$.

$y \leq \frac{-20}{2}$ Divide.

$y \leq$ **−10**

Step 2: Graph the solution. −16 −14 −12 −10 −8 −6 −4 −2 0 2
A(n) **solid** circle should be used and the arrow should point to the **left**.

Multiplying or Dividing by a Negative Number

A. Solve $-6x < 36$.

Isolate *x* by **dividing** both sides of the inequality by −6. If you multiply or divide both sides of an inequality by the same negative number, you must **reverse** the inequality symbol for the statement to be true.

Solve for *x*. $-6x < 36$

$\frac{-6x}{-6} < \frac{36}{-6}$

$x \boxed{>} -6$ Do you need to reverse the inequality sign? **Yes**

B. Solve $2 < -4w$. Then graph the solutions.

Isolate *w* by **dividing** both sides of the inequality by −4.

Solve for *w*. $2 < -4w$

$\frac{2}{-4} < \frac{-4w}{-4}$ −4 −3 −2 −1 0 1 2 3 4 5

$\frac{-1}{2} \boxed{>} w$ Do you need to reverse the inequality sign? **Yes**

Graph the solution.
A(n) **empty** circle should be used and the arrow should point to the **left**.

30
Holt Algebra 1

Ready to Go On? Problem Solving Intervention
3-3 Solving Inequalities by Multiplying or Dividing

Solving one-step inequalities is much like solving one-step equations. To solve an inequality that contains multiplication or division, undo the operation by dividing or multiplying both sides of the inequality by the same number.

A piece of metal tubing is 90 inches long. Jamal needs to cut sections of tubing that are 12 inches long. What are the possible numbers of sections of tubing that Jamal can cut?

Understand the Problem

1. How much tubing does Jamal have? **90 in.**

2. How long does each section of tubing need to be? **12 in.**

3. What do you need to determine? **The possible number of sections of tubing Jamal can cut**

Make a Plan

4. What inequality symbol represents *at most*? **$\leq$**

5. Let *t* represent the length of each section of tubing. Write an inequality for the situation.

12 inches	The length of tubing	is at most	90 inches
12	t	$\leq$	90

Solve

6. Solve the inequality by isolating *t*.

$12t \leq 90$

$\frac{12t}{12} \leq \frac{90}{12}$

$t \leq$ **7.5**

7. Does Jamal want to cut the tubing into partial sections? **No**

8. Round **down** to get the greatest number of sections of tubing Jamal can cut.

9. Jamal can cut the tubing into at most **7** sections.

10. List the number of sections Jamal can cut. **1, 2, 3, 4, 5, 6, 7** sections

Look Back

11. Graph your solution on the number line. −1 0 1 2 3 4 5 6 7 8 9

12. Choose a number that is included in your solution. **Sample answer: 5**

13. Because each section is 12 inches long, multiply the number you chose in Exercise 12 by 12. What is the result? **$5 \times 12 = 60$**

14. Is the result less than or equal to 90 inches? **Yes** Does your solution make sense? **Yes**

31
Holt Algebra 1

Ready To Go On? Skills Intervention
3-4 Solving Two-Step and Multi-Step Inequalities

Solving Two-Step Inequalities

Solve the inequality $8 \geq 1 - 7r$ and graph the solutions.

$8 \geq 1 - 7r$ −5 −4 −3 −2 −1 0 1 2 3 4 5

$\underline{-1} \quad \underline{-1}$

$7 \geq -7r$ Isolate $-7r$ by **subtracting** 1 from both sides.

$\frac{7}{-7} \geq \frac{7r}{-7}$ What is the inverse of multiplication? **Division**

$-1 \boxed{\leq} r$ Do you need to reverse the sign? **Yes**

To graph the solution, a(n) **solid** circle should be used and the arrow should point to the **right**.

Simplifying Before Solving Inequalities

Solve each inequality and graph the solutions.

A. $4(x - 3) > -2$

$4(x - 3) > -2$ −5 −4 −3 −2 −1 0 1 2 3 4 5

$4(x) - 4(3) > -2$ Distribute **4** on the left side.

$4x - 12 > -2$ Simplify the left side.

$4x > 10$ Add **12** to both sides of the equation.

$\frac{4x}{4} > \frac{10}{4}$ Divide both sides by 4.

$x \boxed{>} 2.5$ Do you need to reverse the sign? **No** Graph the solution.

B. $\frac{5}{6}x + \frac{2}{3} > \frac{1}{6}$ What is the LCD of the fractions? **6**

$6\left(\frac{5}{6}x + \frac{2}{3}\right) > 6\left(\frac{1}{6}\right)$ Multiply both sides of the inequality by the LCD.

$6\left(\frac{5}{6}x\right) + 6\left(\frac{2}{3}\right) > 6\left(\frac{1}{6}\right)$ Distribute the LCD on the left side.

$5x + 4 > 1$

$5x > -3$ Subtract **4** from both sides of the inequality.

$\frac{5x}{5} > \frac{-3}{5}$ Divide both sides by 5.

$x \boxed{>} -\frac{3}{5}$ Do you need to reverse the sign? **No**

Graph the solution.   −2 −1 0 1 2

32
Holt Algebra 1

202
Holt Algebra 1

Ready to Go On? Problem Solving Intervention
3-4 Solving Two-Step and Multi-Step Inequalities

Inequalities that contain more than one operation require more than one step to solve. Use inverse operations to undo the operations in the inequality one at a time.

George has scored 21 points and 17 points in his first two basketball games. How many points must he score in his third game to have an average of at least 20 points per game?

Understand the Problem

1. How many games has George played? __2__

2. How many combined points has George scored in the games? __38 points__

3. How many more games will George play? __1__

Make a Plan

4. What are you trying to determine? __The number of points George must score to average at least 20 points per game__

5. How many total points must George score to average 20 points for 3 games? __60__

6. What inequality symbol represents *at least*? __≥__

7. Write an inequality to represent the situation where x equals the number of points in the third game. __38__ $+ x \geq$ 60

Solve

8. Solve the inequality.

$$38 + x \geq 60$$
$$\underline{-38 \quad -38}$$ Subtract to isolate x.
$$x \geq 22$$

9. The number of points that George must score is at least __22__.

Look Back

10. Graph your solution on the number line. 18 19 20 21 22 23 24 25 26 27 28

11. Choose a number that is included in your solution. __Sample answer: 25__

12. Find the average of the number you chose in Exercise 11, and the values 21, and 17. What is the result? $\dfrac{25 + 21 + 17}{3} = \dfrac{63}{3} = 21$

13. Is the result greater than or equal to 20? __Yes__

14. Does your solution make sense? __Yes__

33
Holt Algebra 1

Ready To Go On? Skills Intervention
3-5 Solving Inequalities with Variables on Both Sides

Solving Inequalities with Variables on Both Sides
Solve $x - 10 \geq 4x - 16$.

$$x - 10 \geq 4x - 16$$
$$\underline{+10 \qquad +10}$$ Isolate x by adding 10 to both sides.
$$x \geq 4x - 6$$ Simplify.
$$\underline{-4x \quad -4x}$$ To isolate the constant term, subtract $4x$ from both sides.
$$-3x \geq -6$$

What is the inverse of multiplication? __Division__ Do you need to reverse the sign? __Yes__

The solution is: __$x \leq 2$__

Simplifying Each Side Before Solving
Solve $4(3x - 1) < 2(x + 3)$.

$$4(3x - 1) < 2(x + 3)$$
$$4(3x) - 4(1) < 2(x) + 2(3)$$ Distribute __4__ on the left side of the inequality. Distribute __2__ on the right side of the inequality.
$$12x - 4 < 2x + 6$$ Simplify both sides of the inequality.
$$\underline{-2x \qquad -2x}$$ Subtract $2x$ from both sides so that the coefficient of x is positive.
$$10x - 4 < 6$$
$$\underline{+4 \quad +4}$$ Add 4 to both sides of the equation.
$$10x < 10$$ Divide both sides of the equation by 10.

Do you need to reverse the sign? __No__ The solution is: __$x < 1$__

All Real Numbers as Solutions or No Solutions
Solve $3y + 4 > 3(y + 3)$.

$3y + 4 > 3(y + 3)$ Distribute 3 on the right side of the inequality. Simplify.

$3y + 4 > 3y + $ __9__   The same variable term __$3y$__ appears on both sides of the inequality. Look at the other terms.

For any number $3y$, adding __4__ will never result in a greater number than adding __9__.

No values of y make the inequality __true__.
There are no solutions. The solution set is __∅__.

34
Holt Algebra 1

Ready to Go On? Problem Solving Intervention
3-5 Solving Inequalities with Variables on Both Sides

To solve inequalities that have variables on both sides of the inequality symbol, "collect" all the variable terms on one side of the inequality symbol and all the constant terms on the other side.

Hannah earns $150 per week plus $3 for each jersey she sells. Martin earns $136 per week plus $5 for every jersey he sells. For how many sales of jerseys will Martin make more money?

Understand the Problem

1. How much money does Hannah make per week before she sells any jerseys? __$150__

2. How much money does Hannah make per jersey sold? __$3__

3. How much money does Martin make per week before he sells any jerseys? __$136__

4. How much money does Martin make per jersey sold? __$5__

Make a Plan

Let j represent the number of jerseys sold.

5. Write an expression to represent the amount of money Hannah makes. __150__ + 3j

6. Write an expression to represent the amount of money Martin makes. 136 + __5j__

7. Who are you trying to determine will make more money? __Martin__

8. Write an inequality to represent the situation. __150__ + 3j ≤ 136 + __5j__

Solve

9. Solve the inequality by isolating j.

$$150 + 3j \leq 136 + 5j$$
$$\underline{-3j \qquad -3j}$$
$$150 \leq 136 + 2j$$
$$\underline{-136 \quad -136}$$
$$14 \leq 2j$$
$$\dfrac{14}{2} < \dfrac{2j}{2}$$
$$7 \leq j$$

10. Martin has to sell more than __7__ jerseys to make more money in one week than Hannah.

Look Back

11. Graph your solution on the number line. -2 -1 0 1 2 3 4 5 6 7 8

12. Choose a number that is included in your solution. __Sample answer: 10__

13. Substitute this number for j in the inequality you wrote in Exercise 8. What is the result? __180 < 186__

14. Is the inequality true or false? __True__ Does your solution make sense? __Yes__

35
Holt Algebra 1

Ready To Go On? Skills Intervention
3-6 Solving Compound Inequalities

Find these vocabulary words in Lesson 3-6 and the Multilingual Glossary.

Vocabulary		
compound inequality	intersection	union

Solving Compound Inequalities Involving AND
Solve $-3 \leq x + 2 < 6$. Then graph the solution.

Write each compound inequality. $-3 \leq x + 2$ AND __$x + 2 < 6$__

Solve each simple inequality. __-5__ $\leq x$ AND $x < $ __4__

How can you rewrite the first inequality? $x \geq$ __-5__

To graph this solution, should the circle drawn be solid or empty? __Solid__

In which direction should the arrow point? __Right__

Graph the first inequality. -5 -4 -3 -2 -1 0 1 2 3 4 5

Graph the second inequality. -5 -4 -3 -2 -1 0 1 2 3 4 5

Graph the intersection by finding where the two graphs overlap. -5 -4 -3 -2 -1 0 1 2 3 4 5

Solving Compound Inequalities Involving OR
Solve the compound inequality $3 < d - 4$ OR $d + 4 < 1$ and graph the solution.

Solve each simple inequality. $3 < d - 4$ OR $d + 4 < 1$
__7__ $< d$ OR $d <$ __-3__

For the first inequality, a(n) __empty__ circle should be used and the arrow should point to the __right__. -10 -9 -8 -7 -6 -5 -4 -3 -2 -1 0 1 2 3 4 5 6 7 8 9 10

For the second inequality, a(n) __empty__ circle should be used and the arrow should point to the __left__. -10 -9 -8 -7 -6 -5 -4 -3 -2 -1 0 1 2 3 4 5 6 7 8 9 10

Graph the union by combining the regions. This is the graph of the compound inequality. -10 -9 -8 -7 -6 -5 -4 -3 -2 -1 0 1 2 3 4 5 6 7 8 9 10

36
Holt Algebra 1

203
Holt Algebra 1

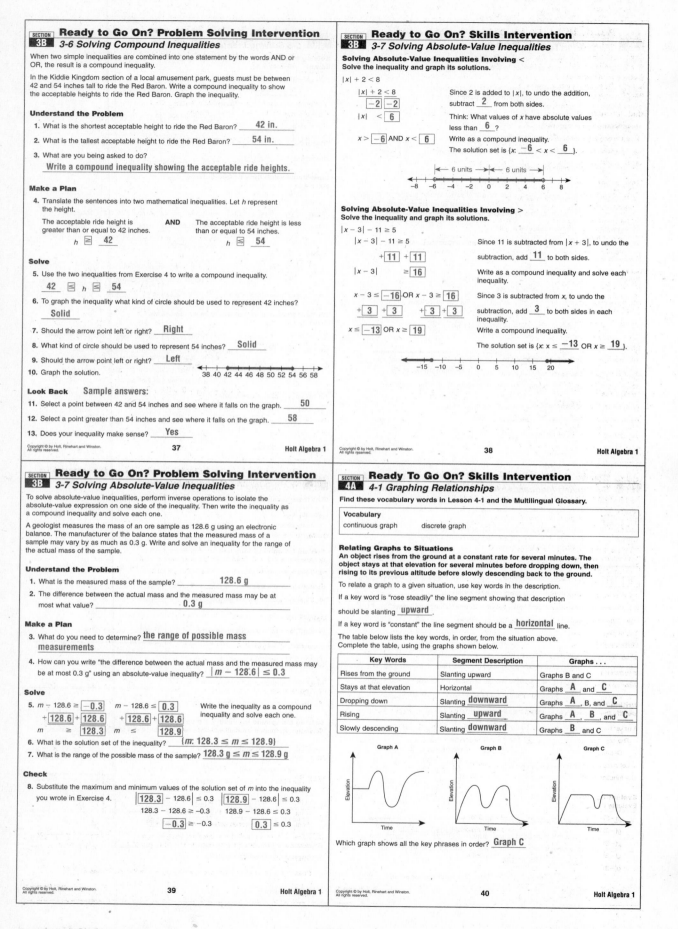

Ready to Go On? Problem Solving Intervention
3-6 Solving Compound Inequalities

When two simple inequalities are combined into one statement by the words AND or OR, the result is a compound inequality.

In the Kiddie Kingdom section of a local amusement park, guests must be between 42 and 54 inches tall to ride the Red Baron. Write a compound inequality to show the acceptable heights to ride the Red Baron. Graph the inequality.

Understand the Problem

1. What is the shortest acceptable height to ride the Red Baron? **42 in.**

2. What is the tallest acceptable height to ride the Red Baron? **54 in.**

3. What are you being asked to do?
   Write a compound inequality showing the acceptable ride heights.

Make a Plan

4. Translate the sentences into two mathematical inequalities. Let h represent the height.

The acceptable ride height is greater than or equal to 42 inches.	**AND**	The acceptable ride height is less than or equal to 54 inches.
$h \geq$ **42**		$h \leq$ **54**

Solve

5. Use the two inequalities from Exercise 4 to write a compound inequality.
   42 $\leq h \leq$ **54**

6. To graph the inequality what kind of circle should be used to represent 42 inches?
   Solid

7. Should the arrow point left or right? **Right**

8. What kind of circle should be used to represent 54 inches? **Solid**

9. Should the arrow point left or right? **Left**

10. Graph the solution.
    38 40 42 44 46 48 50 52 54 56 58

Look Back   Sample answers:

11. Select a point between 42 and 54 inches and see where it falls on the graph. **50**

12. Select a point greater than 54 inches and see where it falls on the graph. **58**

13. Does your inequality make sense? **Yes**

37   **Holt Algebra 1**

Ready to Go On? Skills Intervention
3-7 Solving Absolute-Value Inequalities

Solving Absolute-Value Inequalities Involving <
Solve the inequality and graph its solutions.

$|x| + 2 < 8$

$	x	+ 2 < 8$	Since 2 is added to $	x	$, to undo the addition,
-2 **-2**	subtract **2** from both sides.
$	x	<$ **6**	Think: What values of x have absolute values less than **6** ?
$x >$ **-6** AND $x <$ **6**	Write as a compound inequality.
	The solution set is {x: **-6** $< x <$ **6** }.

|← 6 units →|← 6 units →|
-8 -6 -4 -2 0 2 4 6 8

Solving Absolute-Value Inequalities Involving >
Solve the inequality and graph its solutions.

$|x - 3| - 11 \geq 5$

$	x - 3	- 11 \geq 5$	Since 11 is subtracted from $	x + 3	$, to undo the
+11 **+11**	subtraction, add **11** to both sides.
$	x - 3	\geq$ **16**	Write as a compound inequality and solve each inequality.
$x - 3 \leq$ **-16** OR $x - 3 \geq$ **16**	Since 3 is subtracted from x, to undo the
+3 **+3** **+3** **+3**	subtraction, add **3** to both sides in each inequality.
$x \leq$ **-13** OR $x \geq$ **19**	Write a compound inequality.
	The solution set is {x: $x \leq$ **-13** OR $x \geq$ **19** }.

-15 -10 -5 0 5 10 15 20

38   **Holt Algebra 1**

Ready to Go On? Problem Solving Intervention
3-7 Solving Absolute-Value Inequalities

To solve absolute-value inequalities, perform inverse operations to isolate the absolute-value expression on one side of the inequality. Then write the inequality as a compound inequality and solve each one.

A geologist measures the mass of an ore sample as 128.6 g using an electronic balance. The manufacturer of the balance states that the measured mass of a sample may vary by as much as 0.3 g. Write and solve an inequality for the range of the actual mass of the sample.

Understand the Problem

1. What is the measured mass of the sample? **128.6 g**

2. The difference between the actual mass and the measured mass may be at most what value? **0.3 g**

Make a Plan

3. What do you need to determine? **the range of possible mass measurements**

4. How can you write "the difference between the actual mass and the measured mass may be at most 0.3 g" using an absolute-value inequality? $|m - 128.6| \leq 0.3$

Solve

5. | $m - 128.6 \geq$ **-0.3** | $m - 128.6 \leq$ **0.3** | Write the inequality as a compound |
   | **+128.6** **+128.6** | **+128.6** **+128.6** | inequality and solve each one. |
   | $m \geq$ **128.3** | $m \leq$ **128.9** | |

6. What is the solution set of the inequality? {m: **128.3** $\leq m \leq$ **128.9**}

7. What is the range of the possible mass of the sample? **128.3** g $\leq m \leq$ **128.9** g

Check

8. Substitute the maximum and minimum values of the solution set of m into the inequality you wrote in Exercise 4.
128.3 $- 128.6	\leq 0.3$	**128.9** $- 128.6	\leq 0.3$
$128.3 - 128.6 \geq -0.3$	$128.9 - 128.6 \leq 0.3$
-0.3 ≥ -0.3	**0.3** ≤ 0.3

39   **Holt Algebra 1**

Ready To Go On? Skills Intervention
4-1 Graphing Relationships

Find these vocabulary words in Lesson 4-1 and the Multilingual Glossary.

Vocabulary	
continuous graph	discrete graph

Relating Graphs to Situations
An object rises from the ground at a constant rate for several minutes. The object stays at that elevation for several minutes before dropping down, then rising to its previous altitude before slowly descending back to the ground.

To relate a graph to a given situation, use key words in the description.

If a key word is "rose steadily" the line segment showing that description should be slanting **upward** .

If a key word is "constant" the line segment should be a **horizontal** line.

The table below lists the key words, in order, from the situation above. Complete the table, using the graphs shown below.

Key Words	Segment Description	Graphs . . .
Rises from the ground	Slanting upward	Graphs B and C
Stays at that elevation	Horizontal	Graphs **A** and **C**
Dropping down	Slanting **downward**	Graphs **A** , B, and **C**
Rising	Slanting **upward**	Graphs **A** , **B** , and **C**
Slowly descending	Slanting **downward**	Graphs **B** and C

Which graph shows all the key phrases in order? **Graph C**

40   **Holt Algebra 1**

---

204   **Holt Algebra 1**

Ready to Go On? Problem Solving Intervention
4-1 Graphing Relationships

Graphs with connected curves or lines are called continuous graphs. Graphs that only show distinct points are called discrete graphs.

Dennis has 100 raffle tickets to sell for a school fund-raiser. Each booklet has 10 raffle tickets. Sketch a graph to show how many raffle tickets he has left if he sells 1, 2, 3, 4 or 5 booklets of tickets.

Understand the Problem

1. How many tickets does Dennis have to sell? __100 tickets__
2. Each booklet has how many raffle tickets? __10__
3. If he sells one booklet, he has sold __10__ tickets and 90 remain.
4. If he sells two booklets, he has sold 20 tickets and __80__ tickets remain.

Make a Plan

5. What are you being asked to do? __Sketch a graph showing how many raffle tickets Dennis has left to sell.__
6. Decide the type of graph you should draw. A __continuous__ graph has connected lines or curves. A __discrete__ graph has only distinct points.
   Since you can only count whole numbers of tickets sold, construct a __discrete__ graph.

Solve

7. What should you title the graph? __Dennis' Raffle Tickets__
8. Let the x-axis represent the number of booklets sold. The x-axis should be labeled from 0 to __5__.
9. Let the y-axis represent the number of tickets remaining. The y-axis should be labeled from 0 to __100__.
10. Complete the ordered pairs:
    (1, 90), (2, 80), (3, __70__), (4, __60__), (5, __50__)
11. Plot the ordered pairs.

Look Back

12. If Dennis sells 3 books, how many tickets remain? __70__
13. Is the point shown on your graph? __Yes__

Dennis' Raffle Tickets

41   Holt Algebra 1

Ready To Go On? Skills Intervention
4-2 Relations and Functions

Find these vocabulary words in Lesson 4-2 and the Multilingual Glossary.

Vocabulary			
relation	domain	range	function

Finding the Domain and Range of a Relation
Give the domain and range of each relation.

A set of ordered pairs is called a __relation__.

The __domain__ of a relation is the set of first elements (or x-coordinates) of the ordered pairs.

The __range__ of a relation is the set of second elements (or y-coordinates) of the ordered pairs.

A.

B.

List the ordered pairs: (−3, __6__); (0, __5__); (0, __6__); (3, __4__)
The domain is {−3, __0__, __3__ }.

The range is {4, __5__, __6__ }.

List the ordered pairs of the endpoints:
(−3, __1__); (__2__, 6)
The domain is all x-values from __−3__ to __2__, inclusive: $-3 \le x \le \boxed{2}$
The range is all y-values from 1 to __6__, inclusive: $1 \le y \le \boxed{6}$

Identifying Functions
Tell whether the relation is a function.

x	−4	−2	0	2	4
y	2	2	2	2	2

A function is a special type of relation that pairs each domain value with exactly __one__ range value.

List the ordered pairs (−4, __2__); (−2, __2__); (__0__, 2); (__2__, 2); (__4__, 2)
The domain is {−4, __−2__, __0__, __2__, __4__ }. The range is { __2__ }.
Is a domain value (x-coordinates) paired with more than one range value? __No__
Is the relation a function? __Yes__

42   Holt Algebra 1

Ready To Go On? Skills Intervention
4-3 Writing and Graphing Functions

Find these vocabulary words in Lesson 4-3 and the Multilingual Glossary.

Vocabulary			
independent variable	dependent variable	function rule	function notation

Using a Table to Write an Equation
Determine a relationship between the x- and y-values. Write an equation.

x	1	2	3	4
y	−5	−4	−3	−2

If x = 1, what can you subtract to get −5? $1 - \underline{6} = -5$
If x = 1, what can you multiply by to get −5? $1(\underline{-5}) = -5$
Determine which relationship works for the other x- and y-values.
Subtracting: $2 - 6 = \underline{-4}$ $3 - 6 = \underline{-3}$ $4 - 6 = \underline{-2}$
Multiplying: $2(-5) = \underline{-10}$ $3(-5) = \underline{-15}$ $4(-5) = \underline{-20}$
Which relationship works so that when you input the x-values you get the y-values in the table? __Subtracting__
Write an equation: $y = x - \underline{6}$

Writing Functions
Identify the independent and dependent variables. Write a rule in function notation.

A baker buys flour in 50-pound sacks that cost $18 each.

The cost depends on the number of sacks of flour purchased.

Dependent: __cost__   Independent: __number of sacks__

Let s represent the number of sacks of flour purchased.
The function for the cost of the flour is $f(\underline{s}) = 18\underline{s}$

Evaluating Functions
Evaluate the function $g(x) = 2x^2 - x$ for x = −3.

$g(-3) = 2(\underline{-3})^2 - (-3)$ Substitute −3 for x.
$g(-3) = 2(\underline{9}) - (-3)$ Evaluate the exponent.
$g(-3) = \underline{18} - (-3)$ Multiply.
$g(-3) = \underline{18} + \underline{3}$ Add the opposite.
$g(-3) = \underline{21}$ Simplify.

43   Holt Algebra 1

Ready to Go On? Problem Solving Intervention
4-3 Writing and Graphing Functions

You can graph a function by finding ordered pairs that satisfy the function.

The function $y = 9x$ represents how much money y Cameron earns in x hours. Graph the function.

Understand the Problem

1. What is the given function? __$y = 9x$__
2. What variable represents hours? __x__ What variable represents money? __y__
3. If Cameron works 0 hours, how much money will she earn? __$0__
   If she works 1 hour how much will she earn? __$9__
4. So, the more Cameron works, the more __money__ she will earn.

Make a Plan

5. Can Cameron earn negative money? __No__ So, the domain values for this function should only be __positive__ numbers.
6. The graph will only be graphed in quadrant __I__.

Solve

7. Complete the table for the given function values.
8. The x-coordinate of an ordered pair tells you to move __left or right__ on the grid.
9. The y-coordinate of an ordered pair tells you to move __up or down__ on the grid.
10. Graph each ordered pair.

x	$y = 9x$	(x, y)
0	$y = 9(0) = 0$	(0, __0__)
1	$y = 9(1) = 9$	(1, __9__)
2	$y = 9(\underline{2}) = 18$	(2, __18__)
3	$y = 9(\underline{3}) = 27$	(3, __27__)
4	$y = 9(\underline{4}) = 36$	(__4__, __36__)

Look Back

11. Use your graph to determine:
    What y-value corresponds with an x-value of 2? __$18__
    What y-value corresponds with an x-value of 4? __$36__
    What y-value corresponds with an x-value of 6? __$54__
12. If Cameron works more hours, does the graph show an increase or decrease in the amount of money she earns?
    __Increase__
    Does this correspond to your understanding of the problem in Exercise 4? __Yes__

44   Holt Algebra 1

---

205   Holt Algebra 1

Ready To Go On? Skills Intervention
4-4 Scatter Plots and Trend Lines

Find these vocabulary words in Lesson 4-4 and the Multilingual Glossary.

Vocabulary

scatter plot	correlation	positive correlation
negative correlation	no correlation	trend line

Graphing a Scatter Plot from Given Data
Graph a scatter plot using the given data.

x	2	4	5	7	9	11
y	14	17	19	23	28	34

A __scatter plot__ is a graph with points plotted to show
a possible relationship between two sets of data.

List the sets of ordered pairs: (2, 14); (4, __17__); (5, __19__);
(_7_, _23_); (_9_, _28_); (_11_, _34_).

When plotting an ordered pair the x-coordinate tells you to move __left__ or __right__
and the y-coordinate tells you to move __up__ or __down__.

To plot the point (2, 14) you move 2 units right from the origin and __14__ units up.

To plot the point (4, 17) you move 4 units __right__ from the origin and __17__ units up.

To plot the point (5, 19) you move __5__ units __right__ from the origin and __19__ units __up__.

Plot the ordered pairs on the grid.

Describing Correlations from Scatter Plots
Describe the correlation illustrated by the above scatter plot.

A __correlation__ describes a relationship between two sets of data.

In a positive correlation, both sets of data values __increase__.

In a __negative__ correlation, one set of data values increases as the other set
decreases.

There is __no__ correlation when the data values are scattered about.

Look at the scatter plot you just drew above. As the x-value __increases__ the y-value also
increases. Therefore, a __positive__ correlation exists between the two data sets.

45

Ready to Go On? Problem Solving Intervention
4-4 Scatter Plots and Trend Lines

You can graph a function on a scatter plot to show the relationship of data.
Sometimes the function is a straight line. The line, called a **trend
line** helps show the correlation between data sets more clearly. It
can also be helpful when making predictions based on the data.

The scatter plot shows the estimated annual sales for a
playhouse franchise of stores for the years 2004–2009.
Based on this relationship, predict the total annual
sales in 2012.

Understand the Problem

1. What are you being asked to predict?
   __The total annual sales in 2012__

2. What information are you given?
   __Years and annual sales for 2004 to 2009__

Make a Plan

3. What can be drawn on the scatter plot to help make a prediction? __A trend line__

4. Does your line have to go through all the data points? __No__

5. When drawing a trend line, you want about the same number of points above
   and __below__ the line.

Solve

6. Draw the trend line on the scatter plot above.

7. To make the prediction find the point on the line whose x-value is __2012__.
   The corresponding y-value is the predicted annual sales.

8. The estimated sales for the playground and playhouse franchise in 2012 are
   __$16 million__

Look Back

9. The annual sales increase from year to year, based on the data.
   Is your answer a reasonable prediction of how much in sales the
   playground and playhouse franchise will collect in the year 2012? __Yes__

10. Plot the point (2012, 16) on the grid. Does the point fall near your
    trend line? __Yes__

46

Ready To Go On? Skills Intervention
4-5 Arithmetic Sequences

Find these vocabulary words in Lesson 4-5 and the Multilingual Glossary.

Vocabulary

sequence	term	arithmetic sequence	common difference

Identifying Arithmetic Sequences
Determine whether the sequence 20, 12, 4, −4, ... appears to be an
arithmetic sequence. If so, find the common difference and the next
three terms.

A __sequence__ is a list of numbers that often forms a pattern. Each number
in a sequence is called a __term__.

Find the difference between successive terms:

$12 - 20 = $ __−8__ ; $4 - 12 = $ __−8__ ; $(-4) - 4 = $ __−8__

Is the difference the same between each set of terms? __Yes__

If so, the common difference is __−8__.

Use the common difference to find the next three terms.

20, 12, 4, −4, __−12__ __−20__ __−28__
        −8   8   8

Finding the nth Term of an Arithmetic Sequence
Find the 14th term of the arithmetic sequence 17, 8, −1, −10, ...

What is the common difference, d?

$8 - 17 = $ __−9__

Write the rule to find the nth term:

$a_n = a_1 + (n - 1)d$

In the formula which variable represents

the first term? __a_1__

What is a_1 in the above sequence?

__17__

The variable n represents the number of

term you are looking for, so n = __14__.

Solve for a_n.
$a_n = a_1 + (n - 1)d$
$a_n = $ __17__ $ + (14 - 1)(-9)$ Substitute.
$a_n = $ __17__ $ + 13(-9)$ Subtract.
$a_n = $ __17__ $ - $ __117__   Multiply.
$a_n = $ __−100__   Subtract.

The 14th term of the sequence is __−100__.

47

Ready to Go On? Problem Solving Intervention
4-5 Arithmetic Sequences

The nth term of an arithmetic sequence with common difference d and first term a_1, is:
$a_n = a_1 + (n - 1)d$.

The marching band has 14 marchers in the front row, 16 in the second
row, 18 in the third row, 20 in the fourth row, and so on. How many
marchers are in the 15th row?

Understand the Problem

1. What are you asked to find? __The number of marchers in the 15th row__
2. What are you given? __The number of marchers in the first three rows__

Make a Plan

3. How many marchers are in each of the first four rows? 14, 16, __18__ __20__
4. What is the difference between each two terms? $16 - 14 = $ __2__ ; $18 - 16 = $ __2__
5. What type of sequence does this appear to be? __Arithmetic__

Solve

6. What is the first term of the sequence, a_1? __14__
7. What is the common difference, d? __2__
8. What term in the sequence do you need to find? n = __15__
9. What is the formula for finding the nth term? __$a_n = a_1 + (n - 1)d$__
10. Complete the formula for the number of marchers in the 15th row.
    $a_n = a_1 + (n - 1)d$
    $a_n = 14 + (15 - 1)$ __2__   Substitute for a_1, n, and d.
    $a_n = $ __14__ $ + 14(2)$ Simplify the expression in parentheses.
    $a_n = $ __14__ $ + $ __28__   Multiply.
    $a_n = $ __42__   Add.
11. The number of marchers in the 15th row is __42__.

Look Back

12. Complete the table for the number of marchers in each row.

1	2	3	4	5	6	7	8	9	10	11	12	13	14	15
14	16	18	20	22	24	26	28	30	32	34	36	38	40	42

13. Does your answer from Exercise 11 match the table? __Yes__

48

206
Holt Algebra 1

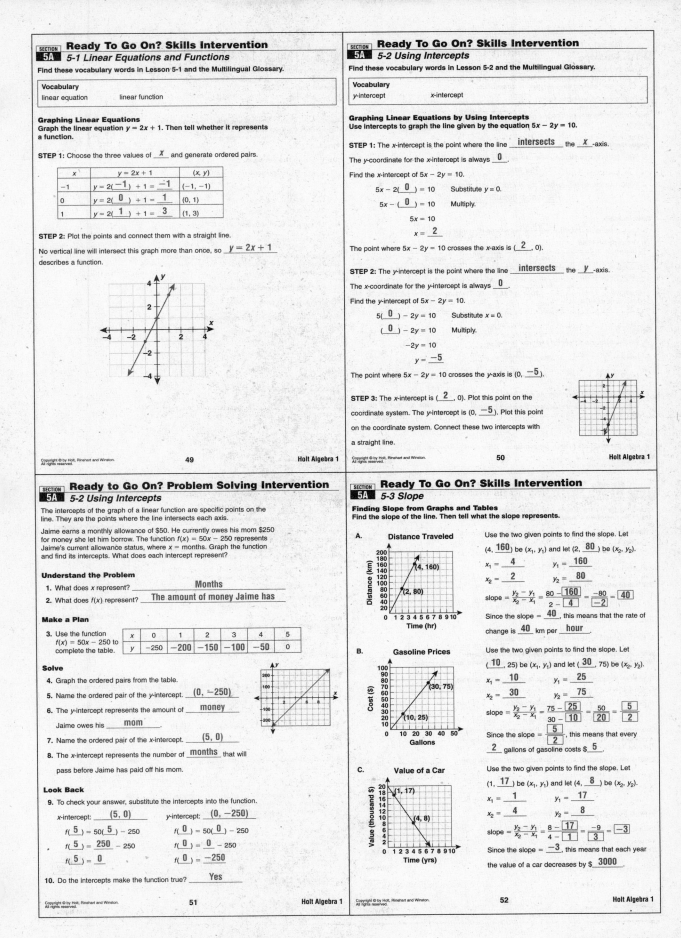

Ready To Go On? Skills Intervention
5A 5-1 Linear Equations and Functions

Find these vocabulary words in Lesson 5-1 and the Multilingual Glossary.

Vocabulary	
linear equation	linear function

Graphing Linear Equations
Graph the linear equation $y = 2x + 1$. Then tell whether it represents a function.

STEP 1: Choose the three values of __x__ and generate ordered pairs.

x	y = 2x + 1	(x, y)
−1	y = 2(−1) + 1 = −1	(−1, −1)
0	y = 2(0) + 1 = 1	(0, 1)
1	y = 2(1) + 1 = 3	(1, 3)

STEP 2: Plot the points and connect them with a straight line.

No vertical line will intersect this graph more than once, so $y = 2x + 1$ describes a function.

49 **Holt Algebra 1**

Ready To Go On? Skills Intervention
5A 5-2 Using Intercepts

Find these vocabulary words in Lesson 5-2 and the Multilingual Glossary.

Vocabulary	
y-intercept	x-intercept

Graphing Linear Equations by Using Intercepts
Use intercepts to graph the line given by the equation $5x − 2y = 10$.

STEP 1: The x-intercept is the point where the line __intersects__ the __x__-axis.

The y-coordinate for the x-intercept is always __0__.

Find the x-intercept of $5x − 2y = 10$.

$$5x − 2(\,0\,) = 10 \quad \text{Substitute } y = 0.$$
$$5x − (\,0\,) = 10 \quad \text{Multiply.}$$
$$5x = 10$$
$$x = 2$$

The point where $5x − 2y = 10$ crosses the x-axis is (2 , 0).

STEP 2: The y-intercept is the point where the line __intersects__ the __y__-axis.

The x-coordinate for the y-intercept is always __0__.

Find the y-intercept of $5x − 2y = 10$.

$$5(\,0\,) − 2y = 10 \quad \text{Substitute } x = 0.$$
$$(\,0\,) − 2y = 10 \quad \text{Multiply.}$$
$$−2y = 10$$
$$y = −5$$

The point where $5x − 2y = 10$ crosses the y-axis is (0, −5).

STEP 3: The x-intercept is (2 , 0). Plot this point on the coordinate system. The y-intercept is (0, −5). Plot this point on the coordinate system. Connect these two intercepts with a straight line.

50 **Holt Algebra 1**

Ready to Go On? Problem Solving Intervention
5A 5-2 Using Intercepts

The intercepts of the graph of a linear function are specific points on the line. They are the points where the line intersects each axis.

Jaime earns a monthly allowance of $50. He currently owes his mom $250 for money she let him borrow. The function $f(x) = 50x − 250$ represents Jaime's current allowance status, where x = months. Graph the function and find its intercepts. What does each intercept represent?

Understand the Problem

1. What does x represent? _____ Months
2. What does f(x) represent? _____ The amount of money Jaime has

Make a Plan

3. Use the function $f(x) = 50x − 250$ to complete the table.

x	0	1	2	3	4	5
y	−250	−200	−150	−100	−50	0

Solve

4. Graph the ordered pairs from the table.
5. Name the ordered pair of the y-intercept. (0, −250)
6. The y-intercept represents the amount of _____ money Jaime owes his _____ mom.
7. Name the ordered pair of the x-intercept. (5, 0)
8. The x-intercept represents the number of _____ months that will pass before Jaime has paid off his mom.

Look Back

9. To check your answer, substitute the intercepts into the function.

x-intercept: (5, 0)   y-intercept: (0, −250)

$f(\,5\,) = 50(\,5\,) − 250$ $f(\,0\,) = 50(\,0\,) − 250$
$f(\,5\,) = 250 − 250$ $f(\,0\,) = 0 − 250$
$f(\,5\,) = 0$ $f(\,0\,) = −250$

10. Do the intercepts make the function true? _____ Yes

51 **Holt Algebra 1**

Ready To Go On? Skills Intervention
5A 5-3 Slope

Finding Slope from Graphs and Tables
Find the slope of the line. Then tell what the slope represents.

A. Distance Traveled

Use the two given points to find the slope. Let (4, 160) be (x_1, y_1) and let (2, 80) be (x_2, y_2).

$x_1 = 4$ $y_1 = 160$
$x_2 = 2$ $y_2 = 80$

$$\text{slope} = \frac{y_2 − y_1}{x_2 − x_1} = \frac{80 − \boxed{160}}{2 − \boxed{4}} = \frac{−80}{\boxed{−2}} = \boxed{40}$$

Since the slope = 40 , this means that the rate of change is 40 km per hour .

B. Gasoline Prices

Use the two given points to find the slope. Let (10 , 25) be (x_1, y_1) and let (30 , 75) be (x_2, y_2).

$x_1 = 10$ $y_1 = 25$
$x_2 = 30$ $y_2 = 75$

$$\text{slope} = \frac{y_2 − y_1}{x_2 − x_1} = \frac{75 − \boxed{25}}{30 − \boxed{10}} = \frac{50}{20} = \frac{5}{2}$$

Since the slope = $\frac{5}{2}$, this means that every 2 gallons of gasoline costs $ 5 .

C. Value of a Car

Use the two given points to find the slope. Let (1, 17) be (x_1, y_1) and let (4, 8) be (x_2, y_2).

$x_1 = 1$ $y_1 = 17$
$x_2 = 4$ $y_2 = 8$

$$\text{slope} = \frac{y_2 − y_1}{x_2 − x_1} = \frac{8 − \boxed{17}}{4 − \boxed{1}} = \frac{−9}{3} = \boxed{−3}$$

Since the slope = −3 , this means that each year the value of a car decreases by $ 3000 .

52 **Holt Algebra 1**

Holt Algebra 1

Ready to Go On? Problem Solving Intervention
5A 5-3 Slope

The rate of change is the ratio of the change in the dependent variable to the change in the independent variable. The rate of change can be determined from ordered pairs, a graph, or an equation.

The chart gives the average price of gasoline in different years. Graph this data and show the annual rates of change.

Year	2000	2001	2002	2003	2004
Cost ($)	1.20	1.50	1.65	2.00	2.15

Understand the Problem

1. What is the independent variable, the year or the cost of gasoline?

   The year

2. What is the dependent variable, the year or the cost of gasoline?

   The cost of gasoline

Make a Plan

3. Look at the table and determine how many rates of change you need to find. 4

4. Complete the table:

	Rate 1	Rate 2	Rate 3	Rate 4
Change in Independent Variable	2001 − 2000 = 1	2002 − 2001 = 1	2003 − 2002 = 1	2004 − 2003 = 1
Change in Dependent Variable	1.50 − 1.20 = 0.30	1.65 − 1.50 = 0.15	2.00 − 1.65 = 0.35	2.15 − 2.00 = 0.15

Solve

5. Find each ratio to determine each rate of change:

   rate 1 $= \frac{0.3}{1} = 0.3$ rate 2 $= \frac{0.15}{1} = 0.15$

   rate 3 $= \frac{0.35}{1} = 0.35$ rate 4 $= \frac{0.15}{1} = 0.15$

6. Graph the ordered pairs from the data table.

7. Write the annual rate of change on the graph between each point.

Look Back

8. Does the steepness of each line correspond to the rates in Exercise 5? Yes

53   Holt Algebra 1

Ready To Go On? Skills Intervention
5A 5-4 Direct Variation

Find these vocabulary words in Lesson 5-4 and the Multilingual Glossary.

Vocabulary

direct variation   constant of variation

Identifying Direct Variations from Ordered Pairs

Tell whether the relationship is a direct variation. If so, identify the constant of variation.

x	3	5	7	9
y	12	20	28	36

Find $\frac{y}{x}$ for each ordered pair.

(3, 12): $\frac{y}{x} = \frac{12}{3} = 4$ (5, 20): $\frac{y}{x} = \frac{20}{5} = 4$

(7, 28): $\frac{y}{x} = \frac{28}{7} = 4$ (9, 36): $\frac{y}{x} = \frac{36}{9} = 4$

Is $\frac{y}{x}$ the same for each ordered pair? Yes

So, this is an example of a direct variation .

Writing and Solving Direct Variation Equations

The value of y varies directly with x, and y = 8 when x = 10. Find y when x = 24.

Since y varies directly with x, you can use the formula $y = k$ x.

It is given that y = 8 when x = 10.

Substitute these values into the direct variation formula: 8 = k(10)

STEP 1: Solve for k.

$8 = 10k$

$\frac{8}{10} = \frac{10}{10}k$

$\frac{4}{5} = k$

Substitute this value for k into the equation $y = kx$.

$y = \frac{4}{5}x$

STEP 2: Find y when x = 24.

Substitute 24 in for x and solve for y.

$y = \frac{4}{5}x$

$y = \frac{4}{5}(24)$

$y = \frac{(96)}{5}$

$y = 19.2$

STEP 3: Complete: When x = 24, y = 19.2 .

54   Holt Algebra 1

Ready To Go On? Skills Intervention
5B 5-5 Slope-Intercept Form

Graphing by Using Slope and y-intercept.

Graph the line given a slope of $\frac{2}{5}$ and y-intercept of −2.

STEP 1: The y-intercept is −2 , so the line contains the point

(0 , −2).

Plot the y-intercept: (0 , −2)

STEP 2: Slope $= \frac{\text{change in } y}{\text{change in } x} = \frac{2}{5}$

Count 2 units up and 5 units right from (0, −2) and plot another point.

STEP 3: Connect these two points with a straight line.

Writing Linear Equations in Slope-Intercept Form

Write the equation, −2x + y = 1, in slope-intercept form, and then graph.

To write an equation in slope-intercept form, isolate the variable, y .

$-2x + y = 1$

$+2x \qquad +2x$ Add 2x to both sides.

$y = 1 + 2x$ Solve for y.

Determine the slope and y-intercept. Remember that y = mx + b.

$m = 2$ $b = 1$

STEP 1: The y-intercept is 1 , so the line contains the point

(0 , 1).

Plot the y-intercept: (0 , 1)

STEP 2: Slope $= \frac{\text{change in } y}{\text{change in } x} = \frac{2}{1}$

Count 2 units up and 1 unit right from (0, 1) and plot another point.

STEP 3: Connect these two points with a straight line.

55   Holt Algebra 1

Ready to Go On? Problem Solving Intervention
5B 5-5 Slope-Intercept Form

A linear equation can be written in slope-intercept form, y = mx + b, where m repeats the slope and b repeats the y-intercept.

At a strawberry festival, each person is charged a $4.00 entrance fee plus $1.50 per pound for the strawberries that they pick. The graph shows the total cost per person as a function of the number of pounds of strawberries picked.

Strawberry Festival

a. Write an equation that represents the total cost per person as a function of the number of pounds of strawberries picked.

b. Identify the slope and the y-intercept and describe the meaning of each in this situation.

Understand the Problem

1. How much does it cost to enter the strawberry festival? $4.00

2. How much does each pound of strawberries cost? $1.50

Make a Plan

3. Let y represent the total cost and x represent the number of pounds of strawberries. Complete the equation: Cost is equal to $4.00 entrance fee plus $1.50 per pound.

   y = 4 + 1.5 · x

4. In slope-intercept form, y = mx + b, m = slope and b = y-intercept .

Solve

5. What is the slope of the equation in Exercise 3? 1.5 Use Exercise 2 and explain what the slope of this equation means.

   The price you pay for each pound of strawberries

6. What is the y-intercept of the equation in Exercise 3? 4 Use Exercise 1 and explain what the y-intercept of this equation means.

   The cost to enter the festival

Look Back

7. Substitute 0 in for x into the equation from Exercise 3.

   $y = 4 + 1.5(0) \longrightarrow y = 4$

   Is the result the same as the y-intercept? Yes

56   Holt Algebra 1

Holt Algebra 1

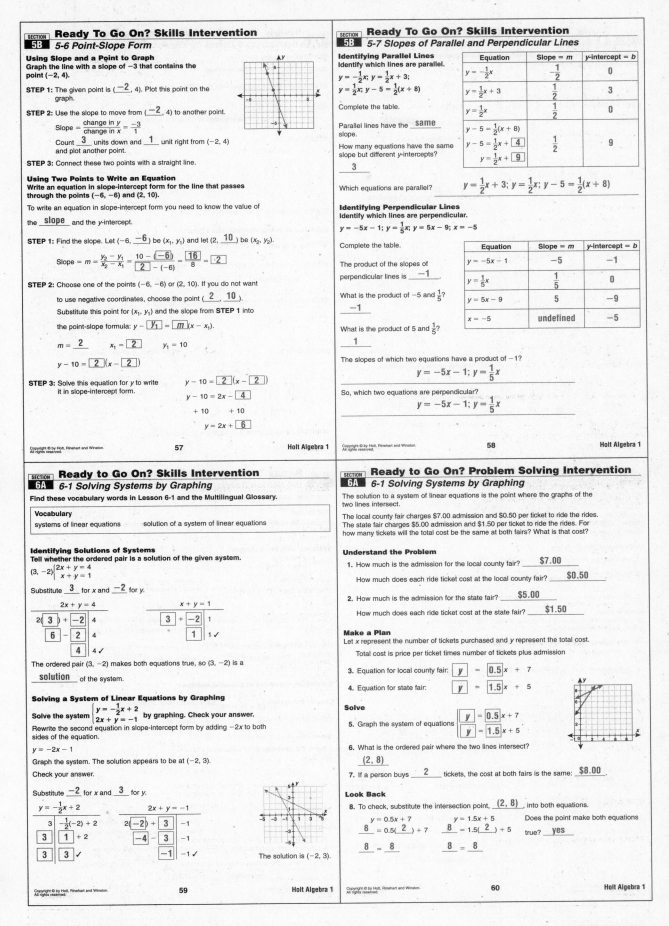

Using Slope and a Point to Graph
Graph the line with a slope of −3 that contains the point (−2, 4).

STEP 1: The given point is (−2, 4). Plot this point on the graph.

STEP 2: Use the slope to move from (−2, 4) to another point.

$\text{Slope} = \dfrac{\text{change in } y}{\text{change in } x} = \dfrac{-3}{1}$

Count 3 units down and 1 unit right from (−2, 4) and plot another point.

STEP 3: Connect these two points with a straight line.

Using Two Points to Write an Equation
Write an equation in slope-intercept form for the line that passes through the points (−6, −6) and (2, 10).

To write an equation in slope-intercept form you need to know the value of the slope and the y-intercept.

STEP 1: Find the slope. Let (−6, −6) be (x_1, y_1) and let (2, 10) be (x_2, y_2).

$\text{Slope} = m = \dfrac{y_2 - y_1}{x_2 - x_1} = \dfrac{10 - (-6)}{2 - (-6)} = \dfrac{16}{8} = 2$

STEP 2: Choose one of the points (−6, −6) or (2, 10). If you do not want to use negative coordinates, choose the point (2, 10).
Substitute this point for (x_1, y_1) and the slope from STEP 1 into the point-slope formula: $y - y_1 = m(x - x_1)$.

$m = 2 \qquad x_1 = 2 \qquad y_1 = 10$

$y - 10 = 2(x - 2)$

STEP 3: Solve this equation for y to write it in slope-intercept form.

$y - 10 = 2(x - 2)$
$y - 10 = 2x - 4$
$\underline{+10 \qquad\quad +10}$
$y = 2x + 6$

Identifying Parallel Lines
Identify which lines are parallel.
$y = -\frac{1}{2}x; \; y = \frac{1}{2}x + 3;$
$y = \frac{1}{2}x; \; y - 5 = \frac{1}{2}(x + 8)$

Complete the table.

Equation	Slope = m	y-intercept = b
$y = -\frac{1}{2}x$	$-\frac{1}{2}$	0
$y = \frac{1}{2}x + 3$	$\frac{1}{2}$	3
$y = \frac{1}{2}x$	$\frac{1}{2}$	0
$y - 5 = \frac{1}{2}(x + 8)$		
$y - 5 = \frac{1}{2}x + 4$	$\frac{1}{2}$	9
$y = \frac{1}{2}x + 9$		

Parallel lines have the same slope.

How many equations have the same slope but different y-intercepts?
3

Which equations are parallel? $y = \frac{1}{2}x + 3; \; y = \frac{1}{2}x; \; y - 5 = \frac{1}{2}(x + 8)$

Identifying Perpendicular Lines
Identify which lines are perpendicular.
$y = -5x - 1; \; y = \frac{1}{5}x; \; y = 5x - 9; \; x = -5$

Complete the table.

The product of the slopes of perpendicular lines is −1.

What is the product of −5 and $\frac{1}{5}$?
−1

What is the product of 5 and $\frac{1}{5}$?
1

Equation	Slope = m	y-intercept = b
$y = -5x - 1$	−5	−1
$y = \frac{1}{5}x$	$\frac{1}{5}$	0
$y = 5x - 9$	5	−9
$x = -5$	undefined	−5

The slopes of which two equations have a product of −1?
$y = -5x - 1; \; y = \frac{1}{5}x$

So, which two equations are perpendicular?
$y = -5x - 1; \; y = \frac{1}{5}x$

Find these vocabulary words in Lesson 6-1 and the Multilingual Glossary.

Vocabulary
systems of linear equations   solution of a system of linear equations

Identifying Solutions of Systems
Tell whether the ordered pair is a solution of the given system.

$(3, -2) \begin{cases} 2x + y = 4 \\ x + y = 1 \end{cases}$

Substitute 3 for x and −2 for y.

$2x + y = 4$				$x + y = 1$		
2(3) + −2	4			3 + −2	1	
6 − 2	4			1	1 ✓	
4	4 ✓					

The ordered pair (3, −2) makes both equations true, so (3, −2) is a solution of the system.

Solving a System of Linear Equations by Graphing
Solve the system $\begin{cases} y = -\frac{1}{2}x + 2 \\ 2x + y = -1 \end{cases}$ by graphing. Check your answer.

Rewrite the second equation in slope-intercept form by adding −2x to both sides of the equation.

$y = -2x - 1$

Graph the system. The solution appears to be at (−2, 3).

Check your answer.

Substitute −2 for x and 3 for y.

$y = -\frac{1}{2}x + 2$			$2x + y = -1$		
3	$-\frac{1}{2}(-2) + 2$		2(−2) + 3	−1	
3	1 + 2		−4 + 3	−1	
3	3 ✓		−1	−1 ✓	

The solution is (−2, 3).

The solution to a system of linear equations is the point where the graphs of the two lines intersect.

The local county fair charges $7.00 admission and $0.50 per ticket to ride the rides. The state fair charges $5.00 admission and $1.50 per ticket to ride the rides. For how many tickets will the total cost be the same at both fairs? What is that cost?

Understand the Problem

1. How much is the admission for the local county fair? $7.00

    How much does each ride ticket cost at the local county fair? $0.50

2. How much is the admission for the state fair? $5.00

    How much does each ride ticket cost at the state fair? $1.50

Make a Plan
Let x represent the number of tickets purchased and y represent the total cost.

    Total cost is price per ticket times number of tickets plus admission

3. Equation for local county fair: y = 0.5 x + 7

4. Equation for state fair: y = 1.5 x + 5

Solve

5. Graph the system of equations $\begin{cases} y = 0.5x + 7 \\ y = 1.5x + 5 \end{cases}$

6. What is the ordered pair where the two lines intersect?
    (2, 8)

7. If a person buys 2 tickets, the cost at both fairs is the same: $8.00

Look Back

8. To check, substitute the intersection point, (2, 8), into both equations.

    $y = 0.5x + 7 \qquad\qquad y = 1.5x + 5$
    $8 = 0.5(2) + 7 \qquad 8 = 1.5(2) + 5$ Does the point make both equations true? yes
    $8 = 8 \qquad\qquad\quad 8 = 8$

Ready To Go On? Skills Intervention
6-2 Solving Systems by Substitution

Solving a System of Linear Equations by Substitution
Solve each system by substitution.

A. $\begin{cases} y = -x + 3 \\ y = \frac{2}{3}x - 2 \end{cases}$

STEP 1 Substitute $-x + 3$ for $\boxed{y}$ in the second equation and solve for x.

STEP 2
$y = \frac{2}{3}x - 2$

$\boxed{-x + 3} = \frac{2}{3}x - 2$

$3(\boxed{-x + 3}) = 3(\frac{2}{3}x - 2)$

$-3x + \boxed{9} = \boxed{2x} - 6$

$\boxed{9} = 5x - 6$

$\boxed{15} = 5x$

$\boxed{3} = x$

STEP 3 Solve for the other variable, y.
You know from Step 2 that $x = \boxed{3}$.

$y = -x + 3$

$y = -(\boxed{3}) + 3$

$y = \boxed{0}$

The solution to the system of equations is $(\underline{3}, 0)$.

B. $\begin{cases} x + y = 4 \\ x + 2y = -2 \end{cases}$

STEP 1 Solve the equation $x + y = 4$ for x.

$x + y = 4$

$x = 4 - \boxed{y}$

STEP 2 Substitute $4 - y$ for $\underline{x}$ in the second equation.

$x + 2y = -2$

$\boxed{4 - y} + 2y = -2$

STEP 3 Solve for $\underline{y}$.

$4 - y + 2y = -2$

$4 + \boxed{y} = -2$

$y = \boxed{-6}$

STEP 4 Solve for the other variable, x.

$x + y = 4$

$x + \boxed{-6} = 4$

$x = \boxed{10}$

The solution to the system is $(10, \boxed{-6})$.

Holt Algebra 1

Ready To Go On? Skills Intervention
6-3 Solving Systems by Elimination

Elimination using Addition
Solve $\begin{cases} x + 4y = 16 \\ 5x - 4y = 8 \end{cases}$ by elimination.

STEP 1 Combine the two equations by addition.

$x + 4y = 16$
$5x - 4y = 8$

$\boxed{6x} + \boxed{0} = 24$ Which variable is eliminated? $\underline{y}$

STEP 2 Solve for $\underline{x}$.

$6x = 24$

$\frac{6x}{\boxed{6}} = \frac{24}{\boxed{6}}$

$x = \boxed{4}$

STEP 3 Substitute and solve for $\underline{y}$.

$x + 4y = 16$

$\boxed{4} + 4y = 16$

$4y = \boxed{12}$

$y = \boxed{3}$

STEP 4 The solution to the system is $(4, \underline{3})$.

Elimination using Multiplication First
Solve $\begin{cases} 3x - y = 4 \\ x + 4y = 10 \end{cases}$ by elimination.

STEP 1 To eliminate y, multiply the first equation by $\underline{4}$.

$4(3x - y) = 4(4) \longrightarrow \boxed{12}x - \boxed{4}y = \boxed{16}$
$x + 4y = 10 \longrightarrow x + 4y = 10$

STEP 2 Combine the two equations using $\underline{addition}$.

$\boxed{12}x - \boxed{4}y = \boxed{16}$
$x + 4y = 10$

$\boxed{13}x + \boxed{0} = 26$

STEP 3 Solve for x.

$13x = 26$

$\frac{\boxed{13}x}{\boxed{13}} = \frac{26}{\boxed{13}}$

$x = \boxed{2}$

STEP 4 Substitute and solve for y.

$x + 4y = 10$

$\boxed{2} + 4y = 10$

$4y = \boxed{8}$

$y = \boxed{2}$

STEP 5 The solution to the system of equations is $(2, \underline{2})$.

Holt Algebra 1

Ready to Go On? Problem Solving Intervention
6-3 Solving Systems by Elimination

You can multiply one or both of the equations in a system by a number so that when the equations are combined, one of the variables is eliminated.

Jack has 38 animals on his farm. Some of the animals have two legs and some of the animals have 4 legs. If Jack counted 128 legs total, how many of each type of animal does he have?

Understand the Problem

1. How many animals does Jack have total? $\underline{38}$

2. What type of animals does Jack have? $\underline{2\text{-legged and } 4\text{-legged}}$

3. How many legs did Jack count on his farm? $\underline{128 \text{ legs}}$

Make a Plan
Let t represent the number of two-legged animals and f represent the number of four-legged animals.

4. Two-legged animals plus four-legged animals equals the total number of animals.

$t + \underline{f} = \underline{38}$

5. (2)(number of two-legged animals) + (4)(number of 4-legged animals) = Total legs

$2(t) + 4(\underline{f}) = \underline{128}$

Solve

6. To eliminate t multiply the first equation by $\underline{-2}$.

$t + f = 38 \longrightarrow \boxed{-2}(t + f) = \boxed{-2}(38) \longrightarrow \boxed{-2}t + \boxed{-2}f = \boxed{-76}$
$2t + 4f = 128 \longrightarrow 2t + 4f = 128 \longrightarrow \underline{2t + 4f = 128}$
$ 2f = 52$
$ f = 26$

7. There are $\underline{26}$ four-legged animals. To find the number of two-legged animals, substitute $\underline{26}$ in for f and solve for t.

$t + 26 = 38$
$t = \boxed{12}$

8. There are $\underline{12}$ two-legged animals.

Look Back

9. To check, substitute the solution, $\underline{(12, 26)}$, into both equations.

$2t + 4f = 128 \qquad t + f = 38$
$2(\underline{12}) + 4(\underline{26}) = 128 \qquad \underline{12} + \underline{26} = 38$
$\underline{128} = 128 \qquad \underline{38} = 38$

Does your solution make both equations true? $\underline{Yes}$

Holt Algebra 1

Ready To Go On? Skills Intervention
6-4 Solving Special Systems

Find these vocabulary words in Lesson 6-4 and the Multilingual Glossary.

Vocabulary
inconsistent system   consistent system   independent system   dependent system

Systems with No Solution
Solve $\begin{cases} y = 4x - 3 \\ -4x + y = 8 \end{cases}$.

Consider $y = 4x - 3$.
What is the slope of this equation?
$\underline{4}$

What is the y-intercept of this equation? $(0, \underline{-3})$

Consider $-4x + y = 8$.
Solve the equation for y.
$-4x + y = 8$
$y = \boxed{4x} + 8$
What is the slope of this equation? $\underline{4}$
What is the y-intercept of this equation? $(0, \underline{8})$

The slopes of both equations are $\underline{equal}$. The y-intercepts of the equations are $\underline{different}$. The lines are $\underline{parallel}$ so the lines do not $\underline{intersect}$. Therefore there is no $\underline{solution}$.

Classifying Systems of Linear Equations

Classify the system $\begin{cases} y = -\frac{1}{3}x + 6 \\ x + 3y = 18 \end{cases}$ Give the number of solutions.

Consider $y = -\frac{1}{3}x + 6$.

What is the slope of this equation? $-\frac{1}{3}$

What is the y-intercept of this equation? $(0, \underline{6})$

Consider $x + 3y = 18$.
To identify the slope and y-intercept solve the equation for $\underline{y}$.

$x + 3y = 18$

$3y = 18 - \boxed{x}$

$\frac{3y}{\boxed{3}} = \frac{18 - \boxed{x}}{\boxed{3}}$

$y = \boxed{6} - \frac{1}{3}x$

What is the slope of this equation? $\underline{-\frac{1}{3}}$

What is the y-intercept of this equation? $(0, \underline{6})$

The slopes of both equations are $\underline{equal}$. The y-intercepts of equations are $\underline{equal}$. Since the lines overlap this system has $\underline{infinitely}$ many solutions.

This system is called $\underline{dependent}$ and $\underline{consistent}$.

Holt Algebra 1

Holt Algebra 1

Ready To Go On? Skills Intervention
6-5 Applying Systems

Writing Systems of Linear Equations

A. Mr. Treaker's rectangular garden has a perimeter of 16 m. Twice the garden's width is 1 meter more than its length. What are the dimensions of the garden?

Let ℓ be the length of the garden and w be the width of the garden. Recall the formula for the perimeter of a rectangle: $2(\ell + w) = p$.

STEP 1 Write the perimeter equation for the garden, substituting known values.

$$2(\ell + w) = \boxed{16}$$

STEP 2 Relate the dimensions ℓ and w of the garden.

Twice the width of the garden	is	one	more than	its length.
$\boxed{2} \cdot w$	$=$	$\boxed{1}$	$+$	ℓ

The system of equations consists of $2(\ell + w) = \boxed{16}$ and $\boxed{2}\,w = \ell + \boxed{1}$.

B. A farmer grows pecan and walnuts. He has a mail-order business selling these nuts. He packs the nuts in bags of one weight for pecans and another weight for walnuts. One shipment contained 5 bags of pecans and 3 bags of walnuts. The total weight of the nuts in this shipment was 108 ounces. Another shipment weighed 144 ounces. It contained 4 bags of pecans and 6 bags of walnuts. What is the weight of a bag of each kind of nut?

Let x be the weight of a bag of pecans and y be the weight of a bag of walnuts.

Write an equation for each shipment.

Total weight	is	number of bags of pecans	times	weight of a bag of pecans	plus	number of bags of walnuts	times	weight of a bag of walnuts.
$\boxed{108}$	$=$	$\boxed{5}$	$\cdot$	x	$+$	$\boxed{3}$	$\cdot$	y
$\boxed{144}$	$=$	$\boxed{4}$	$\cdot$	x	$+$	$\boxed{6}$	$\cdot$	y

The system of equations consists of $\boxed{108} = \boxed{5}\,x + \boxed{3}\,y$ and $\boxed{144} = \boxed{4}\,x + \boxed{6}\,y$.

Ready To Go On? Problem-Solving Intervention
6-5 Applying Systems

A two-digit number can be represented by the expression $10t + u$. Using this idea and a system of equations, you can solve number-digit problems.

The sum of the digits of a two-digit number is 8. When the digits are reversed, the new number is 18 more than the original number. What is the original number?

Understand the Problem

1. What are you being asked to find? _____ **a two-digit number**

2. What expression can be used to represent a two-digit number? _____ **$10t + u$**

Make a Plan

3. If $10t + u$ represents the original number, what expression represents the new two-digit number when the digits are reversed? _____ **$10u + t$**

4. You know that the sum of the digits t and u is 8. How do you write this statement as an equation? _____ **$t + u = 8$**

5. What do you know about the relationship between the original number and the new number?

   The new number is 18 more than the original number.

6. Using the expressions for the original and new numbers, how can you restate your answer to Exercise 5 as an equation? **$(10u + t) = 18 + (10t + u)$**

Solve

Use the equations you wrote in Exercise 4 and 6 to form a system of equations. Solve for t and u.

$t = $ **3** and $u = $ **5**

7. What is the original number? _____ **35**

Check

8. As stated in the problem, the sum of the digits is **3** + **5** = **8** ✓

9. When the digits are reversed, the new number is _____ **53**.

10. Is your answer to Exercise 9 a number that is 18 more than the original number?

   _____ **yes** ✓

Ready To Go On? Skills Intervention
6-6 Solving Linear Inequalities

Find these vocabulary words in Lesson 6-6 and the Multilingual Glossary.

Vocabulary	
linear inequality	solution of a linear inequality

Identifying Solutions of Inequalities

Tell whether the ordered pair, $(-4, -2)$, is a solution of the inequality, $y \le -3x + 6$.

To be a solution to the inequality, the ordered pair must make the inequality **true**.

Substitute the ordered pair $(-4, -2)$ into the inequality. Let $x = $ **-4** and $y = $ **-2**.

$y \le -3x + 6$

$\boxed{-2} \overset{?}{\le} -3(\boxed{-4}) + 6$ Does the ordered pair $(-4, -2)$ make the inequality true? **Yes**

$\boxed{-2} \overset{?}{\le} \boxed{12} + 6$ Therefore the ordered pair $(-4, -2)$ **is** a solution to the inequality $y \le -3x + 6$.

$\boxed{-2} \le \boxed{18}$

Graphing Linear Inequalities in Two Variables

Graph the solutions of the linear inequality, $y > -2x - 3$.

The inequality, $y > -2x - 3$, is in **slope-intercept** form.

The **boundary** line is given by the equation $y \underset{=}{=} -2x - 3$.

The slope of this line is **-2**. The y-intercept of this line is $(0, \underline{-3})$.

Use the slope and y-intercept to plot the boundary line.

Start at the point $(0, \underline{-3})$ and go up **2** units and left **1** unit. Plot the point.

Make the boundary line a **dashed** line because the inequality symbol is not "or equal to."

The inequality symbol is **$>$**, so should the solutions be located in the half-plane above or below the line? **Above** Shade this region to represent the solutions.

Check: Choose the point $(0, 0)$ and substitute it into the inequality.

$y > -2x - 3 \longrightarrow 0 > -2(0) - 3 \longrightarrow 0 > -3$

Does the point make the inequality true? **Yes** Did you shade correctly? **Yes**

Ready to Go On? Problem Solving Intervention
6-6 Solving Linear Inequalities

A solution to a linear equality lies in a half-plane with other ordered pairs that make the inequality true.

Janel has $10 to buy pencils and paper. Pencils sell for $1.50 per dozen and paper sells for $0.50 per package. Write a linear inequality to represent the situation. Then graph the linear inequality and give two possible combinations of pencils and paper that Janel can buy.

Understand the Problem

1. How much money does Janel have? _____ **$10**

2. A dozen pencils cost **$1.50** and a package of paper cost **$0.50**.

Make a Plan

Let x represent the dozens of pencils and y represent the number of packages of paper.

3. $(1.50)(\text{dozens of pencils}) + (0.50)(\text{packages of paper}) \le 10$

   $\boxed{(1.5)} \cdot x + (0.50) \cdot \boxed{y} \le \boxed{10}$

4. Write the inequality in slope-intercept form:

   $1.5x + \boxed{0.5}\,y \le 10$ The slope of the boundary line is **-3**.

   $0.5y \le 10 - \boxed{1.5x}$ The y-intercept of the boundary line is $(0, \boxed{20})$.

   $\dfrac{0.5y}{0.5} \le \dfrac{10}{0.5} - \dfrac{\boxed{1.5x}}{0.5}$ The symbol is "$\le$" so the boundary line is **solid**.

   $y \le 20 - \boxed{3}\,x$ Shade the half-plane **under** the boundary line.

Solve

5. Graph the inequality and shade the correct half-plane.

6. Choose two combinations: $(2, \boxed{2})$ and $(\boxed{1}, 5)$.

Look Back

7. Substitute your combinations into the inequality from Exercise 3.

$y \le 20 - 3x$	$y \le 20 - 3x$
$\boxed{2} \le 20 - 3(\boxed{2})$	$\boxed{5} \le 20 - 3(\boxed{1})$
$\boxed{2} \le 14$	$\boxed{5} \le 17$

So Janel can buy 2 dozen pencils and **2** packages of paper or 1 dozen pencils and **5** packages of paper.

Ready To Go On? Skills Intervention
6-7 Solving Systems of Linear Inequalities

Find these vocabulary words in Lesson 6-7 and the Multilingual Glossary.

Vocabulary
system of linear inequalities   solution of a system of linear inequalities

Identifying Solutions of Systems of Linear Inequalities
Tell whether the ordered pair $(-3, 1)$ is a solution of the system, $\begin{cases} y < -x + 3 \\ y \geq x - 2 \end{cases}$

To be a solution to the system of inequalities, the ordered pair $(-3, 1)$ has to make both inequalities __true__. Let $x =$ __-3__ and let $y =$ __1__.

Substitute $x = -3$ and $y = 1$ into $y < -x + 3$.

$1 < -(-3) + 3$
$1 < 3 + 3$
$1 < 6$

Substitute $x = -3$ and $y = 1$ into $y \geq x - 2$.

$1 \geq -3 - 2$
$1 \geq -5$

The point $(-3, 1)$ makes this inequality __true__.   The point $(-3, 1)$ makes this inequality __true__.

Since the point $(-3, 1)$ makes both inequalities __true__, it is a __solution__ to the system.

Solving a System of Linear Inequalities by Graphing
Graph the system of inequalities $\begin{cases} y > -x + 3 \\ y \leq 2x \end{cases}$. Give two ordered pairs that are solutions and two that are not solutions.

$y > -x + 3$ The y-intercept is $(0, \underline{3})$ and the slope $= \underline{-1}$. Use this information to draw a __dashed__ line. Because the symbol is __greater__ than, shade the half-plane __above__ the line.

$y \leq 2x$ The y-intercept is $(0, \underline{0})$ and the slope $= \underline{2}$. Use this information to draw a __solid__ line. Because the symbol is __less__ than or equal to, shade the half-plane __below__ the line.

Look at the graph. Are $(2, 3)$ and $(4, 1)$ solutions? __Yes__
Are $(0, 0)$ and $(1, -1)$ solutions? __No__
Did you shade the graph correctly? __Yes__

69   **Holt Algebra 1**

Ready to Go On? Problem Solving Intervention
6-7 Solving Systems of Linear Inequalities

The solutions to a system of linear inequalities are located in the intersection of the half-planes.

As a fundraiser, the chess club sells hotdogs and hamburgers. They make $1 for every hotdog and $2 for every hamburger they sell. The club cannot sell more than 100 hotdogs or 200 hamburgers. The club's goal is to make at least $200 in total profit. Show and describe possible combinations of hotdogs and hamburgers that can be sold to meet the goal.

Understand the Problem

1. How much does the club earn from each hotdog? __$1__ Each hamburger? __$2__
2. How many hotdogs do they have to sell? __100__ Hamburgers? __200__
3. How many inequalities need to be written? __3__

Make a Plan
Let x represent the number of hotdogs and y represent the number of hamburgers.

4.

The club cannot sell more than 100 hotdogs.	The club cannot sell more than 200 hamburgers.	Profit from hotdogs + Profit from hamburgers ≥ 200
$x \leq$ __100__	$y \leq$ __200__	$1x +$ __2__ $y \geq$ __200__

5. Graph each inequality on the coordinate system.

Inequality	Boundary Line	Dashed or Solid Line	Shaded Region
$x \leq$ __100__	Vertical line at $x =$ __100__	__Solid__ line	Shade to the __left__ of the line.
$y \leq$ __200__	Horizontal line at $y =$ __200__	__Solid__ line	Shade __under__ the line.
$1x +$ __2__ $y \geq$ __200__	x-intercept: $(200, 0)$ y-intercept: $(0, 100)$	__Solid__ line	Shade above the line.

Solve

6. Graph each inequality and shade the correct half-planes.
7. Are the points $(50, 100)$, $(75, 150)$, and $(80, 175)$ located in the intersection of all three regions? __Yes__

Look Back

8. Check that the x-coordinates of each point are less than 100 and that the y-coordinates are less than 200. Does each point make the inequality $x + 2y \geq 200$ true? __Yes__

70   **Holt Algebra 1**

Ready To Go On? Skills Intervention
7-1 Integer Exponents

Evaluating Expressions with Zero and Negative Exponents
Zero Exponent: Any nonzero number raised to the zero power is __1__.
$4^0 = $ __1__

Negative Exponent: A nonzero number raised to a negative exponent is equal to one divided by that number raised to the __opposite__ exponent.
$3^{-4} = \dfrac{1}{3^{\boxed{4}}}$

Evaluate each expression for the given value(s) of the variable(s).

A. $a^{-3}b^2$ for $a = 2$ and $b = 3$

$2^{-3} \cdot 3^{\boxed{2}}$ Substitute __2__ for a and __3__ for b.

$= \dfrac{1}{2^{\boxed{3}}} \cdot 9$ Use the definition $x^{-n} = \dfrac{1}{x^n}$ and simplify.

$= \dfrac{1}{2 \cdot \boxed{2} \cdot \boxed{2}} \cdot 9$ Write the power in the denominator as a product.

$= \dfrac{1}{\boxed{8}} \cdot 9$ Evaluate the power in the denominator.

$= \dfrac{9}{\boxed{8}}$ Simplify.

B. $x^0 y^{-3}$ for $x = 7$ and $y = -5$

$7^0 \cdot (-5)^{\boxed{-3}}$ Substitute __7__ for x and __-5__ for y.

$= 1 \cdot \dfrac{1}{(-5)^{\boxed{3}}}$ Any nonzero number raised to the zero power is __1__ and $x^{-n} = \dfrac{1}{x^n}$.

$= 1 \cdot \dfrac{1}{\boxed{-125}}$ Evaluate the power.

$= \dfrac{1}{\boxed{125}}$ Simplify.

Simplifying Expressions with Zero and Negative Exponents

A. $9a^{-7}$

$9a^{-7} = 9 \cdot \boxed{a^{-7}}$

$= 9 \cdot \dfrac{1}{\boxed{a^7}}$

$= \dfrac{9}{\boxed{a^7}}$

B. $\dfrac{x^{-6}}{y^{-4}}$

$\dfrac{x^{-6}}{y^{-4}} = x^{-6} \cdot \dfrac{1}{\boxed{y^{-4}}}$

$= \dfrac{1}{\boxed{x^6}} \cdot \dfrac{y^4}{1} = \boxed{\dfrac{y^4}{x^6}}$

71   **Holt Algebra 1**

Ready To Go On? Skills Intervention
7-2 Powers of 10 and Scientific Notation

Find this vocabulary word in Lesson 7-2 and the Multilingual Glossary.

Vocabulary
scientific notation

Positive Integer Exponent: If n is a positive integer, find the value of 10^n by starting with 1 and moving the decimal point __n__ places to the right.

Negative Integer Exponent: If n is a negative integer, find the value of 10^n by starting with 1 and moving the decimal point __n__ places to the left.

Evaluating Powers of 10
Find the value of 10^7.

Is the exponent positive or negative? __Positive__

Start with __1__ and move the decimal point __7__ places to the __right__.

$1\underbrace{0\ 0\ 0\ 0\ 0\ 0\ 0}$ So, $10^7 =$ __10,000,000__

Writing Powers of 10
Write each number as a power of 10.

A. 0.00001

$0.\underbrace{0\ 0\ 0\ 0\ 1}$ The decimal point is __5__ places to the __left__ of 1, so should the exponent be positive or negative? __Negative__

$0.00001 = 10^{\underline{-5}}$

B. 10,000,000,000

$1\underbrace{0\ 0\ 0\ 0\ 0\ 0\ 0\ 0\ 0\ 0}$ The decimal point is __10__ places to the __right__ of 1, so should the exponent be positive or negative? __Positive__

$10,000,000,000 = 10^{\underline{10}}$

Multiplying Powers of 10
Find the value of 16.3×10^6.

Move the decimal point __6__ places to the __right__.

$16\underbrace{3\ 0\ 0\ 0\ 0\ 0} = $ __16,300,000__

72   **Holt Algebra 1**

---

212   **Holt Algebra 1**

Ready To Go On? Skills Intervention
7-3 Multiplication Properties of Exponents

Finding Product of Powers

Product of Powers Property: The product of two powers with the same base equals

that base raised to the __sum__ of the exponents. For example $5^4 \cdot 5^2 = 5^{4+2}$.

Simplify.

A. $2^7 \cdot 2^3$ What is the base of each expression? __2__

$2^7 \cdot 2^3 = 2^{\underline{7}} + 3 = 2^{\underline{10}}$ Add the exponents.

B. $a^4 \cdot a^{-3} \cdot a^2$ Are the bases the same? __Yes__ So, __add__ the exponents.

$a^{4-3+\underline{2}} = a^{\underline{3}}$

Finding Powers of Powers

Power of a Power Property: A power raised to another power equals that base

raised to the __product__ of the exponents. For example $(4^3)^5 = 4^{3 \cdot 5} = 4^{15}$.

Power of a Product Property: A product raised to a power equals the __product__ of

each factor raised to that __power__. For example $(2^2 y^3)^4 = (2^2)^4 (y^3)^4 = 2^8 y^{12}$.

Simplify.

A. $(2x^3)^4$

$(2)^4 \cdot (\underline{x^3})^4$ Use the Power of a Product Property.

$16 \cdot x^{3 \cdot \underline{4}}$ When you raise a power to another power, __multiply__ exponents.

$16 \cdot x^{\underline{12}}$ Simplify.

B. $(-5a^3)^2$

$(\underline{-5})^2 \cdot (a^3)^{\underline{2}}$ Use the Power of a Product Property.

$\underline{25} \cdot (a^{3 \cdot \underline{2}})$ Simplify.

$25a^{\underline{8}}$

C. $(ab^2)^3 \cdot (a^4 b^2)^2$

$a^3 b^{\underline{2 \cdot 3}} \cdot a^{4 \cdot 2} b^{\underline{2 \cdot 2}}$ Use the Power of a Product Property.

$a^3 b^{\underline{6}} \cdot a^8 b^{\underline{4}}$ Simplify.

$a^{3+8} b^{\underline{6+4}}$ Use the Product of Powers Property.

$a^{11} b^{\underline{10}}$ Simplify.

73   **Holt Algebra 1**

Ready to Go On? Problem Solving Intervention
7-3 Multiplication Properties of Exponents

A number written in scientific notation has two parts that are multiplied. The first part is a number that is greater than or equal to 1 and less than 10. The second part is a power of 10.

Light travels at a speed of 3.0×10^8 meters per second. If light travels for 4.5 seconds, how far does it travel? Write your answer in scientific notation and in standard form.

Understand the Problem

1. What number(s) are given in scientific notation? __3.0×10^8 m/s__

2. What number(s) are given in standard form? __4.5 seconds__

3. What are you being asked to find? __How far light travels in 4.5 seconds.__

Make a Plan

4. What operation must be used to solve the problem? __Multiplication__

5. Write the multiplication expression. $4.5 \cdot (3.0 \times 10^{\underline{8}})$

Solve

6. What is the product of the expression? $(4.5)(3.0) \times 10^8 = \underline{13.5} \times 10^8$

7. What units should your answer have? __Meters__

8. Is the answer 13.5×10^8 written in scientific notation? __No__

    a. How many places does the decimal point need to be moved? __1__

    b. In what direction does the decimal point need to be moved? __Left__

    c. Write the answer in scientific notation. $\underline{1.35} \times 10^9$

9. Write the answer in standard form.

    a. How many places does the decimal point need to be moved? __9__

    b. In what direction does the decimal point need to be moved? __Right__

    c. Write the answer in standard form. __1,350,000,000__ meters

Look Back

10. Estimate your answer to see if it is correct.

    What does 4.5 round to? __5__

    What is $(5 \cdot 3) \times 10^8$? $\underline{15 \times 10^8}$

11. Is your estimate close to your numeric answers in Exercises 8c and 9c? __Yes__

74   **Holt Algebra 1**

Ready To Go On? Skills Intervention
7-4 Division Properties of Exponents

Finding Quotients of Powers

Quotient of Powers Property: The quotient of two nonzero powers with

the same base equals the base raised to the __difference__ of

the exponents. For example $\frac{5^8}{5^3} = 5^{8-3}$.

Simplify $\dfrac{3a^7 y^{10}}{a^2 y^8}$**.**

When finding the quotient of two powers you __subtract__ the exponents.

$\dfrac{3a^7 y^{10}}{a^2 y^8} = 3a^{7-2} y^{10-8} = 3a^{\underline{5}} y^{\underline{2}}$

Dividing Numbers in Scientific Notation

Simplify $(3 \times 10^8) \div (6 \times 10^5)$ **and write the answer in scientific notation.**

$(3 \times 10^8) \div (6 \times 10^5) = \dfrac{\boxed{3} \times 10^8}{\boxed{6} \times 10^5}$ Rewrite as a quotient.

$= \dfrac{\boxed{3}}{6} \times \dfrac{10^8}{10^{\underline{5}}}$ Write as a product of quotients.

$= \boxed{0.5} \times 10^{\underline{3}}$ Simplify each quotient and simplify the exponent.

$= 5 \times \boxed{10^{-1}} \times 10^3$ Write 0.5 in scientific notation.

$= 5 \times 10^{\underline{2}}$ Add the exponents.

Finding Positive Powers of Quotients

Positive Power of a Quotient Property: A quotient raised to a positive power

equals the quotient of each base raised to that __power__.

Simplify $\left(\dfrac{3a^4}{6a^2 b^2}\right)^2$**.**

$\left(\dfrac{3a^4}{6a^2 b^2}\right)^2 = \dfrac{(3a^4)^{\underline{2}}}{(6a^2 b^2)^{\underline{2}}}$ Use the Power of a Quotient Property.

$= \dfrac{(3)^2 (a^4)^{\underline{2}}}{(6)^2 (a^2)^2 (b^2)^2}$ Use the Power of a Product Property.

$= \dfrac{\boxed{9} a^{4 \cdot \underline{2}}}{\boxed{36}(a^{2 \cdot \underline{2}})(b^{2 \cdot \underline{2}})}$ Simplify and Use the Power of a Power Property.

$= \dfrac{\boxed{9} a^8}{\boxed{36}(a^{\underline{4}})(b^{\underline{4}})} = \dfrac{a^4}{4b^{\underline{4}}}$ Simplify.

75   **Holt Algebra 1**

Ready To Go On? Skills Intervention
7-5 Fractional Exponents

Find this vocabulary word in Lesson 7-5 and the Multilingual Glossary.

Vocabulary
index

Simplifying $b^{\frac{1}{n}}$

Simplify the expression.

$8^{\frac{1}{3}}$

$8^{\frac{1}{3}} = \boxed{3\sqrt{8}}$ Use definition of $b^{\frac{1}{n}}$ as $(\sqrt[n]{b})$. Think: $?^3 = \underline{8}$.

$= \boxed{2}$

Simplifying Expressions with Fractional Exponents

Simplify the expression.

$16^{\frac{5}{4}}$

$16^{\frac{5}{4}} = (\boxed{4}\sqrt{16}\,)^{\boxed{5}}$ Use the definition of $b^{\frac{m}{n}}$ as $(\sqrt[n]{b})^m$.

    Think $?^4 = \underline{16}$.

$= (\boxed{2})^{\boxed{5}}$ Evaluate the expression.

$= \boxed{32}$

Using Properties of Exponents to Simplify Expressions

Simplify. All variables represent nonnegative numbers.

$\sqrt[4]{x^4 y^8}$

$\sqrt[4]{x^4 y^8} = (x^4 y^8)^{\boxed{\frac{1}{4}}}$ Use the definition of $b^{\frac{1}{n}}$.

$= \boxed{(x^4)^{\frac{1}{4}}} \cdot \boxed{(y^8)^{\frac{1}{4}}}$ Power of a Product Property

$= \left(x^{\boxed{4} \cdot \frac{1}{4}} \cdot x^{\boxed{8} \cdot \frac{1}{4}}\right)$ Power of a Product Property

$= (x)^{\boxed{1}} \cdot (y)^{\boxed{2}}$ Simplify exponents.

$= xy^{\boxed{2}}$

76   **Holt Algebra 1**

Holt Algebra 1

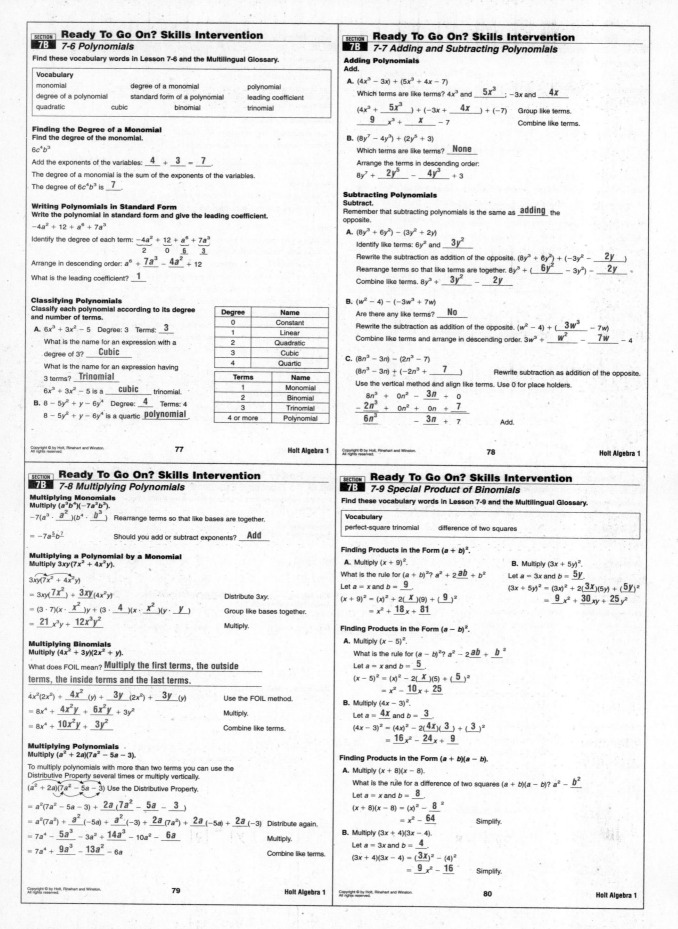

Ready To Go On? Skills Intervention

7-6 Polynomials

Find these vocabulary words in Lesson 7-6 and the Multilingual Glossary.

Vocabulary

monomial	degree of a monomial	polynomial
degree of a polynomial	standard form of a polynomial	leading coefficient
quadratic	cubic	binomial	trinomial

Finding the Degree of a Monomial
Find the degree of the monomial.

$6c^4b^3$

Add the exponents of the variables: $\underline{4} + \underline{3} = \underline{7}$.

The degree of a monomial is the sum of the exponents of the variables.

The degree of $6c^4b^3$ is $\underline{7}$.

Writing Polynomials in Standard Form
Write the polynomial in standard form and give the leading coefficient.

$-4a^2 + 12 + a^6 + 7a^3$

Identify the degree of each term: $\underset{2}{-4a^2} + \underset{0}{12} + \underset{6}{a^6} + \underset{3}{7a^3}$

Arrange in descending order: $a^6 + \underline{7a^3} - \underline{4a^2} + 12$

What is the leading coefficient? $\underline{1}$

Classifying Polynomials
Classify each polynomial according to its degree and number of terms.

A. $6x^3 + 3x^2 - 5$ Degree: 3   Terms: $\underline{3}$

What is the name for an expression with a degree of 3? $\underline{Cubic}$

What is the name for an expression having 3 terms? $\underline{Trinomial}$

$6x^3 + 3x^2 - 5$ is a $\underline{cubic}$ trinomial.

B. $8 - 5y^2 + y - 6y^4$ Degree: $\underline{4}$ Terms: 4

$8 - 5y^2 + y - 6y^4$ is a quartic $\underline{polynomial}$.

Degree	Name
0	Constant
1	Linear
2	Quadratic
3	Cubic
4	Quartic

Terms	Name
1	Monomial
2	Binomial
3	Trinomial
4 or more	Polynomial

77   Holt Algebra 1

Ready To Go On? Skills Intervention

7-7 Adding and Subtracting Polynomials

Adding Polynomials
Add.

A. $(4x^3 - 3x) + (5x^3 + 4x - 7)$

Which terms are like terms? $4x^3$ and $\underline{5x^3}$; $-3x$ and $\underline{4x}$

$(4x^3 + \underline{5x^3}) + (-3x + \underline{4x}) + (-7)$ Group like terms.

$\underline{9}x^3 + \underline{x} - 7$ Combine like terms.

B. $(8y^7 - 4y^3) + (2y^5 + 3)$

Which terms are like terms? $\underline{None}$

Arrange the terms in descending order:

$8y^7 + \underline{2y^5} - \underline{4y^3} + 3$

Subtracting Polynomials
Subtract.

Remember that subtracting polynomials is the same as $\underline{adding}$ the opposite.

A. $(8y^3 + 6y^2) - (3y^2 + 2y)$

Identify like terms: $6y^2$ and $\underline{3y^2}$

Rewrite the subtraction as addition of the opposite. $(8y^3 + 6y^2) + (-3y^2 - \underline{2y})$

Rearrange terms so that like terms are together. $8y^3 + (\underline{6y^2} - 3y^2) - \underline{2y}$

Combine like terms. $8y^3 + \underline{3y^2} - \underline{2y}$

B. $(w^2 - 4) - (-3w^3 + 7w)$

Are there any like terms? $\underline{No}$

Rewrite the subtraction as addition of the opposite. $(w^2 - 4) + (\underline{3w^3} - 7w)$

Combine like terms and arrange in descending order. $3w^3 + \underline{w^2} - \underline{7w} - 4$

C. $(8n^3 - 3n) - (2n^3 - 7)$

$(8n^3 - 3n) + (-2n^3 + \underline{7})$ Rewrite subtraction as addition of the opposite.

Use the vertical method and align like terms. Use 0 for place holders.

$$\begin{array}{r} 8n^3 + 0n^2 - \underline{3n} + 0 \\ \underline{-2n^3 + 0n^2 + 0n + 7} \\ 6n^3 - 3n + 7 \end{array}$$ Add.

78   Holt Algebra 1

Ready To Go On? Skills Intervention

7-8 Multiplying Polynomials

Multiplying Monomials
Multiply $(a^3b^4)(-7a^2b^3)$.

$-7(a^3 \cdot \underline{a^2})(b^4 \cdot \underline{b^3})$ Rearrange terms so that like bases are together.

$= -7a^5b^7$ Should you add or subtract exponents? $\underline{Add}$

Multiplying a Polynomial by a Monomial
Multiply $3xy(7x^2 + 4x^2y)$.

$3xy(7x^2 + 4x^2y)$

$= 3xy(\underline{7x^2}) + \underline{3xy}(4x^2y)$ Distribute $3xy$.

$= (3 \cdot 7)(x \cdot \underline{x^2})y + (3 \cdot \underline{4})(x \cdot \underline{x^2})(y \cdot \underline{y})$ Group like bases together.

$= \underline{21}x^3y + \underline{12}x^3y^2$ Multiply.

Multiplying Binomials
Multiply $(4x^2 + 3y)(2x^2 + y)$.

What does FOIL mean? $\underline{Multiply\ the\ first\ terms,\ the\ outside}$
$\underline{terms,\ the\ inside\ terms\ and\ the\ last\ terms.}$

$4x^2(2x^2) + \underline{4x^2}(y) + \underline{3y}(2x^2) + \underline{3y}(y)$ Use the FOIL method.

$= 8x^4 + \underline{4x^2y} + \underline{6x^2y} + 3y^2$ Multiply.

$= 8x^4 + \underline{10x^2y} + \underline{3y^2}$ Combine like terms.

Multiplying Polynomials
Multiply $(a^2 + 2a)(7a^2 - 5a - 3)$.

To multiply polynomials with more than two terms you can use the Distributive Property several times or multiply vertically.

$(a^2 + 2a)(7a^2 - 5a - 3)$ Use the Distributive Property.

$= a^2(7a^2 - 5a - 3) + \underline{2a}(\underline{7a^2} - \underline{5a} - \underline{3})$

$= a^2(7a^2) + \underline{a^2}(-5a) + \underline{a^2}(-3) + \underline{2a}(7a^2) + \underline{2a}(-5a) + \underline{2a}(-3)$ Distribute again.

$= 7a^4 - \underline{5a^3} - 3a^2 + \underline{14a^3} - 10a^2 - \underline{6a}$ Multiply.

$= 7a^4 + \underline{9a^3} - \underline{13a^2} - 6a$ Combine like terms.

79   Holt Algebra 1

Ready To Go On? Skills Intervention

7-9 Special Product of Binomials

Find these vocabulary words in Lesson 7-9 and the Multilingual Glossary.

Vocabulary

perfect-square trinomial   difference of two squares

Finding Products in the Form $(a + b)^2$.

A. Multiply $(x + 9)^2$.

What is the rule for $(a + b)^2$? $a^2 + 2\underline{ab} + b^2$

Let $a = x$ and $b = \underline{9}$.

$(x + 9)^2 = (x)^2 + 2(\underline{x})(9) + (\underline{9})^2$

$= x^2 + \underline{18}x + \underline{81}$

B. Multiply $(3x + 5y)^2$.

Let $a = 3x$ and $b = \underline{5y}$.

$(3x + 5y)^2 = (3x)^2 + 2(\underline{3x})(5y) + (\underline{5y})^2$

$= \underline{9}x^2 + \underline{30}xy + \underline{25}y^2$

Finding Products in the Form $(a - b)^2$.

A. Multiply $(x - 5)^2$.

What is the rule for $(a - b)^2$? $a^2 - 2\underline{ab} + \underline{b}^2$

Let $a = x$ and $b = \underline{5}$.

$(x - 5)^2 = (x)^2 - 2(\underline{x})(5) + (\underline{5})^2$

$= x^2 - \underline{10}x + \underline{25}$

B. Multiply $(4x - 3)^2$.

Let $a = \underline{4x}$ and $b = \underline{3}$.

$(4x - 3)^2 = (4x)^2 - 2(\underline{4x})(\underline{3}) + (\underline{3})^2$

$= \underline{16}x^2 - \underline{24}x + \underline{9}$

Finding Products in the Form $(a + b)(a - b)$.

A. Multiply $(x + 8)(x - 8)$.

What is the rule for a difference of two squares $(a + b)(a - b)$? $a^2 - \underline{b}^2$

Let $a = x$ and $b = \underline{8}$.

$(x + 8)(x - 8) = (x)^2 - \underline{8}^2$

$= x^2 - \underline{64}$ Simplify.

B. Multiply $(3x + 4)(3x - 4)$.

Let $a = 3x$ and $b = \underline{4}$.

$(3x + 4)(3x - 4) = (\underline{3x})^2 - (4)^2$

$= \underline{9}x^2 - \underline{16}$ Simplify.

80   Holt Algebra 1

Ready to Go On? Problem Solving Intervention
7-9 Special Products of Binomials

A circular fish pond has a radius of $(x - 12)$ feet. Write a polynomial that represents the area of the fish pond. The formula for the area of a circle is $A = \pi r^2$, where r represents the radius of the circle. Leave the symbol π in your answer.

Understand the Problem

1. What are you being asked to find? _____ The area of the pond
2. What piece of information are you given regarding the pond?
   The radius is $(x - 12)$ feet.
3. How do you find the area of a circle? _____ $A = \pi r^2$

Make a Plan

4. Write an expression representing the area of the fish pond. _____ $\pi(x - 12)^2$
5. What are two possible ways that $(x - 12)^2$ can be simplified?
   Using the Distributive Property more than once, FOIL or a perfect-square trinomial

Solve

6. What is $(x - 12)^2$? $x^2 - \underline{24x} + \underline{144}$
7. Write an expression representing the area of the pond. $\pi x^2 - \underline{24\pi x} + \underline{144\pi}$

Look Back

8. Suppose that $x = 20$. What would the length of the radius be $(x - 12)$? _____ 8
9. What would the area of the pond equal using $A = \pi r^2$?

   $A = \pi \; \underline{8} \;^2$

   $A = \underline{64} \; \pi$

10. What is the value of the expression in Exercise 7, using $x = 20$?

    $A = \pi x^2 - 24\pi x + 144\pi$

    $= \pi(20)^2 - 24\pi(\underline{20}) + 144\pi$

    $= \underline{400}\pi - \underline{480}\pi + 144\pi$

    $= \underline{64}\pi$

11. Are your answers to Exercises 9 and 10 the same? _____ Yes

81
Holt Algebra 1

Ready To Go On? Skills Intervention
8-1 Factors and Greatest Common Factors

Find these vocabulary words in Lesson 8-1 and the Multilingual Glossary.

Vocabulary	
prime factorization	greatest common factor

Writing Prime Factorizations
Write the prime factorization of 48.

What is a prime number? A number with only two factors, itself and 1.

Method 1 Factor tree
Choose any two factors of 48 to begin. Keep finding factors until each branch ends in a prime factor. Circle the prime factors.

Method 2 Ladder diagram
Choose a prime factor of 48 to begin. Keep dividing by prime factors until the quotient is 1.

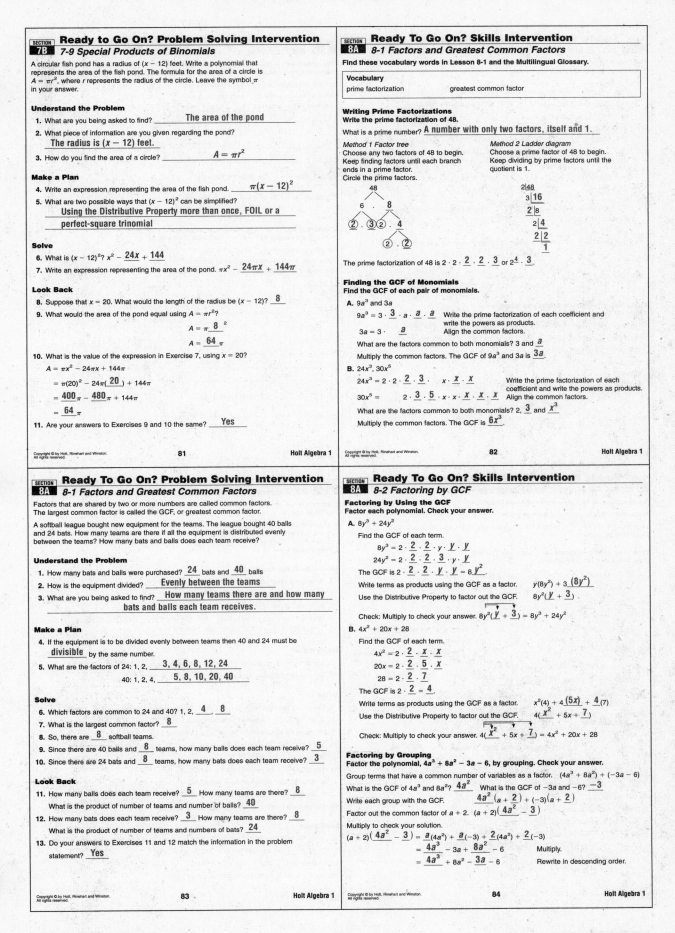

The prime factorization of 48 is $2 \cdot 2 \cdot \underline{2} \cdot \underline{2} \cdot \underline{3}$ or $2^{\underline{4}} \cdot \underline{3}$.

Finding the GCF of Monomials
Find the GCF of each pair of monomials.

A. $9a^3$ and $3a$

   $9a^3 = 3 \cdot \underline{3} \cdot a \cdot \underline{a} \cdot \underline{a}$ Write the prime factorization of each coefficient and write the powers as products.

   $3a = 3 \cdot \underline{a}$ Align the common factors.

   What are the factors common to both monomials? 3 and $\underline{a}$

   Multiply the common factors. The GCF of $9a^3$ and $3a$ is $\underline{3a}$

B. $24x^3$, $30x^5$

   $24x^3 = 2 \cdot 2 \cdot \underline{2} \cdot \underline{3} \cdot x \cdot \underline{x} \cdot \underline{x}$ Write the prime factorization of each coefficient and write the powers as products.

   $30x^5 = \underline{2} \cdot \underline{3} \cdot \underline{5} \cdot x \cdot x \cdot \underline{x} \cdot \underline{x} \cdot \underline{x}$ Align the common factors.

   What are the factors common to both monomials? 2, $\underline{3}$ and $\underline{x^3}$

   Multiply the common factors. The GCF is $\underline{6x^3}$

82
Holt Algebra 1

Ready To Go On? Problem Solving Intervention
8-1 Factors and Greatest Common Factors

Factors that are shared by two or more numbers are called common factors. The largest common factor is called the GCF, or greatest common factor.

A softball league bought new equipment for the teams. The league bought 40 balls and 24 bats. How many teams are there if all the equipment is distributed evenly between the teams? How many bats and balls does each team receive?

Understand the Problem

1. How many bats and balls were purchased? $\underline{24}$ bats and $\underline{40}$ balls
2. How is the equipment divided? Evenly between the teams
3. What are you being asked to find? How many teams there are and how many bats and balls each team receives.

Make a Plan

4. If the equipment is to be divided evenly between teams then 40 and 24 must be $\underline{divisible}$ by the same number.
5. What are the factors of 24: 1, 2, $\underline{3, 4, 6, 8, 12, 24}$

   40: 1, 2, 4, $\underline{5, 8, 10, 20, 40}$

Solve

6. Which factors are common to 24 and 40? 1, 2, $\underline{4}$, $\underline{8}$
7. What is the largest common factor? $\underline{8}$
8. So, there are $\underline{8}$ softball teams.
9. Since there are 40 balls and $\underline{8}$ teams, how many balls does each team receive? $\underline{5}$
10. Since there are 24 bats and $\underline{8}$ teams, how many bats does each team receive? $\underline{3}$

Look Back

11. How many balls does each team receive? $\underline{5}$ How many teams are there? $\underline{8}$
    What is the product of number of teams and number of balls? $\underline{40}$
12. How many bats does each team receive? $\underline{3}$ How many teams are there? $\underline{8}$
    What is the product of number of teams and numbers of bats? $\underline{24}$
13. Do your answers to Exercises 11 and 12 match the information in the problem statement? $\underline{Yes}$

83
Holt Algebra 1

Ready To Go On? Skills Intervention
8-2 Factoring by GCF

Factoring by Using the GCF
Factor each polynomial. Check your answer.

A. $8y^3 + 24y^2$

   Find the GCF of each term.

   $8y^3 = 2 \cdot \underline{2} \cdot \underline{2} \cdot y \cdot \underline{y} \cdot \underline{y}$

   $24y^2 = 2 \cdot \underline{2} \cdot \underline{2} \cdot \underline{3} \cdot y \cdot \underline{y}$

   The GCF is $2 \cdot \underline{2} \cdot \underline{2} \cdot \underline{y} \cdot \underline{y} = 8\underline{y^2}$

   Write terms as products using the GCF as a factor. $y(8y^2) + 3 \underline{(8y^2)}$

   Use the Distributive Property to factor out the GCF. $8y^2(\underline{y} + \underline{3})$

   Check: Multiply to check your answer. $8y^2(\underline{y} + \underline{3}) = 8y^3 + 24y^2$

B. $4x^2 + 20x + 28$

   Find the GCF of each term.

   $4x^2 = 2 \cdot \underline{2} \cdot \underline{x} \cdot \underline{x}$

   $20x = 2 \cdot \underline{2} \cdot \underline{5} \cdot \underline{x}$

   $28 = 2 \cdot \underline{2} \cdot \underline{7}$

   The GCF is $2 \cdot \underline{2} = \underline{4}$

   Write terms as products using the GCF as a factor. $x^2(4) + 4\underline{(5x)} + \underline{4}(7)$

   Use the Distributive Property to factor out the GCF. $4(\underline{x^2} + 5x + \underline{7})$

   Check: Multiply to check your answer. $4(\underline{x^2} + 5x + \underline{7}) = 4x^2 + 20x + 28$

Factoring by Grouping
Factor the polynomial, $4a^3 + 8a^2 - 3a - 6$, by grouping. Check your answer.

Group terms that have a common number of variables as a factor. $(4a^3 + 8a^2) + (-3a - 6)$

What is the GCF of $4a^3$ and $8a^2$? $\underline{4a^2}$ What is the GCF of $-3a$ and -6? $\underline{-3}$

Write each group with the GCF. $\underline{4a^2}(a + \underline{2}) + (-3)(a + \underline{2})$

Factor out the common factor of $a + 2$. $(a + 2)\underline{(4a^2 - 3)}$

Multiply to check your solution.

$(a + 2)\underline{(4a^2 - 3)} = \underline{a}(4a^2) + \underline{a}(-3) + \underline{2}(4a^2) + \underline{2}(-3)$

$= \underline{4a^3} - 3a + \underline{8a^2} - 6$ Multiply.

$= \underline{4a^3} + 8a^2 - \underline{3a} - 6$ Rewrite in descending order.

84
Holt Algebra 1

Ready To Go On? Skills Intervention
8-3 Factoring $x^2 + bx + c$

Factoring $x^2 + bx + c$ When c is Positive.
Factor each trinomial. Check your answer.

A. $x^2 + 9x + 14$
When the constant term is positive, its factors have the __same__ sign.
What is the value of the c term? __14__ What is the value of the b term? __9__

Factors of 14	Sum
1 and __14__	15
2 and __7__	__9__

What are the factors of c whose sum is b? __2__ and __7__
Complete: $(x + \underline{2})(x + \underline{7})$

Check using FOIL $(x + \underline{2})(x + \underline{7}) = x^2 + \underline{7x} + 2x + \underline{14}$
$x^2 + \underline{9x} + \underline{14}$

B. $x^2 + 8x + 15$
What is the value of the c term? __15__ What is the value of the b term? __8__

Factors of 15	Sum
1 and __15__	16
3 and __5__	__8__

What are the factors of c whose sum is b? __3__ and __5__
Complete: $(x + \underline{3})(x + \underline{5})$

Check using FOIL $(x + \underline{3})(x + \underline{5}) = x^2 + 5x + \underline{3x} + \underline{15}$
$x^2 + \underline{8x} + \underline{15}$

Factoring $x^2 + bx + c$ When c is Negative
Factor the trinomial $x^2 + 3x - 18$. Check your answer.

When the constant term of a trinomial is negative, its factors have __opposite__ signs.
What is the value of the c term? __−18__ What is the value of the b term? __3__

Factors of −18	Sum
−1 and __18__	17
−2 and __9__	__7__
−3 and __6__	__3__

What are the factors of c whose sum is b? __−3__ and __6__
Complete: $(x − \underline{3})(x + \underline{6})$

Check using FOIL $(x − \underline{3})(x + \underline{6}) = x^2 + \underline{6x} − 3x − \underline{18}$
$x^2 + \underline{3x} − \underline{18}$

85

Ready To Go On? Problem Solving Intervention
8-4 Factoring $ax^2 + bx + c$

Factoring $ax^2 + bx + c$ when c is Positive.
Factor the trinomial $2x^2 + 9x + 10$. Check your answer.

What is the value of a? __2__ What is the value of c? __10__
What is the sum of the inner and outer products? __9__

Factors of 2	Factors of 10	Outer + Inner
1 · 2	1 · 10	1 · 10 + 2 · 1 = 12
1 · 2	10 · 1	1 · 1 + 2 · __10__ = 21
1 · 2	5 · __2__	1 · 2 + 2 · __5__ = __12__
1 · 2	2 · __5__	1 · 5 + 2 · __2__ = __9__

$(x + \underline{2})(2x + \underline{5})$ Complete the factoring.

Check $(x + \underline{2})(2x + \underline{5}) = 2x^2 + \underline{5x} + \underline{4x} + \underline{10}$
$= 2x^2 + \underline{9x} + 10$

Factoring $ax^2 + bx + c$ when c is Negative
Factor the trinomial $4x^2 + 21x - 18$. Check your answer.

What is the value of a? __4__ What is the value of c? __−18__
What is the sum of the inner and outer products? __21__

Factors of 4	Factors of −18	Outer + Inner
1 · 4	1(−18)	1 · −18 + 4 · 1 = −14
1 · 4	−18(1)	1 · 1 + 4 · −18 = __−71__
1 · 4	2 · __−9__	1 · −9 + 4 · __2__ = __−1__
1 · 4	−9 · __2__	1 · __2__ + 4 · __−9__ = __−34__
1 · 4	3 · __−6__	1 · __−6__ + 4 · __3__ = __6__
1 · 4	−6 · __3__	1 · __3__ + 4 · __−6__ = __−21__
1 · 4	−3 · __6__	1 · __6__ + 4 · __−3__ = __−6__
1 · 4	6 · __−3__	1 · __−3__ + 4 · __6__ = __21__

$(x + \underline{6})(4x − \underline{3})$ Complete the factoring.

Check $(x + \underline{6})(4x − \underline{3}) = 4x^2 − \underline{3x} + \underline{24x} − \underline{18}$
$= 4x^2 + \underline{21x} − 18$

86

Ready To Go On? Skills Intervention
8-5 Factoring Special Products

Recognizing and Factoring Perfect-Square Trinomials

A trinomial is a perfect square if the first and the __last__ terms are perfect
squares. The __middle__ term is two times one factor from the first term and one
factor from the last term.

**Determine whether each trinomial is a perfect square.
If so, factor it. If not, explain why.**

A. $x^2 + 14x + 42$
Method 1 Factor.

Factors of 42	Sum
1 and 42	43
2 and 21	__23__
__3__ and 14	__17__
6 and __7__	__13__

Is $x^2 + 14x + 42$ a perfect square
trinomial? __No__ Why? __No factors
give the sum of 14.__

B. $9x^2 - 24x + 16$
Method 2 Use the pattern.
$9x^2 - 24x + 16$
$3x · 3x - 2(3x \cdot \underline{4}) + 4 \cdot 4$
The trinomial is a perfect __square__.
$a = 3x, b = \underline{4}$
$(3x)^2 - 2(\underline{3x})(4) + 4^2$ Write the trinomial as $a^2 - 2ab + b^2$.
$(\underline{3x} - 4)^2$ Write as $(a - b)^2$.

**Determine whether each binomial is the difference of two squares. If so, factor
it. If not explain why.**

A. $x^2 - 16$
$(x \cdot x) - (4 \cdot \underline{4})$ The polynomial is the difference of two __squares__.
$a = x, b = 4$
$(x + 4)(x - \underline{4})$ Write the polynomial as $(a + b)(a - b)$.
So $x^2 - 16 = (x + \underline{4})(x - \underline{4})$.

B. $9x^6 - 17y^2$
Is $9x^6$ a perfect square? __Yes__
Is $-17y^2$ a perfect square? __No__
Is $9x^6 - 17y^2$ the difference of two squares? __No__
Why? __Because $-17y^2$ is not a perfect square.__

87

Ready To Go On? Problem Solving Intervention
8-5 Factoring Special Products

If a trinomial is a perfect square, it can be factored to determine measurements of
real-world objects.

A community garden, rectangular in shape, has an area of $(25x^2 + 20x + 4)$ ft^2.
The dimensions of the garden are approximately $ax + b$, where a and b are whole
numbers. Find an expression for the perimeter of the garden. Then find the
perimeter where $x = 12$.

Understand the Problem

1. What is the shape of the garden? __Rectangle__
2. What is the area of the garden? __$(25x^2 + 20x + 4)$ ft^2__
3. What kind of numbers are a and b? __Whole numbers__
4. What are you being asked to find? __The expression for the perimeter of the
garden__ and __the perimeter when $x = 12$.__

Make a Plan

5. The formula for the area of a rectangle is: Area = length × __width__
6. What must be done to the trinomial to find the length and width? __Factor it__

Solve

7. Does the trinomial $25x^2 + 20x + 4$ have a common factor? __No__
8. Is $25x^2 + 20x + 4$ a perfect square trinomial? __Yes__ So, $a =$ __5x__ and $b = 2$.
9. What are the factors of the perfect square trinomial? __$(5x + 2)^2$__
10. Since the length and width of the garden are equal, what is the actual shape of
the garden? __A square__
11. The formula for the perimeter of a square is $P = 4s$.
    a. What should you substitute in the perimeter formula for s? __5x + 2__
    b. Simplify $4(5x + 2)$ to find an expression for the perimeter. __20x + 8__
12. Evaluate the expression when $x = 12$. What is the perimeter? __248 ft__

Look Back

13. Using the perimeter from Exercise 12, what is the length of one side of the square?
    __62 ft__ Use this side length to find the area. __3844 ft^2__
14. Evaluate $25x^2 + 20x + 4$ for $x = 12$: $25(12)^2 + 20(12) + 4 =$ __3844__
15. Are the areas in Exercises 13 and 14 equal? __Yes__

88

216
Holt Algebra 1

Determining Whether an Expression Is Completely Factored
Tell whether each expression is completely factored. If not, factor it.

A. $4x^2 + 2x - 6 = 2(2x^2 + x - 3)$

The greatest common factor is __2__.

Is $(2x^2 + x - 3)$ factorable? __Yes__

Is $2(2x^2 + x - 3)$ completely factored? __No__

Factor: $2(2x^2 + x - 3) \Rightarrow 2(2x + \underline{3})(x - \underline{1})$

B. $42x - 14x^3 = 14(3x - x^3)$

What is the greatest common factor? __14x__

Is the polynomial factored completely? __No__

Factor: $42x - 14x^3 \Rightarrow 14x(\underline{3} - \underline{x^2})$

Can the polynomial be factored any further? __No__

Factoring by Multiple Methods
Factor the polynomial $6x^3 + 21x^2 + 15x$ completely. Check your answer.

Consider $6x^3 + 21x^2 + 15x$.

What is the GCF? __3x__

Factor out the GCF: $3x(\underline{2x^2} + \underline{7x} + 5)$

What is the value of a? __2__ What is the value of c? __5__

The Outer + Inner terms = __7__.

Factors of 2	Factors of 5	Outer + Inner
1 · 2	5· 1	$1 \cdot 1 + 2 \cdot 5 = $ __11__
1 · 2	1· __5__	$1 \cdot \underline{5} + 2 \cdot \underline{1} = 7$

Complete the binomial: $(x + \underline{1})(2x + \underline{5})$

Write as a factored polynomial: $3x(x + 1)(2x + \underline{5})$

Check: $3x(x + 1)(2x + 5)$

$= 3x(2x^2 + \underline{5x} + \underline{2x} + 5)$ FOIL

$= 3x(2x^2 + \underline{7x} + 5)$ Combine like terms.

$= 6x^3 + \underline{21}x^2 + \underline{15}x$ Distribute the 3x.

Is this the original polynomial? __Yes__

Find these vocabulary words in Lesson 9-1 and the Multilingual Glossary.

Vocabulary

quadratic equation   quadratic function   parabola   vertex   minimum   maximum

Identifying Quadratic Functions
The quadratic function $y = x^2$ does not have constant first differences. It

has constant __second__ differences. This is true for all quadratic
functions.

A. Tell whether the point $(-2, 7)$ is on the graph of $y = 2x^2 - 1$. Explain.

Substitute $(-2, 7)$ into $y = ax^2 - 1$.

$\underline{7} = 2(\underline{-2})^2 - 1$

$\underline{7} = 2 \cdot \underline{4} - 1$

$\underline{7} = \underline{8} - 1$

$7 = \underline{7}$ ✓

Is the point $(-2, 7)$ on the graph of $y = 2x^2 - 1$?

__yes__

How do you know?

Since $(-2, 7)$ is a solution of $y = 2x^2 - 1$, $(-2, 7)$ is on the graph.

B. Graph the function $y = \frac{1}{2}x^2 - 4$ and give the domain and range.

Make a table of values. Choose values of x and use them to find values of y.
Graph the points and connect with a smooth curve.

x	$y = \frac{1}{2}x^2 - 4$
-4	4
-2	-2
0	-4
2	-2
4	4

Is the value of a positive or negative? __Positive__
Therefore, the graph opens
__upward__
The vertex is located at
$(0, \underline{-4})$.
Is the vertex a maximum or
a minimum? __Minimum__

The domain is all __real__ numbers. All the y-values of the function

are greater than or equal to __-4__. So the range is $y \underline{\geq} -4$.

Find these vocabulary words in Lesson 9-2 and the Multilingual Glossary.

Vocabulary

zero of a function   axis of symmetry

Finding Zeros of Quadratic Functions From Graphs
Find the zeros of the quadratic function from its graph. Then find its axis of
symmetry.
The zero of a function is an x-value that makes the function equal to zero.
The zero of a function is the same as an x-intercept.

A quadratic function may have one, __two__, or no zeros.

The axis of symmetry always passes through the __vertex__ of the parabola.

A.

B.

Where does the graph cross the x-axis?

__-4__ and __3__
To determine the axis of symmetry,
find the average of the zeros.

$\frac{-4 + \underline{3}}{2} = \underline{-\frac{1}{2}}$ $x = \underline{-\frac{1}{2}}$

Where does the graph cross the x-axis?

__2__
In this case, the x-coordinate is the
axis of symmetry.

$x = \underline{2}$

Finding the Vertex of a Parabola
Find the vertex of the parabola $y = -2x^2 + 4x - 3$.

Step 1 Find the x-coordinate using the formula $x = -\frac{b}{2a}$.

What does a equal? __-2__ What does b equal? __4__

$x = -\frac{b}{2a} = -\frac{\underline{4}}{2(\underline{-2})} = -\frac{\underline{4}}{\underline{-4}} = \underline{1}$

Step 2 Find the corresponding y-coordinate.

$y = -2x^2 + 4x - 3$

$y = -2(\underline{1})^2 + 4(\underline{1}) - 3$

$y = -2 + \underline{4} - 3 = \underline{-1}$

Step 3 Write the coordinates as an ordered
pair. The vertex is $(1, \underline{-1})$.

The x-coordinate of the vertex of a parabola can be found by $x = -\frac{b}{2a}$.

The height above water of a curved arch support for a bridge can be modeled by
$y = -0.004x^2 + 0.68x + 0.6$, where x is the distance in feet from where the arch
support enters the water. How tall is the arched bridge?

Understand the Problem

1. What are you being asked to find? __The height of the arched bridge__

2. What formula are you given? __$y = -0.004x^2 + 0.68x + 0.6$__

Make a Plan

3. The __vertex__ represents the highest point of a parabola.

4. The formula for the vertex of a parabola is $x = -\frac{b}{2a}$.

Solve

5. Given the equation $y = -0.004x^2 + 0.68x + 0.6$,

$a = \underline{-0.004}$ and $b = \underline{0.68}$.

6. Substitute the values for a and b into the vertex formula.

$x = -\frac{\underline{b}}{2a}$

$x = -\frac{\underline{0.68}}{2(-0.004)} = \underline{85}$

7. Find the corresponding y-coordinate. $y = -0.004x^2 + 0.68x + 0.6$

$= -0.004(\underline{85})^2 + 0.68(\underline{85}) + 0.6$

$= \underline{29.5}$

8. The height of the bridge is __29.5__ feet.

Look Back

9. Graph the function $y = -0.004x^2 + 0.68x + 0.6$ on a graphing calculator.
Viewing window: x-values -5 to 200 by 25, y-values -10 to 50 by 10.

10. Use the Calc feature on your calculator and determine the maximum point on

the parabola. __29.49__

11. Do your heights in Exercise 8 and Exercise 10 match? __Yes__

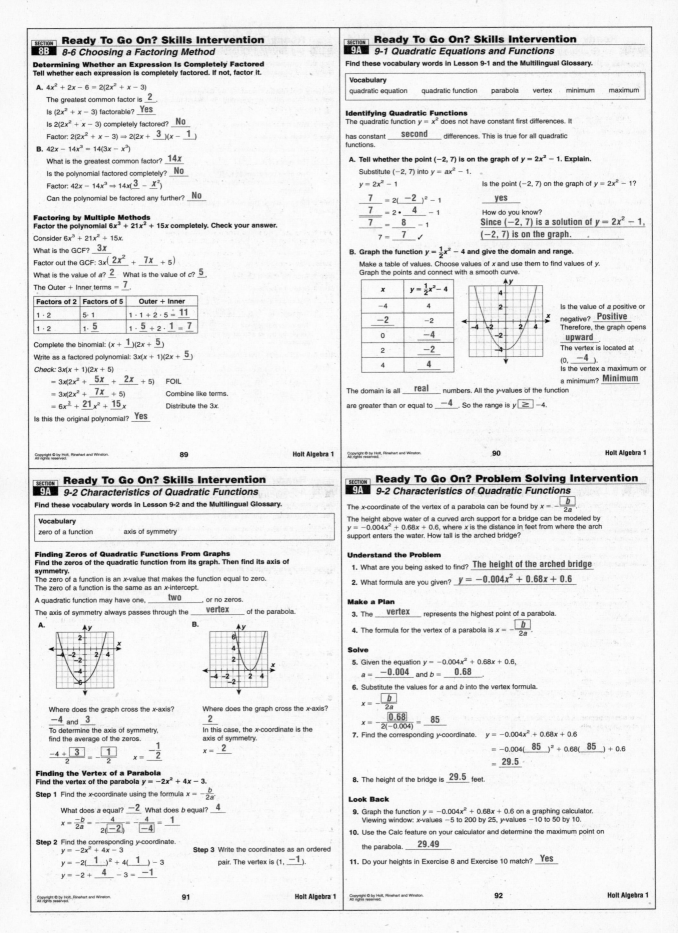

Ready To Go On? Skills Intervention
9-3 Graphing Quadratic Functions

Graphing a Quadratic Function

Graph $y = 2x^2 + 4x + 1$.

Step 1 Find the axis of symmetry.

$x = -\dfrac{b}{2a}$ What does a equal? __2__ What does b equal? __4__

$x = -\dfrac{4}{2(\underline{2})} = -\dfrac{4}{\underline{4}} = \underline{-1}$ Substitute known values and solve for x.

Step 2 Find the vertex. Substitute the x-coordinate into the equation.

$y = 2x^2 + 4x + 1$

$y = 2(\underline{-1})^2 + 2(\underline{-1}) + 1$

$y = 2 - \underline{2} + 1$

$y = \underline{1}$ The vertex is ($\underline{-1}$, $\underline{1}$).

Step 3 Find the y-intercept.

$y = 2x^2 + 4x + 1$ Identify c. __1__

The y-intercept is 1; the graph passes through (0, __1__).

Step 4 Find two more points on the same side of the axis of symmetry as the point containing the y-intercept. Use -3 and -2.

Let $x = -3$
$y = 2x^2 + 4x + 1$
$y = 2(\underline{-3})^2 + 4(\underline{-3}) + 1$
$y = 2(\underline{9}) - \underline{12} + 1$
$y = \underline{7}$
The point is (-3, $\underline{7}$).

Let $x = -2$
$y = 2x^2 + 4x + 1$
$y = 2(\underline{-2})^2 + 4(\underline{-2}) + 1$
$y = 2(\underline{4}) - \underline{8} + 1$
$y = \underline{1}$
The point is (-2, $\underline{1}$).

Step 5 Graph the axis of symmetry, vertex, y-intercept, and the two other points.

Step 6 Now, reflect the points across the axis of symmetry to graph points on the other side of the parabola. Connect the points with a smooth curve.

93 **Holt Algebra 1**

Ready To Go On? Skills Intervention
9-4 Solving Quadratic Equations by Graphing

Find this vocabulary word in Lesson 9-4 and the Multilingual Glossary.

Vocabulary
quadratic equation

Solving Quadratic Equation by Graphing

Solve each equation by graphing the related function.

A. $x^2 - 4$

Step 1 Write the related function. $y = x^2 - \underline{4}$

Step 2 Graph the function.

The axis of symmetry is $x = \underline{0}$.

The vertex is (0, $\underline{-4}$).

Two other points are (-1, $\underline{-3}$) and (-3, $\underline{5}$). Graph the points and reflect them across the axis of symmetry.

Step 3 Find the zeros. The zeros appear to be -2 and $\underline{2}$.

Check

$x^2 - 4 = 0$	
$(-2)^2 - 4$	0
$4 - 4$	0
0	0

$x^2 - 4 = 0$	
$(2)^2 - 4$	0
$4 - 4$	0
0	0

B. $x^2 + 3x - 10$

Step 1 Write the related function. $y = x^2 + \underline{3x} - \underline{10}$

Step 2 Graph the function.

The axis of symmetry is $x = \underline{-1.5}$.

The vertex is (-1.5, $\underline{-12.25}$).

Two other points are (-4, $\underline{-6}$) and (-3, $\underline{-10}$). Graph the points and reflect them across the axis of symmetry.

Step 3 Find the zeros. The zeros appear to be $\underline{-5}$ and 2.

Check

$x^2 + 3x - 10 = 0$	
$(-5)^2 + 3(\underline{-5}) - 10$	0
$25 - \underline{15} - 10$	0
0	

$x^2 + 3x - 10 = 0$	
$(2)^2 + 3(\underline{2}) - 10$	0
$4 + \underline{6} - 10$	0
0	

94 **Holt Algebra 1**

Ready To Go On? Problem Solving Intervention
9-4 Solving Quadratic Equations by Graphing

Given a quadratic equation, you can write and graph the related function to determine the zeros of the function.

The height of a water rocket is launched upward with an initial velocity of 48 feet per second. Its height h, from the ground can be approximated by $h = -16t^2 + 48t$, where t is the time in seconds. Find the time it takes for the rocket to reach the ground after it is launched.

Understand the Problem

1. What are you being asked to determine?
   The time it takes the rocket to reach the ground.

2. What equation approximates the height? $h = -16t^2 + 48t$

Make a Plan

3. Write the related function and graph the function.

   The related function: $h = -16t^2 + 48t$
   $0 = -16t^2 + 48t$
   $\underline{y} = -16t^2 + 48t$

Solve

4. Graph the function from Exercise 3. Use a graphing calculator.

5. Use the TRACE key to estimate the zeros.

   The zeros appear to be $\underline{0}$ and $\underline{3}$.

6. The rocket leaves the launch pad at $\underline{0}$ seconds and reaches the ground in $\underline{3}$ seconds.

7. The rocket is in the air for about $\underline{3}$ seconds.

Look Back

8. Substitute your value in Exercise 7 for t and see if the answer checks.

   $0 = -16t^2 + 48t$

0	$-16(\underline{3})^2 + 48(\underline{3})$
0	$-16(\underline{9}) + \underline{144}$
0	$-144 + \underline{144}$
0	0 ✓

95 **Holt Algebra 1**

Ready To Go On? Skills Intervention
9-5 Solving Quadratic Equations by Factoring

Using the Zero Product Property

If the product of two quantities equal zero, at least one of the quantities equals __zero__. If a quadratic equation is written in standard form, $ax^2 + bx + c = 0$, then to solve the equation, you may need to __factor__ before using the Zero Product Property.

Using the Zero Product Property.

A. $(x + 7)(x + 3) = 0$

$x + \underline{7} = 0$ or $x + 3 = \underline{0}$ Use the __Zero Product__ Property.

$x = -7$ or $x = \underline{-3}$ Solve each equation.

Check: $x = -7$
$(x + 7)(x + 3) = 0$
$(\underline{-7} + 7)(\underline{-7} + 3) = 0$
$(0)(\underline{-4}) = 0$
$0 = 0$

Check: $x = -3$
$(x + 7)(x + 3) = 0$
$(\underline{-3} + 7)(\underline{-3} + 3) = 0$
$(4)(\underline{0}) = 0$
$0 = 0$

B. $x(x - 3) = 10$

$x^2 - \underline{3x} = 10$ Multiply.

$x^2 - 3x - 10 = \underline{0}$ Write the equation in __standard__ form.

$(x - \underline{5})(x + \underline{2}) = 0$ Factor.

$x - 5 = 0$ or $x + \underline{2} = 0$ Use the Zero Product Property.

$x = \underline{5}$ or $x = \underline{-2}$ Solve each equation.

C. $(x + 5)(x - 8) = -22$

$x^2 - \underline{8x} + 5x - \underline{40} = -22$ Multiply using the FOIL method.

$x^2 - \underline{3x} - 40 = -22$ Combine like terms.

$x^2 - 3x - \underline{18} = 0$ Write the equation in standard form.

$(x - \underline{6})(x + \underline{3}) = 0$ __Factor__ the trinomial.

$x - \underline{6} = 0$ or $x + \underline{3} = 0$ Use the Zero Product Property.

$x = \underline{6}$ or $x = \underline{-3}$ Solve each equation.

96 **Holt Algebra 1**

218

Holt Algebra 1

Ready To Go On? Problem Solving Intervention
9-6 Solving Quadratic Equations by Factoring

A bottle rocket is launched upward with an initial velocity of 48 feet per second. The rocket's height h, in feet, after t seconds is given by $h = -16t^2 + 48t$. When will the rocket hit the ground?

Understand the Problem

1. Which direction is the bottle rocket launched? __Upward__

2. What is the initial velocity of the rocket? __48 ft/sec__

3. What is height represented by in the problem? __h__

4. What is the time represented by in the problem? __t__

5. What is the equation given that models the launched rocket? __$h = -16t^2 + 48t$__

6. What are you asked to find? __When the rocket will hit the ground__

Make a Plan

7. Which variable does the equation need to be solved for? __t__

8. When the rocket hits the ground what does h equal? __0__

Write the equation substituting this value for h. __$0 = -16t^2 + 48t$__

Solve

9. What is the GCF of the equation in Exercise 8? __$-16t$__

10. Factor out the GCF and rewrite the equation in Exercise 8. __$0 = -16t(t - 3)$__

11. Using the Zero Product Property, solve.
$-16t = 0 \qquad t - 3 = 0$
$t = $ __0__ $\qquad t = $ __3__

12. Which value for t is the only one that makes sense, why?
__$t = 3$, because time has occurred so $t \neq 0$.__

13. How long will it take for the rocket to hit the ground? __3 seconds__

Look Back

14. Substitute your answer in Exercise 13 into the original equation, $0 = -16(\underline{3})^2 + 48(\underline{3})$.

15. Does the value found satisfy the equation to make it true? __Yes__

Ready To Go On? Skills Intervention
9-6 Solving Quadratic Equations by Using Square Roots

Using Square Roots to Solve Quadratic Equations

Every positive real number has __two__ square roots, one __positive__ and one __negative__. When you take the square root of a positive real number and the sign of the square root is not indicated, you must find both the positive and negative square root. This is indicated by $\pm \sqrt{\ }$. The square root of __zero__ is neither positive nor negative.

Solve using square roots. Round to the nearest hundredth if necessary.

A. $6x^2 = 216$

$\dfrac{6x^2}{6} = \dfrac{216}{6}$ Divide each side by __6__.

$x^2 = 36$

$\sqrt{x^2} = \sqrt{36}$ Solve for x by taking the __square root__ of both sides.

$x = \pm 6$ Use $\pm$ to show both square roots.

B. $18 = x^2 - 31$

$18 = x^2 - 31$

$\underline{+31 \quad +31}$ Add __31__ to each side of the equation.

$49 = x^2$

$\sqrt{49} = \sqrt{x^2}$ Solve for x by taking the square root of both sides.

$x = \pm 7$ Use $\pm$ to show both square roots.

C. $5x^2 + 6 = 34$

$5x^2 + 6 = 34$

$\underline{-6 \quad -6}$ Subtract __6__ from each side of the equation.

$5x^2 = 28$

$\dfrac{5x^2}{5} = \dfrac{28}{5}$ Divide each side by __5__.

$x^2 = \dfrac{28}{5}$

$\sqrt{x^2} = \sqrt{\dfrac{28}{5}}$ Solve for x by taking the __square root__ of each side.

$x = \pm 2.37$ Use $\pm$ to show __both__ square roots. Round to the nearest hundredth.

Ready To Go On? Skills Intervention
9-7 Completing the Square

Find this vocabulary word in Lesson 9-7 and the Multilingual Glossary.

Vocabulary
completing the square

Solving $x^2 + bx = c$ by Completing the Square
Solve each equation by completing the square.

A. $x^2 + 12x = 45$

Step 1 Write the equation in the form $x^2 + bx = c$. __$x^2 + 12x = 45$__

Step 2 What is the value of b in the equation? __12__ What is $\left(\dfrac{b}{2}\right)^2$? __36__

Step 3 $x^2 + 12x + \underline{36} = 45 + \underline{36}$ Complete the square by adding 36 to both sides.

Step 4 $(x + 6)^2 = \underline{81}$ Factor the perfect-square trinomial on the left.

Step 5 $x + \underline{6} = \pm \underline{9}$ Take the square root of both sides.

Step 6 $x + 6 = \underline{9}$ or $x + 6 = -\underline{9}$ Write and solve two equations.

$x = 3 \qquad\quad x = \underline{-15}$ Solve for x.

The solutions of the equation are __3__ and __−15__.

Check: Substitute the solutions into the original equation $x^2 + 12x = 45$ and solve.

$x = 3$
$(\underline{3})^2 + 12(\underline{3}) = 45$
$\underline{45} = 45$

$x = \underline{-15}$
$(\underline{-15})^2 + 12(\underline{-15}) = 45$
$\underline{45} = 45$

Do your solutions check? __Yes__

B. $x^2 - 11 = 4x$

Step 1 Write the equation in the form $x^2 + bx = c$. $x^2 - \underline{4x} = 11$

Step 2 What is the value of b in the equation? __−4__ What is $\left(\dfrac{b}{2}\right)^2$? __4__

Step 3 $x^2 - 4x + \underline{4} = 11 + \underline{4}$ Complete the square by adding 4 to both sides.

Step 4 $(x - 2)^2 = \underline{15}$ Factor the perfect-square trinomial on the left.

Step 5 $x - \underline{2} = \pm \sqrt{15}$ Take the square root of both sides.

Step 6 $x - 2 = \sqrt{15}$ or $x - 2 = -\sqrt{15}$ Write and solve two equations.

$x = 2 + \sqrt{15}$ or $x = 2 - \sqrt{15}$

The solutions of the equation are __$2 + \sqrt{15}$__ and __$2 - \sqrt{15}$__.

Check: You can use a graphing calculator to check your answer.

Ready To Go On? Skills Intervention
9-8 The Quadratic Formula

Using the Quadratic Formula

A. Solve $x^2 + 7x + 2 = 0$ using the Quadratic Formula.

What is the quadratic formula?

$x = \dfrac{-b \pm \sqrt{b^2 - 4ac}}{2a}$

In the equation $x^2 + 7x + 2 = 0$, $a = $ __1__ $b = $ __7__ and $c = $ __2__.

Substitute for a, b, c in the quadratic formula.

$x = \dfrac{-7 \pm \sqrt{7^2 - 4(1)(2)}}{2(1)}$

$x = \dfrac{-7 \pm \sqrt{49 - 8}}{2(1)}$ Simplify.

$x = \dfrac{-7 \pm \sqrt{41}}{2}$

$x = \dfrac{-7 + \sqrt{41}}{2}$ or $x = \dfrac{-7 - \sqrt{41}}{2}$

B. Solve $3x = x^2 - 10$ using the Quadratic Formula.

Write the equation in standard form. $x^2 - 3x - 10 = 0$

In the equation $x^2 - 3x - 10 = 0$, $a = $ __1__, $b = $ __−3__, and $c = $ __−10__.

Substitute for a, b, and c in the quadratic formula.

$x = \dfrac{-(-3) \pm \sqrt{(-3)^2 - 4(1)(-10)}}{2(1)}$

$x = \dfrac{-(-3) \pm \sqrt{9 + 40}}{2(1)}$ Simplify.

$x = \dfrac{-(-3) \pm \sqrt{49}}{2(1)}$

$x = \dfrac{3 + 7}{2}$ or $x = \dfrac{3 - 7}{2}$

$x = \dfrac{10}{2}$ or $x = \dfrac{-4}{2}$

$x = \underline{5}$ or $x = \underline{-2}$

Ready To Go On? Skills Intervention
10-6 Dividing Polynomials

Dividing a Polynomial by a Monomial
Divide. $(2x^3 + 6x^2 - 8x + 10) \div 2x$

$$\frac{(2x^3 + 6x^2 - 8x + 10)}{\boxed{2x}}$$ Write as a rational expression.

$$\frac{2x^3}{2x} + \frac{\boxed{6x^2}}{2x} - \frac{\boxed{8x}}{2x} + \frac{10}{\boxed{2x}}$$ Divide each term in the polynomial by the monomial.

$$\frac{2x\boxed{x^2}}{2x} + \frac{\boxed{6x^2}}{2x} - \frac{\boxed{8x}}{2x} + \frac{10}{\boxed{2x}}$$ Divide out common factors.

$$x^2 + \boxed{3x} - \boxed{4} + \frac{5}{x}$$ Simplify.

Polynomial Long Division
Divide using long division. $(28 + 4x^2 - 23x) \div (x - 4)$

Step 1 $x - 4 \overline{)4x^2 - \boxed{23x} + \boxed{28}}$ Write in long division form with expressions in standard form.

Step 2 $x - 4 \overline{)4x^2 - 23x + 28}$ (with $\boxed{4}x$ above)   Divide the first term of the dividend $4x^2$ by the first term of the divisor x to get the first term of the quotient.

Step 3 $x - 4 \overline{)4x^2 - 23x + 28}$ (with $\boxed{4}x$ above)
$4x^2 - \boxed{16}x$ Multiply the first term of the quotient $4x$ by the binomial divisor $(x - 4)$. Place the product under the dividend, aligning like terms.

Step 4 $x - 4 \overline{)4x^2 - 23x + 28}$ (with $\boxed{4}x$ above)
$-(4x^2 - \boxed{16}x)$
$0 - \boxed{7x}$ Subtract the product from the dividend.

Step 5 $x - 4 \overline{)4x^2 - 23x + 28}$ (with $\boxed{4}x$ above)
$-(4x^2 - \boxed{16}x) \downarrow$
$0 - \boxed{7x} + \boxed{28}$ Bring down the next term in the dividend.

Step 6 $x - 4 \overline{)4x^2 - 23x + 28}$ (with $\boxed{4}x - \boxed{7}$ above)
$-(4x^2 - \boxed{16}x)$
$-\boxed{7x} + \boxed{28}$
$-(-7x + 28))$
0 Repeat Steps 2–5 as necessary.

109   Holt Algebra 1

Ready To Go On? Skills Intervention
10-7 Solving Rational Equations

Find this vocabulary word in Lesson 10-7 and the Multilingual Glossary.

Vocabulary
rational equation
extraneous solution

Solving Rational Equations by Using Cross Products

Solve $\frac{6}{x+7} = \frac{1}{x+2}$. Identify any extraneous solutions.

$6(x + \boxed{2}) = x + \boxed{7}$ Multiply cross products.
$6x + \boxed{12} = x + \boxed{7}$ Distribute 6 on the left side.
$\boxed{5}x + \boxed{12} = 7$ Subtract x from both sides.
$\boxed{5}x = \boxed{-5}$ Subtract 12 from both sides.
$x = \boxed{-1}$ Divide both sides by 5.

Solve Rational Equations by Using the LCD.

Solve $\frac{8}{n^2} = \frac{14}{n} + 4$. Identify any extraneous solutions. Check your answer.

Step 1 Find the LCD. Include every factor of the denominators.

The LCD is n^2.

Step 2 Multiply both sides of the equation by the LCD. Distribute on the left side.

$$n^2 \left(\frac{8}{n^2}\right) = \frac{n^2}{1}\left(\frac{14}{n} + 4\right)$$

$$8 = \boxed{14}n + \boxed{4}n^2$$

Step 3 Simplify and solve.

$8 = 14n + 4n^2$
$0 = 4n^2 + 14n - \boxed{8}$
$0 = \boxed{2}(2n^2 + \boxed{7}n - \boxed{4})$
$0 = 2(2n - \boxed{1})(n + \boxed{4})$
$0 = 2n - \boxed{1}$ or $n + \boxed{4} = 0$
$\boxed{\frac{1}{2}} = n$ or $n = -4$

Check: Verify that your solutions make the equation true.

$n = \frac{1}{2}$
$\frac{8}{\left(\frac{1}{2}\right)^2} = \frac{14}{\boxed{\frac{1}{2}}} + 4$
$\frac{8}{\boxed{\frac{1}{4}}} = \boxed{\frac{28}{1}} + 4$
$32 = \boxed{32}$

$n = -4$
$\frac{8}{(-4)^2} = \frac{14}{\boxed{-4}} + 4$
$\frac{8}{\boxed{16}} = -\frac{7}{2} + \frac{8}{2}$
$\frac{1}{2} = \frac{1}{2}$

The solutions are $\boxed{\frac{1}{2}}$, and $\boxed{4}$.
There are $\boxed{no}$ extraneous solutions.

110   Holt Algebra 1

Ready To Go On? Problem Solving Intervention
10-7 Solving Rational Equations

A rational equation is an equation that contains one or more rational expressions.

Mort can refinish a wood table in 6 hours. It takes his business partner Rebecca 10 hours to refinish the same table. How long will it take them to refinish the table if they work together?

Understand the Problem

1. What are you being asked to determine? How long it will take Mort and Rebecca to refinish a table working together.

2. Mort refinishes the table in $\boxed{6}$ hours, so he completes $\frac{1}{6}$ of the table per hour.

3. Rebecca refinishes the table in $\boxed{10}$ hours, so she completes $\boxed{\frac{1}{10}}$ of the table per hour.

Make a Plan

4. Mort's rate, times the number of hours worked, plus Rebecca's rate, times the number of hours worked, equals the complete time to refinish the table.

Let h = the number of hours worked.

Mort's rate + Rebecca's rate = complete job

$$\boxed{\frac{1}{6}h} + \boxed{\frac{1}{10}h} = 1$$

Solve

5. Solve the rational equation.

$\frac{1}{6}h + \frac{1}{10}h = 1$ What is the LCD? $\boxed{60}$

$\boxed{60}\left(\frac{1}{6}h + \frac{1}{10}h\right) = \boxed{60} \cdot 1$ Multiply both sides by the LCD.

$10h + \boxed{6h} = 60$ Distribute 60 on the left side and solve the equation.

$\boxed{16h} = 60$

$h = \frac{60}{\boxed{16}} = \boxed{3\frac{3}{4}}$

6. Mort and Rebecca, working together, can refinish the table in $\boxed{3\frac{3}{4}}$ hours.

Look Back

7. In $3\frac{3}{4}$ hours, Mort completes $\frac{15}{4} \cdot \frac{1}{6} = \boxed{\frac{5}{8}}$ of the table and Rebecca completes $\frac{15}{4} \cdot \boxed{\frac{1}{10}} = \boxed{\frac{3}{8}}$ of the table. Together, they complete $\frac{5}{8} + \frac{3}{8}$ or 1 table.

111   Holt Algebra 1

Ready To Go On? Skills Intervention
10-8 Applying Rational Equations

Writing Rational Equations

A. Silas helps pick grapes during the harvest season. As an experienced grape harvester, he can pick a bushel of grapes in 6 minutes. Fran is a less experienced harvester. It takes her 9 minutes to pick a bushel of grapes. How long will it take them to pick 1 bushel of grapes if they work together?

The sum of the amount of grapes picked by Silas and the amount of grapes picked by Fran as they work together equals 1 bushel.

The amount of grapes Silas picks equals the product of his picking rate and the time.

The amount of grapes Fran picks equals the product of her picking rate and the time.

Step 1 Write the expression for the rate at which Silas picks grapes.

$\frac{1 \text{ bushel}}{6 \text{ min}} = -\frac{1}{6}$ bushel per minute

Step 2 Write the expression for the amount of grapes Silas picks in time t.

$\frac{1}{6} \cdot t$

Step 3 Write the expression for the rate at which Fran picks grapes.

$\frac{1 \text{ bushel}}{9 \text{ min}} = \frac{1}{9}$ bushel per minute

Step 4 Write the expression for the amount of grapes Fran picks in time t.

$\frac{1}{9} \cdot t$

Step 5 Write an equation to show that the sum of the amounts of grapes that Silas and Fran each pick in time t equals the amount that they both pick in time t.

$\frac{1}{6} \cdot t + \frac{1}{9} \cdot t = \boxed{1}$

Step 6 Solve the equation for t.

B. Silas and Fran continue to pick grapes at their same rates. Complete the equation that you could solve to find the time that it takes them to pick 5 bushels of grapes together.

$\frac{1}{6} \cdot t + \frac{1}{9} \cdot t = \boxed{5}$

112   Holt Algebra 1

---

222   Holt Algebra 1

Ready To Go On? Problem Solving Intervention
10-8 Applying Rational Equations

You can use rational equations to calculate amounts of substances used to prepare solutions of given concentrations.

A lab technician has 60 milliliters of a solution that is 50% ethanol. He needs a solution that is 75% ethanol. How many milliliters of ethanol should he add?

Understand the Problem

1. What are you being asked to find? <u>the volume of ethanol that must be added to</u>
   <u>60 mL of a solution that is 50% ethanol to make a solution that is 75% ethanol</u>

2. What volume of ethanol is in 60 milliliters of a solution that is 50% ethanol? <u>30 mL</u>

3. If the volume of ethanol added to the original solution is represented by v, what
   expression represents the volume of ethanol in the new solution? <u>30 mL + v</u>

4. In terms of v, what expression represents the total volume of the new solution? <u>60 mL + v</u>

Make a Plan

5. Construct a table that shows the volume of ethanol and the total volume of the solution.

	Ethanol (mL)	Total (mL)
Original	30	60
New	30 + v	60 + v

6. Write an equation to express the 75% concentration of the new
   solution in terms of the volume of ethanol and the total volume of the solution.

   $$\frac{30 + v}{60 + v} = 0.75$$

Solve

5. Solve this equation for v.

   $$\frac{30 + v}{60 + v} = 0.75$$
   $$0.25v = 15$$
   $$v = \underline{60}$$

   The technician must add <u>60</u> milliliters of ethanol to the 60 milliliters of the 50% solution.

Check

6. If 60 mL is substituted into the concentration formula,
   is the new concentration 75%? <u>yes</u>
   $$\frac{30 + 60}{60 + 60} = \frac{90}{120} = 0.75$$

 Holt Algebra 1

Ready To Go On? Skills Intervention
11-1 Square-Root Functions

Find this vocabulary word in Lesson 11-1 and the Multilingual Glossary.

Vocabulary
square-root function

Finding the Domain of Square-Root Functions
Find the domain of the function $y = \sqrt{2x} + 4$.

The domain of a function is the <u>set</u> of x-coordinates.
To be part of the domain, the values in the radicand must be greater than
or equal to <u>zero</u>.

What is the expression inside the square root? <u>2x</u>

Complete the inequality. $2x \geq \underline{0}$

Solve the inequality.

$$2x \geq \underline{0}$$
$$\frac{2x}{2} \geq \frac{\underline{0}}{\underline{2}}$$
$$x \geq \underline{0}$$

The domain of the function is $x \geq \underline{0}$.

Graphing Square-Root Functions
Graph $y = \sqrt{x} - 2$.

Complete the table to graph
the function $y = \sqrt{x}$.

x	0	1	4	9
y	0	1	2	3

Move the function to the right <u>2</u> units
to graph the function $y = \sqrt{x} - 2$.

 Holt Algebra 1

Ready To Go On? Problem Solving Intervention
11-1 Square-Root Functions

A square-root function is a function in which the variable is included in the radicand.

On wet concrete, the function $y = \sqrt{12x}$ gives the speed in miles per hour when the length of the skid mark is x feet. Find the speed that the car was traveling if it left a skid mark that was 210 ft long. Round your answer to the nearest hundredth.

Understand the Problem

1. What does x represent in the function? <u>It represents the length of the skid mark.</u>
2. What does y represent? <u>The speed in mi/hr.</u>
3. What are you asked to find? <u>The speed of the car.</u>

Make a Plan

4. How long was the skid mark? <u>210 ft</u>
5. For which variable do you substitute the value 210? <u>x</u>

Solve

6. Substitute the given value for x into the function.
   $$y = \sqrt{12(\underline{210})}$$
   $$y = \sqrt{\underline{2520}}$$
   $$y = \underline{50.1996}$$

7. To which place are you asked to round your answer? <u>Hundredths place</u>
8. Which number is in the thousandths place? <u>9</u>
9. The speed of the car was <u>50.20</u> mi/h.

Look Back

10. To check your answer, substitute it in for y and solve for x.
    $$\underline{50.20} = \sqrt{12x}$$
    $$(\underline{50.20})^2 = (\sqrt{12x})^2$$
    $$\underline{2520.04} = 12x$$
    $$\frac{\boxed{2520.04}}{12} = \frac{12x}{12}$$
    $$\underline{210} = x$$

11. Does your answer check? <u>Yes</u>

 Holt Algebra 1

Ready To Go On? Skills Intervention
11-2 Radical Expressions

Find this vocabulary word in Lesson 11-2 and the Multilingual Glossary.

Vocabulary
square-root

Simplifying Square-Root Expressions
Simplify the expression $\sqrt{\frac{125}{5}}$.

Simplify the expression inside the radicand.
$$\frac{125}{5} = \frac{\boxed{5} \cdot \boxed{5} \cdot \boxed{5}}{5} = \underline{25}$$

Find the square root of the simplified expression.

Which number multiplied by itself is 25? <u>5</u> $\sqrt{25} = \underline{5}$

So $\sqrt{\frac{125}{5}} = \underline{5}$.

Using the Product Property of Square Roots
Simplify the expression $\sqrt{j^6 k^3}$. All variables represent nonnegative numbers.

The square root of $j^6 k^3$ is equal to the product of the <u>square root</u> of j^6 and the
square root of $\underline{k^3}$.

$$\sqrt{j^6 k^3} = \sqrt{j^6} \cdot \sqrt{k^3}$$

$(j^3)^{\underline{2}} = j^6 \longrightarrow \sqrt{j^6} = j^{\underline{3}}$ | $\sqrt{k^3} = \sqrt{k^{\underline{2}}} \cdot \sqrt{k^{\underline{1}}}$ $\sqrt{k^2} = k^{\underline{1}}$

$$\sqrt{j^6 k^3} = j^{\underline{3}} k^{\underline{1}} \sqrt{k}$$

Using the Quotient Property of Square Roots
Simplify the expression $\sqrt{\frac{9}{121z^2}}$. All variables represent nonnegative numbers.

The square root of $\frac{9}{121z^2}$ is equal to the quotient of the <u>square root</u> of 9 and the
square root of $\underline{121z^2}$.

$$\sqrt{\frac{9}{121z^2}}$$

$$= \frac{\sqrt{9}}{\sqrt{121z^2}}$$ Use the Quotient Property to rewrite the expression.

$$= \frac{\boxed{3}}{11\boxed{z}}$$ Find the square root of the numerator and the denominator.

 Holt Algebra 1

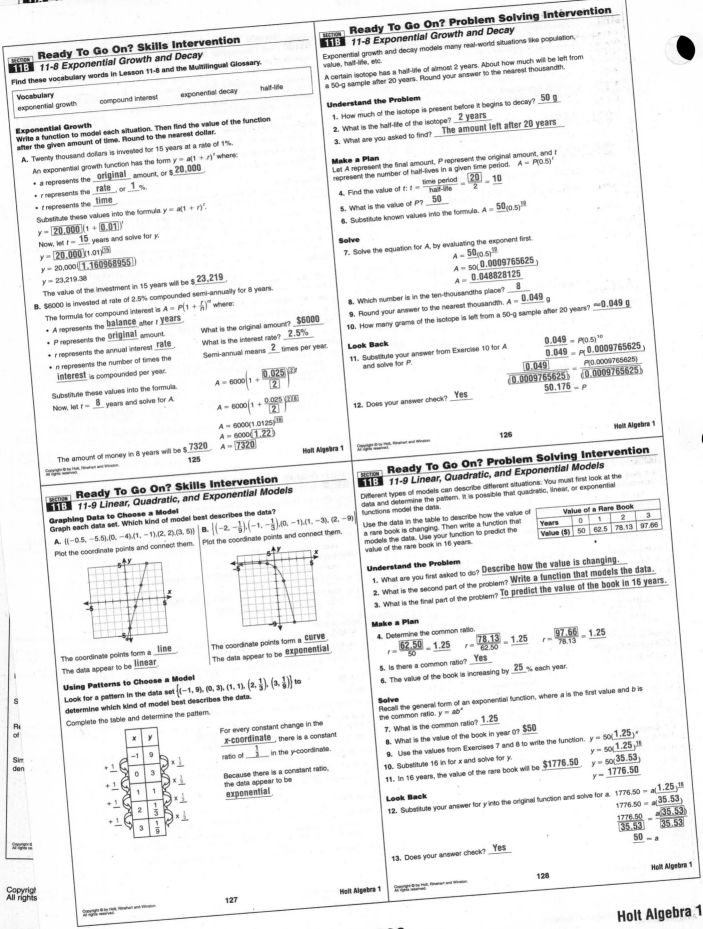

Ready To Go On? Skills Intervention
SECTION 11B 11-8 Exponential Growth and Decay

Find these vocabulary words in Lesson 11-8 and the Multilingual Glossary.

Vocabulary
exponential growth   compound interest   exponential decay   half-life

Exponential Growth
Write a function to model each situation. Then find the value of the function after the given amount of time. Round to the nearest dollar.

A. Twenty thousand dollars is invested for 15 years at a rate of 1%.

An exponential growth function has the form $y = a(1 + r)^t$ where:

- a represents the __original__ amount, or $ __20,000__ .
- r represents the __rate__ , or __1__ %.
- t represents the __time__ .

Substitute these values into the formula $y = a(1 + r)^t$.

$y = \boxed{20,000}\left(1 + \boxed{0.01}\right)^t$

Now, let $t = $ __15__ years and solve for y.

$y = \boxed{20,000}(1.01)^{\boxed{15}}$

$y = 20,000\left(\boxed{1.160968955}\right)$

$y = 23,219.38$

The value of the investment in 15 years will be $ __23,219__ .

B. $6000 is invested at rate of 2.5% compounded semi-annually for 8 years.

The formula for compound interest is $A = P\left(1 + \frac{r}{n}\right)^{nt}$ where:

- A represents the __balance__ after t __years__ .
- P represents the __original__ amount.
- r represents the annual interest __rate__ .
- n represents the number of times the __interest__ is compounded per year.

What is the original amount? __$6000__
What is the interest rate? __2.5%__
Semi-annual means __2__ times per year.

$A = 6000\left(1 + \dfrac{\boxed{0.025}}{\boxed{2}}\right)^{\boxed{2}t}$

Substitute these values into the formula.
Now, let $t = $ __8__ years and solve for A.

$A = 6000\left(1 + \dfrac{0.025}{\boxed{2}}\right)^{\boxed{2}\boxed{8}}$

$A = 6000(1.0125)^{\boxed{16}}$

$A = 6000\left(\boxed{1.22}\right)$

$A = \boxed{7320}$

The amount of money in 8 years will be $ __7320__ .

Holt Algebra 1

Ready To Go On? Problem Solving Intervention
SECTION 11B 11-8 Exponential Growth and Decay

Exponential growth and decay models many real-world situations like population, value, half-life, etc.

A certain isotope has a half-life of almost 2 years. About how much will be left from a 50-g sample after 20 years. Round your answer to the nearest thousandth.

Understand the Problem

1. How much of the isotope is present before it begins to decay? __50 g__
2. What is the half-life of the isotope? __2 years__
3. What are you asked to find? __The amount left after 20 years__

Make a Plan
Let A represent the final amount, P represent the original amount, and t represent the number of half-lives in a given time period. $A = P(0.5)^t$

4. Find the value of t: $t = \dfrac{\text{time period}}{\text{half-life}} = \dfrac{\boxed{20}}{2} = \boxed{10}$
5. What is the value of P? __50__
6. Substitute known values into the formula. $A = \underline{50}(0.5)^{\underline{10}}$

Solve

7. Solve the equation for A, by evaluating the exponent first.

$A = \underline{50}(0.5)^{\underline{10}}$

$A = 50(\underline{0.0009765625})$

$A = \underline{0.048828125}$

8. Which number is in the ten-thousandths place? __8__
9. Round your answer to the nearest thousandth. $A = \underline{0.049}$ g
10. How many grams of the isotope is left from a 50-g sample after 20 years? $\approx \underline{0.049}$ g

Look Back

11. Substitute your answer from Exercise 10 for A and solve for P.

$0.049 = P(0.5)^{10}$

$0.049 = P(\underline{0.0009765625})$

$\dfrac{\boxed{0.049}}{\boxed{0.0009765625}} = \dfrac{P(0.0009765625)}{\boxed{0.0009765625}}$

$50.176 = P$

12. Does your answer check? __Yes__

Holt Algebra 1

Ready To Go On? Skills Intervention
SECTION 11B 11-9 Linear, Quadratic, and Exponential Models

Graphing Data to Choose a Model
Graph each data set. Which kind of model best describes the data?

A. $\{(-0.5, -5.5), (0, -4), (1, -1), (2, 2), (3, 5)\}$

Plot the coordinate points and connect them.

The coordinate points form a __line__ .
The data appear to be __linear__ .

B. $\left\{\left(-2, -\frac{1}{9}\right), \left(-1, -\frac{1}{3}\right), (0, -1), (1, -3), (2, -9)\right\}$

Plot the coordinate points and connect them.

The coordinate points form a __curve__ .
The data appear to be __exponential__ .

Using Patterns to Choose a Model
Look for a pattern in the data set $\left\{(-1, 9), (0, 3), (1, 1), \left(2, \frac{1}{3}\right), \left(3, \frac{1}{9}\right)\right\}$ to determine which kind of model best describes the data.

Complete the table and determine the pattern.

x	y
-1	9
0	3
1	1
2	$\frac{1}{3}$
3	$\frac{1}{9}$

$+1$ ... $\times \frac{1}{3}$
$+1$ ... $\times \frac{1}{3}$
$+1$ ... $\times \frac{1}{3}$
$+1$ ... $\times \frac{1}{3}$

For every constant change in the __x-coordinate__ , there is a constant ratio of __$\frac{1}{3}$__ in the y-coordinate.

Because there is a constant ratio, the data appear to be __exponential__ .

Holt Algebra 1

Ready To Go On? Problem Solving Intervention
SECTION 11B 11-9 Linear, Quadratic, and Exponential Models

Different types of models can describe different situations. You must first look at the data and determine the pattern. It is possible that quadratic, linear, or exponential functions model the data.

Use the data in the table to describe how the value of a rare book is changing. Then write a function that models the data. Use your function to predict the value of the rare book in 16 years.

Value of a Rare Book

Years	0	1	2	3
Value ($)	50	62.5	78.13	97.66

Understand the Problem

1. What are you first asked to do? __Describe how the value is changing.__
2. What is the second part of the problem? __Write a function that models the data.__
3. What is the final part of the problem? __To predict the value of the book in 16 years.__

Make a Plan

4. Determine the common ratio.

$r = \dfrac{\boxed{62.50}}{50} = 1.25$ $r = \dfrac{\boxed{78.13}}{62.50} = 1.25$ $r = \dfrac{\boxed{97.66}}{78.13} = 1.25$

5. Is there a common ratio? __Yes__
6. The value of the book is increasing by __25__ % each year.

Solve
Recall the general form of an exponential function, where a is the first value and b is the common ratio. $y = ab^x$

7. What is the common ratio? __1.25__
8. What is the value of the book in year 0? __$50__
9. Use the values from Exercises 7 and 8 to write the function. $y = 50(\underline{1.25})^x$
10. Substitute 16 in for x and solve for y. __$1776.50__
    $y = 50(\underline{1.25})^{\underline{16}}$
    $y = 50(\underline{35.53})$
    $y \approx \underline{1776.50}$
11. In 16 years, the value of the rare book will be __$1776.50__

Look Back

12. Substitute your answer for y into the original function and solve for a.
    $1776.50 = a(\underline{1.25})^{16}$
    $1776.50 = a(\underline{35.53})$
    $\dfrac{1776.50}{\underline{35.53}} = \dfrac{a(\boxed{35.53})}{\boxed{35.53}}$
    $50 \approx a$

13. Does your answer check? __Yes__

Holt Algebra 1

Holt Algebra 1

1-1 Variables and Expressions
Give two ways to write each algebraic expression in words.

1. $6 + z$ ___The sum of 6 and z; 6 increased by z___

2. $r - 4$ ___The difference of r and 4; 4 subtracted from r___

3. $\frac{s}{5}$ ___s divided by 5; the quotient of s and 5___

4. $9m$ ___9 times m, the product of 9 and m___

5. Jane bikes at a rate of 12 miles per hour. Write an expression for the amount she bikes in h hours.

___$12h$___

6. It takes 35 minutes for a pan of brownies to bake. Write an expression for the number of minutes left after m minutes have elapsed.

___$35 - m$___

Evaluate each expression for $x = 2$, $y = 10$, and $z = 3$.

7. $y \div x$

___5___

8. xy

___20___

9. $x + y$

___12___

10. $y - z$

___7___

1-2 Adding and Subtracting Real Numbers
Add or subtract.

11. $76 + (-19)$

___57___

12. $54 - 21$

___33___

13. $6 - \left(-2\frac{1}{2}\right)$

___8.5 or $8\frac{1}{2}$___

14. $x + (-12)$ for $x = -6$

___-18___

15. Taylor's credit card balance shows a balance of $-\$50$. What will the balance be after Taylor makes a credit card payment of $85?

___$35___

Holt Algebra 1

1-3 Multiplying and Dividing Real Numbers
Find the value of each expression.

16. $-6(6)$ ___-36___

17. $8 \div \frac{4}{9}$ ___18___

18. $5.6 \div 0$ ___Undefined___

19. $-\frac{1}{4}x$ for $x = -\frac{1}{4}$ ___$\frac{1}{16}$___

20. Alex babysat for $8\frac{1}{2}$ hours. Alex charges $8.00 per hour. How much money did Alex earn babysitting? ___$68___

1-4 Powers and Exponents
Simplify each expression.

21. $(-6)^2$

___36___

22. -3^2

___-9___

23. $\left(-\frac{2}{5}\right)^3$

___$\frac{8}{125}$___

24. $\left(-\frac{1}{3}\right)^5$

___$\frac{1}{243}$___

25. A gigameter is a unit of length equal to 10 to the 9th power. Express this number in two ways. ___10^9; $10 \times 10 \times 10 \times 10 \times 10 \times 10 \times 10 \times 10 \times 10$___

1-5 Roots and Irrational Numbers
Find each square root.

26. $\sqrt{169}$ ___13___

27. $-\sqrt{81}$ ___-9___

28. $\sqrt{196}$ ___14___

29. $\sqrt{\frac{4}{100}}$ ___$\frac{2}{10}$ or $\frac{1}{5}$___

30. Tom is building a square kitchen table. The table will cover 39 square feet. Find the length of a side of the table to the nearest tenth of a foot.

___6.2 ft___

Classify each real number. Write all classifications that apply.

31. $\frac{1}{9}$ ___Rational___

32. $\sqrt{15}$ ___Irrational___

33. $\sqrt{900}$ ___Rational, Integer, Whole, Natural___

34. -9 ___Rational, Integer___

Holt Algebra 1

1-6 Properties of Real Numbers
Name the property that is illustrated in each equation.

1. $12 \cdot 26 = 26 \cdot 12$ ___Commutative Property of Multiplication___

2. $3 + (2 + 11) = (3 + 2) + 11$ ___Associative Property of Addition___

3. $a(-7) = -7a$ ___Commutative Property of Multiplication___

4. $ar + 25 = 25 + ar$ ___Commutative Property of Addition___

Write each product using the Distributive Property. Then simplify.

5. $8(56)$

___$8(50 + 6) = 400 + 48 = 448$___

6. $6(26)$

___$6(20 + 6) = 120 + 36 = 156$___

7. $13(16)$

___$13(10 + 6) = 130 + 78 = 208$___

8. $4(102)$

___$4(100 + 2) = 400 + 8 = 408$___

Find a counterexample to show that each statement is false.

9. The set of odd numbers is closed under subtraction.

___$3 - 1 = 2$___

10. The set of negative integers is closed under subtraction.

___$-1 - (-3) = 2$___

1-7 Simplifying Expressions
Simplify each expression.

11. $-8 + 16 \div (-2)$

___-16___

12. $28 - 7 + 5$

___26___

Holt Algebra 1

---

13. $\frac{28 - 3 \cdot (2)^2}{2}$

___8___

14. $|2 - 7| \div 5 + 9$

___10___

Answer the following question.

15. The formula for a baseball player's total number of bases is $Hits + D + 2T + 3H$. Use this expression and the information in the table to determine the player's total number of bases.

Batting Information	Number
Hits	16
Double (D)	0
Triple (T)	3
Home run (H)	1

___$16 + (0) + 2(3) + 3(1) = 25$___

Simplify each expression by combining like terms.

16. $6s + 20s$

___$26s$___

17. $28x + 3$

___$28x + 3$___

18. $-6.3d + 9.5d$

___$3.2d$___

19. $5b - 3b$

___$2b$___

20. $7x + 3 - 2x$

___$5x + 3$___

21. $5t + 4 + 2t - 3$

___$7t + 1$___

Use properties and operations to show that the first expression simplifies to the second expression.

22. $5x^2 + 6x - 9x^2 + x$; $-4x^2 + 7x$

___$(-9x^2 + 5x^2) + (6x + x)$___

___$-4x^2 + 7x$___

23. $-3(4x + 3y + 5x - 2y)$; $-27x - 3y$

___$-3(4x + 5x) - 3(3y - 2y) = -3(9x) - 3(y)$___

___$-27x - 3y$___

Holt Algebra 1

Holt Algebra 1

2-1 Solving One-Step Equations
Solve each equation.

1. $x - 42 = 16$
$$x = 58$$

2. $2.3 = k - 0.7$
$$k = 3$$

3. $j + 2 = -11$
$$j = -13$$

4. $52 = 4y$
$$y = 13$$

5. $3.4 = \frac{n}{2}$
$$n = 6.8$$

6. $\frac{2}{3} = g - \frac{1}{6}$
$$g = \frac{5}{6}$$

7. At the beginning of the week, Joshua had $356 in his savings account. At the end of the week, he had only $123 in his savings account. Write and solve an equation to find the amount of money that Joshua spent during the week.
$$356 - x = 123;\ \$233$$

8. There are 450 students who participate in extracurricular activities at school. This is $\frac{5}{8}$ of the total number of students enrolled in the school. Write and solve an equation to find the number of students enrolled in the school.
$$450 = \frac{5}{8}x;\ 720\ students$$

2-2 Solving Two-Step Equations
Solve each equation.

9. $4r + 60 = 400$
$$r = 85$$

10. $3.0 + 0.2g = 3.8$
$$g = 4$$

11. $60 - 2j = 40$
$$j = 10$$

12. $\frac{x}{5} - 2 = 6$
$$x = 40$$

13. $\frac{7}{8}x + 3 = 17$
$$x = 16$$

14. $2 - \frac{1}{2}x = 3$
$$x = -2$$

15. A house painter charges each customer a $50 estimation fee and then $30 per hour. Write and solve an equation to find the number of hours the painter worked if she earned $1250 at the job.
$$50 + 30h = 1250;\ 40\ hours$$

16. Jan's charm bracelet weighs a total of 9.0 ounces with each charm having a weight of 1.2 ounces. Write and solve an equation to find the number of charms on her bracelet if the bracelet chain itself weighs 3.0 ounces.
$$9.0 = 1.2n + 3.0;\ 5\ charms$$

133   Holt Algebra 1

2-3 Solving Multi-Step Equations
Solve each equation.

17. $\frac{5n - 3}{2} = 6$
$$n = 3$$

18. $8b - 4 + 2b = 16$
$$b = 2$$

19. $2(f - 7) = 10$
$$f = 12$$

20. $5d - 4 - 8d = 2$
$$d = -2$$

21. $\frac{3}{2}(x - 2) = 6$
$$x = 6$$

22. $2(1 + 3y) = 11$
$$y = \frac{3}{2}$$

23. A small nursery displays 34 potted trees in four rows. The first row has 7 maple trees. The second and third rows each have the same number of dogwood trees. The fourth row has 11 willow trees. Write and solve an equation to determine the number of dogwood trees in each row.
$$7 + 2x + 11 = 34;\ x = 8$$

24. An ice cream shop sells a sundae with 1 topping for $2.75. A sundae with 2 or more toppings costs $2.00 plus $0.60 for each topping. Anna bought 2 sundaes and her bill was $6.55. One sundae had one topping. Write and solve an equation to find the number of toppings on the second sundae.
$$6.55 = 2.75 + 2.00 + 0.60x;\ 3\ toppings$$

2-4 Solving Equations with Variables on Both Sides

25. $6x - 5 = 4x + 7$
$$x = 6$$

26. $4(3x - 6) = 3(4x - 3)$
The solution set is $\varnothing$.

27. $4(2n - 5) = 7(2n + 4)$
$$n = -8$$

28. $6(k + 7) = -6(k + 7)$
$$k = -7$$

29. On the first day of the month, one investment began with $1568 and started losing $16 each day. Another investment began with $854 and started earning $26 each day. Write and solve an equation to determine the number of days in which the two investments will have the same amount of money. What will that amount be?
$$1568 - 16d = 854 + 26d;\ 17\ days;\ \$1296$$

30. Twice June's age increased by one is three times her age decreased by 10. Write and solve an equation to find June's age.
$$2x + 1 = 3x - 10;\ 11\ years\ old$$

134   Holt Algebra 1

2-5 Solving Proportions

1. Last month, the ratio of DVDs to VHS tapes sold at a video store was 8:3. Sixty VHS tapes were sold. How many DVDs were sold?
160 DVDs

2. A florist designs an arrangement of roses to have a ratio of 1 red rose to 3 white roses. If the arrangement has two dozen white roses, how many red roses will it have?
8 red roses

Find the unit rate.

3. An 8-oz can of corn costs $0.96.
$0.12 per ounce

4. Brian can type 990 words in 30 minutes.
33 words per minute

5. A potter makes 110 pots in 5 days.
22 pots per day

6. A farmer harvests 180 bushels of apples from an orchard of 9 trees.
20 bushels per tree

Solve each proportion.

7. $\frac{-12}{x} = \frac{3}{2}$
$$x = -8$$

8. $\frac{k}{9} = \frac{6}{12}$
$$k = 4.5$$

9. $\frac{2}{6} = \frac{r + 2}{11}$
$$r = \frac{5}{3}$$

10. $\frac{-5}{9} = \frac{10}{x + 8}$
$$x = -26$$

11. Find 25% of 60. **15**

12. Find 160% of 12. **19.2**

13. 27 is what percent of 60? **45%**

14. What percent of 125 is 400? **320%**

15. 12 is 75% of what number? **16**

16. 160% of what number is 64? **40**

17. A college savings fund has 30% of the money invested in stocks. If the stocks have a value of $3000, what is the value of the college fund?
$10,000

18. An architectural drawing of a building has a scale of 1 in. = 2 ft. The length of a wall in the drawing is 6.5 in. What is the length of the wall in the building?
13 ft

135   Holt Algebra 1

2-6 Solving Literal Equations for a Variable

19. Solve $6m + n = p - 7$ for p.
$$p = 6m + n + 7$$

20. Solve $a + b = 4(c - 5)$ for c.
$$c = \frac{a + b}{4} + 5$$

21. Solve $6k + 7n = 12$ for k.
$$k = 2 - \frac{7n}{6}$$

22. Solve $I = V/R$ for V.
$$V = IR$$

23. A simple microscope can produce an enlarged image of an object. The formula $m = \frac{i}{o}$ relates the magnification of the microscope, m, to the length of the image, i, and the length of the object, o.

  a. Solve $m = \frac{i}{o}$ for i. $i = mo$

  b. A student views a 0.03-mm strand of algae under a microscope that has a magnification of 50. The image of the strand will have what length?
    1.5 mm

2-7 Solving Absolute-Value Equations
Solve each equation.

24. $|m| = 3$
$$\{-3, 3\}$$

25. $11 = |q|$
$$\{-11, 11\}$$

26. $|2y| = 8$
$$\{-4, 4\}$$

27. $|2n + 1| = 7$
$$\{-4, 3\}$$

28. $|z| + 7 = 5$
$$\varnothing$$

29. $2|q| + 1 = 3$
$$\{-1, 1\}$$

30. A hose clamp has a diameter of $2\frac{1}{2}$ inches. The screw can be used to increase or decrease the diameter of the clamp by $\frac{1}{8}$ of an inch. Write and solve an absolute-value equation to find the minimum and maximum diameter of the clamp.
$$\left|d - 2\frac{1}{2}\right| = \frac{1}{8};\ \text{The minimum diameter is}$$
$$2\frac{3}{8}\ \text{in. and the maximum diameter is}\ 2\frac{5}{8}\ \text{in.}$$

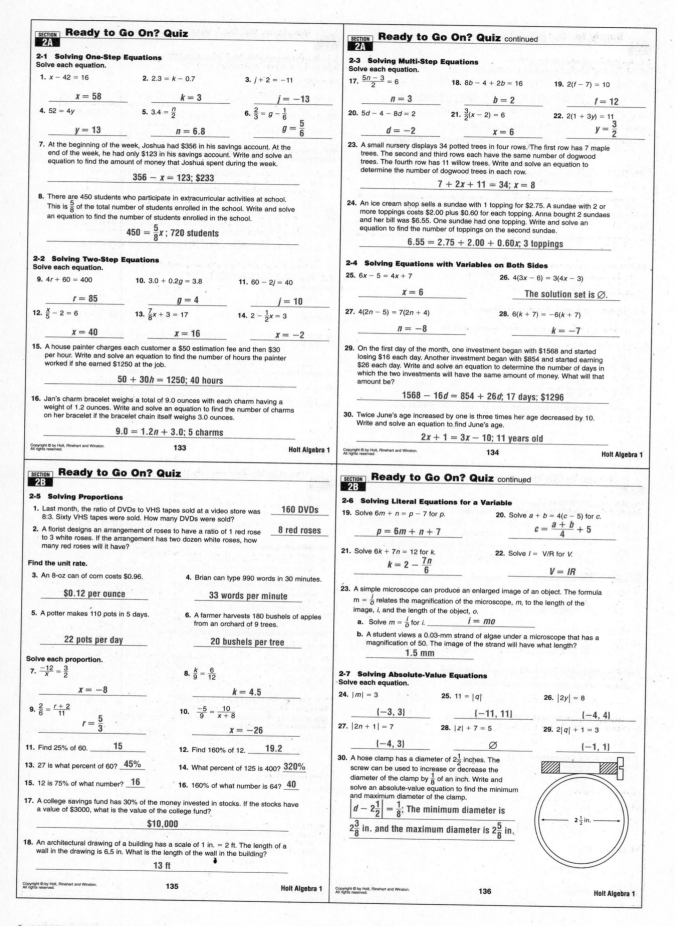

$2\frac{1}{2}$ in.

136   Holt Algebra 1

---

228   **Holt Algebra 1**

3-1 Graphing and Writing Inequalities
Describe the solutions of each inequality in words.

1. $-3 < x$

<u>All real numbers greater than -3</u>

2. $t - 3 \le 8$

<u>All real numbers less than or equal to 11</u>

3. $4w \ge 12$

<u>All real numbers greater than or equal to 3</u>

4. $5 > 6 - x$

<u>All real numbers greater than 1</u>

Graph each inequality.

5. $x > -4$

6. $m \le 2\frac{1}{2}$

7. $g < \sqrt{8 + 8}$

8. $h \ge 3^2$

Write the inequality shown by each graph.

9. $x \ge -4$

10. $x < 6$

11. $x \le -2\frac{1}{2}$

Write an inequality for each situation and graph the solutions.

12. You must spend at least 50 dollars to use a coupon. $\underline{x \ge 50}$

13. The speed limit is less than 55 miles per hour. $\underline{s < 55}$

14. To qualify, earnings cannot be more than $200. $\underline{e \le \$200}$

3-2 Solving Inequalities by Adding and Subtracting
Solve each inequality and graph the solutions.

15. $k + 6 \le 9$ $\qquad k \le 3$

16. $5 > p - 2$ $\qquad p < 7$

17. $r - 9 \ge -4$ $\qquad r \ge 5$

18. $-4 + p < -8$ $\qquad p < -4$

19. Donna must sell at least 45 raffle tickets for the community fund-raiser. She already sold 27 tickets. Write and solve an inequality to determine how many more raffle tickets Donna must sell for the fund-raiser.

$\underline{x + 27 \ge 45;\ x \ge 18;\ \text{at least 18 more tickets}}$

20. Micah has at most $52.00 to spend on office supplies each month. So far this month, he has spent $21.75. Write and solve an inequality to determine how much more money Micah can spend on office supplies the rest of the month.

$\underline{m + 21.75 \le 52.00;\ m \le 30.25;\ \text{at most \$30.25 more}}$

3-3 Solving Inequalities by Multiplying and Dividing
Solve each inequality and graph the solutions.

21. $-5x < 10$ $\qquad x > -2$

22. $\frac{d}{4} \ge -2$ $\qquad d \ge -8$

23. $\frac{2}{3}t \le 6$ $\qquad t \le 9$

24. $6 > -24x$ $\qquad x > -\frac{1}{4}$

25. Romans' new ink cartridge will print up to 250 pages. Roman's printing a 15-page booklet to hand out at a presentation. What are the possible number of booklet's Roman can print?

$\underline{15r \le 250;\ r \le 16.7;\ \text{from 1 to 16 booklets}}$

3-4 Solving Two-Step and Multi-Step Inequalities
Solve each inequality and graph the solutions.

1. $3x + 9 < 27$ $\qquad x < 6$

2. $8x - 5 > 11$ $\qquad x > 2$

3. $8 \ge 1 - 7t$ $\qquad t \ge -1$

Solve each inequality.

4. $3(x - 4) > -2$ $\qquad x > \frac{10}{3}$

5. $\frac{1}{2}a + \frac{1}{3} > \frac{3}{4}$ $\qquad a > \frac{5}{6}$

6. $3^2 - x > 3(4 - 6)$ $\qquad x < 15$

7. $18y + 9 - 7y \le 42$ $\qquad y \le 3$

8. The average of Lynn's two test scores must be at least 93 to make an A. Lynn got an 88 on her first test. What scores can she get on her second test to make an A in the class?

<u>Lynn must make a score of 98 or higher.</u>

3-5 Solving Inequalities with Variables on Both Sides
Solve each inequality and graph the solutions.

9. $6x < 4x + 10$ $\qquad x < 5$

10. $7y - 21 > 4y$ $\qquad y > 7$

11. $h - 5 \ge 2h + 4$ $\qquad h \le -9$

Solve each inequality.

12. $3(x - 4) > 2(x + 6)$ $\qquad x > 24$

13. $3(4 - y) \ge y$ $\qquad y \le 3$

14. $6(t + 4) < 6t - 24$ $\qquad$ <u>No solution</u>

15. $-4(8 + y) < 5(1 + y)$ $\qquad y > \frac{-37}{9}$

16. Catherine has $57 in the bank and deposits $12 per month. Nicholas has $120 in the bank and deposits $9 per month. For how many months will Nicholas have the larger balance than Catherine?

<u>Nicholas will have a larger balance than Catherine for 21 months.</u>

3-6 Solving Compound Inequalities
Solve each compound inequality and graph the solutions.

17. $-1 < x + 3 \le 7$ $\qquad -4 < x \le 4$

18. $m - 3 < -4$ OR $m + 3 > 5$ $\qquad m < -1$ or $m > 2$

19. $-4 \ge x - 1$ AND $x - 6 > 3$ $\qquad$ <u>No solution</u>

20. $-3 > w + 4$ OR $w + 5 < 8$ $\qquad w < 3$

21. The directions on a package of pasta say to cook for 7 to 9 minutes. Write a compound inequality to show the acceptable cooking times for this pasta.

$\underline{7 \le t \le 9}$

3-7 Solving Absolute-Value Inequalities
Solve each inequality and graph the solutions.

22. $|x| + 1 < 4$ $\qquad x > -3$ AND $x < 3$

23. $|x| - 1 > 3$ $\qquad x < -4$ OR $x > 4$

Solve each inequality.

24. $|w - 2| + 4 \le 10$ $\qquad w \ge -4$ AND $w \le 8$

25. $|z - 2| + 1 \ge 6$ $\qquad z \le -3$ OR $z \ge 7$

26. The density, d, of a 100-kg plastic block is listed as 1.70 g/cm^3. The manufacturer states that the actual density of the block may vary by as much as 0.03 g/cm^3. Write and solve an absolute-value inequality for the range of possible densities of the block.

$\underline{|d - 1.70| \le 0.03;\ 1.67 \text{ g/cm}^3 \le d \le 1.73 \text{ g/cm}^3}$

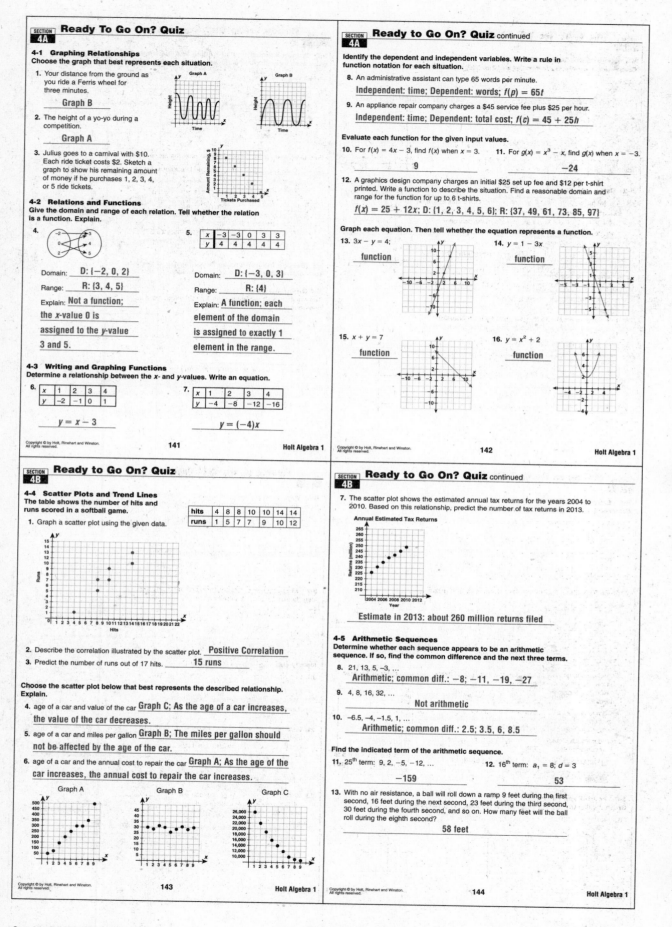

Ready To Go On? Quiz

SECTION 4A

4-1 Graphing Relationships
Choose the graph that best represents each situation.

1. Your distance from the ground as you ride a Ferris wheel for three minutes.

    Graph B

2. The height of a yo-yo during a competition.

    Graph A

3. Julius goes to a carnival with $10. Each ride ticket costs $2. Sketch a graph to show his remaining amount of money if he purchases 1, 2, 3, 4, or 5 ride tickets.

4-2 Relations and Functions
Give the domain and range of each relation. Tell whether the relation is a function. Explain.

4.

Domain: **D: {−2, 0, 2}**

Range: **R: {3, 4, 5}**

Explain: **Not a function; the x-value 0 is assigned to the y-value 3 and 5.**

5.

x	−3	−3	0	3	3
y	4	4	4	4	4

Domain: **D: {−3, 0, 3}**

Range: **R: {4}**

Explain: **A function; each element of the domain is assigned to exactly 1 element in the range.**

4-3 Writing and Graphing Functions
Determine a relationship between the x- and y-values. Write an equation.

6.
x	1	2	3	4
y	−2	−1	0	1

y = x − 3

7.
x	1	2	3	4
y	−4	−8	−12	−16

y = (−4)x

141

Ready to Go On? Quiz continued

SECTION 4A

Identify the dependent and independent variables. Write a rule in function notation for each situation.

8. An administrative assistant can type 65 words per minute.

    Independent: time; Dependent: words; $f(p) = 65t$

9. An appliance repair company charges a $45 service fee plus $25 per hour.

    Independent: time; Dependent: total cost; $f(c) = 45 + 25h$

Evaluate each function for the given input values.

10. For $f(x) = 4x − 3$, find $f(x)$ when $x = 3$.

    9

11. For $g(x) = x^3 − x$, find $g(x)$ when $x = −3$.

    −24

12. A graphics design company charges an initial $25 set up fee and $12 per t-shirt printed. Write a function to describe the situation. Find a reasonable domain and range for the function for up to 6 t-shirts.

    $f(x) = 25 + 12x$; D: {1, 2, 3, 4, 5, 6}; R: {37, 49, 61, 73, 85, 97}

Graph each equation. Then tell whether the equation represents a function.

13. $3x − y = 4$;

    function

14. $y = 1 − 3x$

    function

15. $x + y = 7$

    function

16. $y = x^2 + 2$

    function

142

Ready to Go On? Quiz

SECTION 4B

4-4 Scatter Plots and Trend Lines
The table shows the number of hits and runs scored in a softball game.

hits	4	8	8	10	10	14	14
runs	1	5	7	7	9	10	12

1. Graph a scatter plot using the given data.

2. Describe the correlation illustrated by the scatter plot. **Positive Correlation**

3. Predict the number of runs out of 17 hits. **15 runs**

Choose the scatter plot below that best represents the described relationship. Explain.

4. age of a car and value of the car **Graph C; As the age of a car increases, the value of the car decreases.**

5. age of a car and miles per gallon **Graph B; The miles per gallon should not be affected by the age of the car.**

6. age of a car and the annual cost to repair the car **Graph A; As the age of the car increases, the annual cost to repair the car increases.**

Graph A

Graph B

Graph C

143

Ready to Go On? Quiz continued

SECTION 4B

7. The scatter plot shows the estimated annual tax returns for the years 2004 to 2010. Based on this relationship, predict the number of tax returns in 2013.

    Annual Estimated Tax Returns

    Estimate in 2013: about 260 million returns filed

4-5 Arithmetic Sequences
Determine whether each sequence appears to be an arithmetic sequence. If so, find the common difference and the next three terms.

8. 21, 13, 5, −3, …

    Arithmetic; common diff.: −8; −11, −19, −27

9. 4, 8, 16, 32, …

    Not arithmetic

10. −6.5, −4, −1.5, 1, …

    Arithmetic; common diff.: 2.5; 3.5, 6, 8.5

Find the indicated term of the arithmetic sequence.

11. 25th term: 9, 2, −5, −12, …

    −159

12. 16th term: $a_1 = 8$; $d = 3$

    53

13. With no air resistance, a ball will roll down a ramp 9 feet during the first second, 16 feet during the next second, 23 feet during the third second, 30 feet during the fourth second, and so on. How many feet will the ball roll during the eighth second?

    58 feet

144

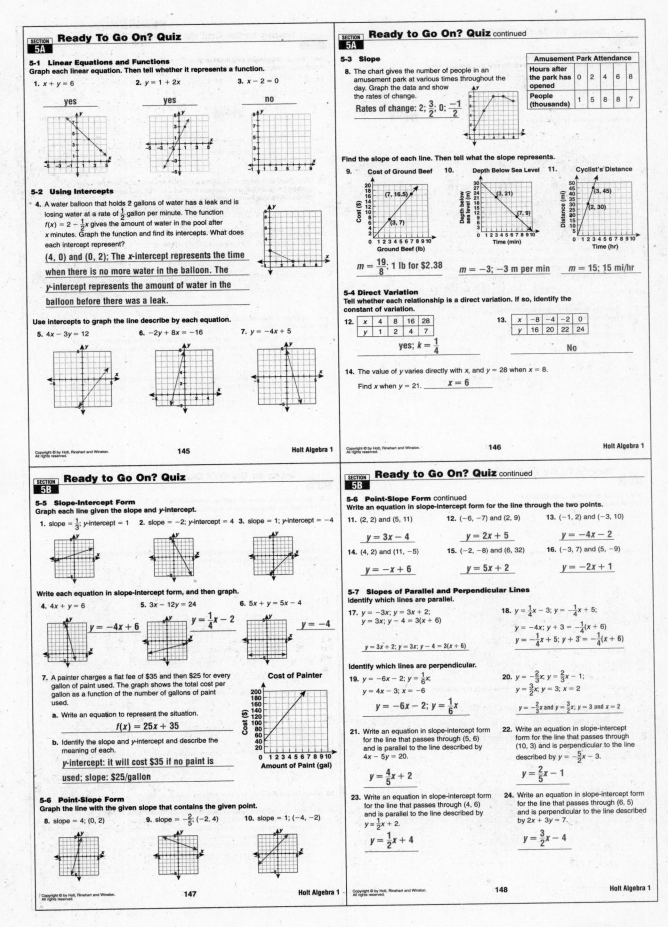

5-1 Linear Equations and Functions
Graph each linear equation. Then tell whether it represents a function.

1. $x + y = 6$
yes

2. $y = 1 + 2x$
yes

3. $x - 2 = 0$
no

5-2 Using Intercepts

4. A water balloon that holds 2 gallons of water has a leak and is losing water at a rate of $\frac{1}{2}$ gallon per minute. The function $f(x) = 2 - \frac{1}{2}x$ gives the amount of water in the pool after x minutes. Graph the function and find its intercepts. What does each intercept represent?

(4, 0) and (0, 2); The x-intercept represents the time when there is no more water in the balloon. The y-intercept represents the amount of water in the balloon before there was a leak.

Use intercepts to graph the line describe by each equation.

5. $4x - 3y = 12$

6. $-2y + 8x = -16$

7. $y = -4x + 5$

5-3 Slope

8. The chart gives the number of people in an amusement park at various times throughout the day. Graph the data and show the rates of change.

Rates of change: $2; \frac{3}{2}; 0; \frac{-1}{2}$

Amusement Park Attendance					
Hours after the park has opened	0	2	4	6	8
People (thousands)	1	5	8	8	7

Find the slope of each line. Then tell what the slope represents.

9. Cost of Ground Beef
(7, 16.5)
(3, 7)
$m = \frac{19}{8}$; 1 lb for $2.38

10. Depth Below Sea Level
(3, 21)
(7, 9)
$m = -3$; -3 m per min

11. Cyclist's Distance
(3, 45)
(2, 30)
$m = 15$; 15 mi/hr

5-4 Direct Variation
Tell whether each relationship is a direct variation. If so, identify the constant of variation.

12.

x	4	8	16	28
y	1	2	4	7

yes; $k = \frac{1}{4}$

13.

x	-8	-4	-2	0
y	16	20	22	24

No

14. The value of y varies directly with x, and $y = 28$ when $x = 8$.
Find x when $y = 21$. $x = 6$

5-5 Slope-Intercept Form
Graph each line given the slope and y-intercept.

1. slope $= \frac{1}{3}$; y-intercept $= 1$

2. slope $= -2$; y-intercept $= 4$

3. slope $= 1$; y-intercept $= -4$

Write each equation in slope-intercept form, and then graph.

4. $4x + y = 6$
$y = -4x + 6$

5. $3x - 12y = 24$
$y = \frac{1}{4}x - 2$

6. $5x + y = 5x - 4$
$y = -4$

7. A painter charges a flat fee of $35 and then $25 for every gallon of paint used. The graph shows the total cost per gallon as a function of the number of gallons of paint used.

a. Write an equation to represent the situation.
$f(x) = 25x + 35$

b. Identify the slope and y-intercept and describe the meaning of each.
y-intercept: it will cost $35 if no paint is used; slope: $25/gallon

Cost of Painter

5-6 Point-Slope Form
Graph the line with the given slope that contains the given point.

8. slope = 4; (0, 2)

9. slope $= -\frac{2}{5}$; (-2, 4)

10. slope = 1; (-4, -2)

5-6 Point-Slope Form continued
Write an equation in slope-intercept form for the line through the two points.

11. (2, 2) and (5, 11)
$y = 3x - 4$

12. (-6, -7) and (2, 9)
$y = 2x + 5$

13. (-1, 2) and (-3, 10)
$y = -4x - 2$

14. (4, 2) and (11, -5)
$y = -x + 6$

15. (-2, -8) and (6, 32)
$y = 5x + 2$

16. (-3, 7) and (5, -9)
$y = -2x + 1$

5-7 Slopes of Parallel and Perpendicular Lines
Identify which lines are parallel.

17. $y = -3x$; $y = 3x + 2$;
$y = 3x$; $y - 4 = 3(x + 6)$
$y = 3x + 2$; $y = 3x$; $y - 4 = 3(x + 6)$

18. $y = \frac{1}{4}x - 3$; $y = -\frac{1}{4}x + 5$;
$y = -4x$; $y + 3 = -\frac{1}{4}(x + 6)$
$y = -\frac{1}{4}x + 5$; $y + 3 = -\frac{1}{4}(x + 6)$

Identify which lines are perpendicular.

19. $y = -6x - 2$; $y = \frac{1}{6}x$;
$y = 4x - 3$; $x = -6$
$y = -6x - 2$; $y = \frac{1}{6}x$

20. $y = -\frac{2}{3}x$; $y = \frac{2}{3}x - 1$;
$y = \frac{3}{2}x$; $y = 3$; $x = 2$
$y = -\frac{2}{3}x$ and $y = \frac{3}{2}x$; $y = 3$ and $x = 2$

21. Write an equation in slope-intercept form for the line that passes through (5, 6) and is parallel to the line described by $4x - 5y = 20$.
$y = \frac{4}{5}x + 2$

22. Write an equation in slope-intercept form for the line that passes through (10, 3) and is perpendicular to the line described by $y = -\frac{5}{2}x - 3$.
$y = \frac{2}{5}x - 1$

23. Write an equation in slope-intercept form for the line that passes through (4, 6) and is parallel to the line described by $y = \frac{1}{2}x + 2$.
$y = \frac{1}{2}x + 4$

24. Write an equation in slope-intercept form for the line that passes through (6, 5) and is perpendicular to the line described by $2x + 3y = 7$.
$y = \frac{3}{2}x - 4$

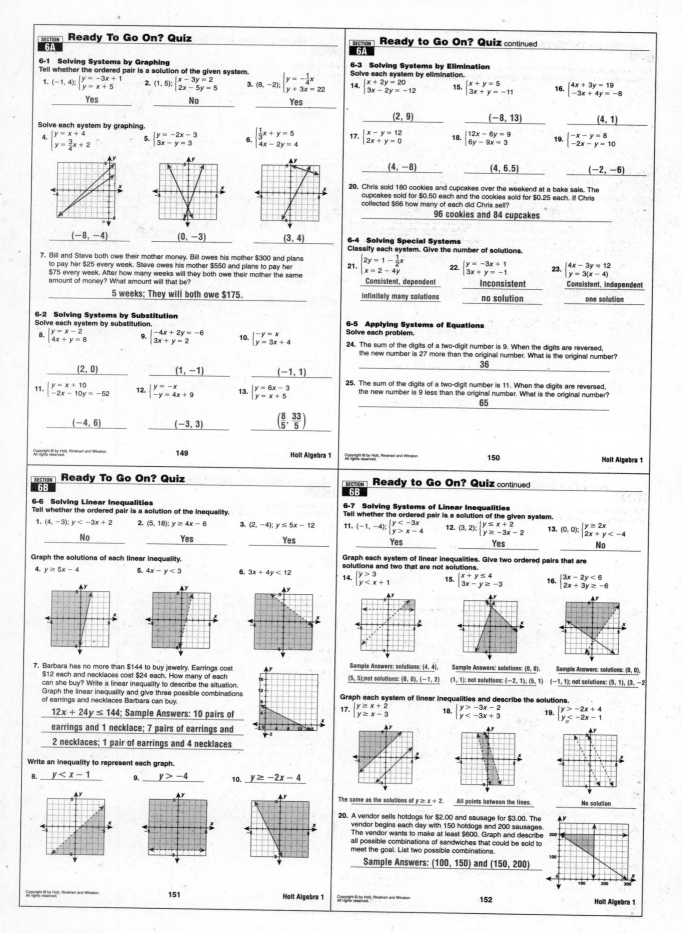

Ready To Go On? Quiz

SECTION 6A

6-1 Solving Systems by Graphing
Tell whether the ordered pair is a solution of the given system.

1. $(-1, 4)$; $\begin{cases} y = -3x + 1 \\ y = x + 5 \end{cases}$ **Yes**

2. $(1, 5)$; $\begin{cases} x - 3y = 2 \\ 2x - 5y = 5 \end{cases}$ **No**

3. $(8, -2)$; $\begin{cases} y = -\frac{1}{4}x \\ y + 3x = 22 \end{cases}$ **Yes**

Solve each system by graphing.

4. $\begin{cases} y = x + 4 \\ y = \frac{3}{4}x + 2 \end{cases}$ **$(-8, -4)$**

5. $\begin{cases} y = -2x - 3 \\ 3x - y = 3 \end{cases}$ **$(0, -3)$**

6. $\begin{cases} \frac{1}{3}x + y = 5 \\ 4x - 2y = 4 \end{cases}$ **$(3, 4)$**

7. Bill and Steve both owe their mother money. Bill owes his mother $300 and plans to pay her $25 every week. Steve owes his mother $550 and plans to pay her $75 every week. After how many weeks will they both owe their mother the same amount of money? What amount will that be?

5 weeks; They will both owe $175.

6-2 Solving Systems by Substitution
Solve each system by substitution.

8. $\begin{cases} y = x - 2 \\ 4x + y = 8 \end{cases}$ **$(2, 0)$**

9. $\begin{cases} -4x + 2y = -6 \\ 3x + y = 2 \end{cases}$ **$(1, -1)$**

10. $\begin{cases} -y = x \\ y = 3x + 4 \end{cases}$ **$(-1, 1)$**

11. $\begin{cases} y = x + 10 \\ -2x - 10y = -52 \end{cases}$ **$(-4, 6)$**

12. $\begin{cases} y = -x \\ -y = 4x + 9 \end{cases}$ **$(-3, 3)$**

13. $\begin{cases} y = 6x - 3 \\ y = x + 5 \end{cases}$ **$\left(\frac{8}{5}, \frac{33}{5}\right)$**

149   **Holt Algebra 1**

Ready to Go On? Quiz continued

SECTION 6A

6-3 Solving Systems by Elimination
Solve each system by elimination.

14. $\begin{cases} x + 2y = 20 \\ 3x - 2y = -12 \end{cases}$ **$(2, 9)$**

15. $\begin{cases} x + y = 5 \\ 3x + y = -11 \end{cases}$ **$(-8, 13)$**

16. $\begin{cases} 4x + 3y = 19 \\ -3x + 4y = -8 \end{cases}$ **$(4, 1)$**

17. $\begin{cases} x - y = 12 \\ 2x + y = 0 \end{cases}$ **$(4, -8)$**

18. $\begin{cases} 12x - 6y = 9 \\ 6y - 9x = 3 \end{cases}$ **$(4, 6.5)$**

19. $\begin{cases} -x - y = 8 \\ -2x - y = 10 \end{cases}$ **$(-2, -6)$**

20. Chris sold 180 cookies and cupcakes over the weekend at a bake sale. The cupcakes sold for $0.50 each and the cookies sold for $0.25 each. If Chris collected $66 how many of each did Chris sell?

96 cookies and 84 cupcakes

6-4 Solving Special Systems
Classify each system. Give the number of solutions.

21. $\begin{cases} 2y = 1 - \frac{1}{2}x \\ x = 2 - 4y \end{cases}$ **Consistent, dependent** **infinitely many solutions**

22. $\begin{cases} y = -3x + 1 \\ 3x + y = -1 \end{cases}$ **Inconsistent** **no solution**

23. $\begin{cases} 4x - 3y = 12 \\ y = 3(x - 4) \end{cases}$ **Consistent, independent** **one solution**

6-5 Applying Systems of Equations
Solve each problem.

24. The sum of the digits of a two-digit number is 9. When the digits are reversed, the new number is 27 more than the original number. What is the original number?

36

25. The sum of the digits of a two-digit number is 11. When the digits are reversed, the new number is 9 less than the original number. What is the original number?

65

150   **Holt Algebra 1**

Ready To Go On? Quiz

SECTION 6B

6-6 Solving Linear Inequalities
Tell whether the ordered pair is a solution of the inequality.

1. $(4, -3)$; $y < -3x + 2$ **No**

2. $(5, 18)$; $y \geq 4x - 6$ **Yes**

3. $(2, -4)$; $y \leq 5x - 12$ **Yes**

Graph the solutions of each linear inequality.

4. $y \geq 5x - 4$

5. $4x - y < 3$

6. $3x + 4y < 12$

7. Barbara has no more than $144 to buy jewelry. Earrings cost $12 each and necklaces cost $24 each. How many of each can she buy? Write a linear inequality to describe the situation. Graph the linear inequality and give three possible combinations of earrings and necklaces Barbara can buy.

$12x + 24y \leq 144$; Sample Answers: 10 pairs of earrings and 1 necklace; 7 pairs of earrings and 2 necklaces; 1 pair of earrings and 4 necklaces

Write an inequality to represent each graph.

8. **$y < x - 1$**

9. **$y > -4$**

10. **$y \geq -2x - 4$**

151   **Holt Algebra 1**

Ready to Go On? Quiz continued

SECTION 6B

6-7 Solving Systems of Linear Inequalities
Tell whether the ordered pair is a solution of the given system.

11. $(-1, -4)$; $\begin{cases} y < -3x \\ y > x - 4 \end{cases}$ **Yes**

12. $(3, 2)$; $\begin{cases} y \leq x + 2 \\ y \geq -3x - 2 \end{cases}$ **Yes**

13. $(0, 0)$; $\begin{cases} y \geq 2x \\ 2x + y < -4 \end{cases}$ **No**

Graph each system of linear inequalities. Give two ordered pairs that are solutions and two that are not solutions.

14. $\begin{cases} y > 3 \\ y < x + 1 \end{cases}$

Sample Answers: solutions: (4, 4), (5, 5); not solutions: (0, 0), (-1, 2)

15. $\begin{cases} x + y \leq 4 \\ 3x - y \geq -3 \end{cases}$

Sample Answers: solutions: (0, 0), (1, 1); not solutions: (-2, 1), (5, 1)

16. $\begin{cases} 3x - 2y < 6 \\ 2x + 3y \geq -6 \end{cases}$

Sample Answers: solutions: (0, 0), (-1, 1); not solutions: (5, 1), (3, -2)

Graph each system of linear inequalities and describe the solutions.

17. $\begin{cases} y \geq x + 2 \\ y \geq x - 3 \end{cases}$

The same as the solutions of $y \geq x + 2$.

18. $\begin{cases} y > -3x - 2 \\ y < -3x + 3 \end{cases}$

All points between the lines.

19. $\begin{cases} y > -2x + 4 \\ y < -2x - 1 \end{cases}$

No solution

20. A vendor sells hotdogs for $2.00 and sausage for $3.00. The vendor begins each day with 150 hotdogs and 200 sausages. The vendor wants to make at least $600. Graph and describe all possible combinations of sandwiches that could be sold to meet the goal. List two possible combinations.

Sample Answers: (100, 150) and (150, 200)

152   **Holt Algebra 1**

232

Holt Algebra 1

7-1 Integer Exponents
Evaluate each expression for the given value(s) of the variable(s).

1. a^{-4} for $a = 3$
$\dfrac{1}{81}$

2. w^{-6} for $w = -5$
$\dfrac{1}{15,625}$

3. $w^{-2}y$ for $w = 5$ and $y = -3$
$-\dfrac{3}{25}$

4. a^0 for $a = 12$
1

5. $(6 - w)^{-8}$ for $w = 7$
1

6. $a^0 b^{-3}$ for $a = 5$ and $b = 10$
$\dfrac{1}{1000}$

Simplify.

7. $6w^{-4}$
$\dfrac{6}{w^4}$

8. $\dfrac{y^7}{w^{-3}}$
$w^3 y^7$

9. $3x^{-2}y^0$
$\dfrac{3}{x^2}$

10. $\dfrac{w^{-6}}{b^{-4}}$
$\dfrac{b^4}{w^6}$

11. Engineering notation can be written in terms of a base unit, with a power of 10 that is a multiple of 3. The table shows some of these equivalences. Simplify each expression.

Selected Engineering Prefixes					
Giga	Mega	Kilo	Milli	Micro	Nano
10^9	10^6	10^3	10^{-3}	10^{-6}	10^{-9}

Giga 1,000,000,000   Kilo 1000

Milli 0.001   Micro 0.000001

Mega 1,000,000   Nano 0.000000001

7-2 Powers of 10 and Scientific Notation

12. Find the value of 10^5.
100,000

13. Write 0.00000004 as a power of 10.
4×10^{-8}

14. Write 1,000,000,000,000 as a power of 10.
10^{12}

15. Find the value of 15.7×10^5.
1,570,000

16. The wavelength of red light is 0.0000007 m. Write this length in scientific notation.
7×10^{-7} m

153   Holt Algebra 1

7-3 Multiplication Properties of Exponents
Simplify.

17. $3^5 \cdot 3^2$
3^7

18. $5^4 \cdot 5^{-2}$
5^2 or 25

19. $(2x^5)^3$
$8x^{15}$

20. $(-6w^6)^2$
$36w^{12}$

21. The closest star to Earth is Proxima Centauri, which is 4.3 light-years away (one light-year equals 5.88×10^{12} miles). How far, in miles, is Proxima Centauri from Earth? Write your answer in scientific notation and standard form.
2.5284×10^{13} miles; 25,284,000,000,000 miles

7-4 Division Properties of Exponents
Simplify.

22. $\dfrac{7^9}{7^7}$
49

23. $\dfrac{15x^6}{5x^3}$
$3x^3$

24. $\dfrac{a^9 b^{10}}{a^{11} b^3}$
$\dfrac{b^7}{a^2}$

25. $\dfrac{8x^3 y^5}{x^3 y}$
$8y^4$

26. $\left(\dfrac{2}{3}\right)^3$
$\dfrac{8}{27}$

27. $\left(\dfrac{5w^4}{w^2 y^6}\right)^2$
$\dfrac{25w^4}{y^{12}}$

28. $\left(\dfrac{3}{4}\right)^{-3}$
$\dfrac{64}{27}$

29. $\left(\dfrac{a^2 b^5}{ab^6}\right)^{-2}$
$\dfrac{b^2}{a^2}$

Simplify each quotient and write the answers in scientific notation.

30. $(9 \times 10^{10}) \div (3 \times 10^4)$
3×10^6

31. $(4.5 \times 10^6) \div (9 \times 10^9)$
5×10^{-4}

32. $(2 \times 10^5) \div (5 \times 10^5)$
4×10^{-1}

7-5 Fractional Exponents
Simplify each expression. All variables represent nonnegative numbers.

33. $36^{\frac{1}{2}}$
6

34. $27^{\frac{1}{3}}$
3

35. $1^{\frac{2}{3}}$
1

36. $16^{\frac{3}{2}}$
64

37. $\sqrt{x^4 y^2}$
$x^2 y$

38. $\sqrt[3]{q^6}$
q^2

39. $\sqrt[3]{k^{15}}$
k^5

40. $\sqrt[3]{r^3 s^9}$
rs^3

154   Holt Algebra 1

7-6 Polynomials
Write each polynomial in standard form and give the leading coefficient.

1. $7x^2 + 4x^5 - 2r$
$4x^5 + 7x^2 - 2r$; 4

2. $y^3 + 3 - 8y^2 + 4y$
$y^3 - 8y^2 + 4y + 3$; 1

3. $-8w^4 - 3w + w^5$
$w^5 - 8w^4 - 3w$; 1

4. $3 + y + 5y^2$
$5y^2 + y + 3$; 5

5. $9 + 4x^4$
$4x^4 + 9$; 4

6. $-2a^2 + 9 + a^8 + 2a$
$a^8 - 2a^2 + 2a + 9$; 1

Classify each polynomial according to its degree and number of terms.

7. $3a^2 + 4a - a^4 + 3a^3$
Quartic polynomial

8. $4x^2 + 8 - 3x$
Quadratic trinomial

9. $3x^3 + 5x^2 - 1$
Cubic trinomial

10. $7 - 5b^4 + 2b + 5b^2$
Quartic polynomial

11. $7w^2$
Quadratic monomial

12. $3a^4 - 6a^8 + 2a + 9$
8th degree polynomial

13. The function $P(x) = x^3 - 3x^2 + 12$ gives the profit on a product. What is the profit on 800 units? $510,080,012

7-7 Adding and Subtracting Polynomials
Add or subtract.

14. $(12x^4 + 5x^3) + (6x^3 + 7x)$
$12x^4 + 11x^3 + 7x$

15. $(4x^2 - 3) + (10x^2 + 5x - 7)$
$14x^2 + 5x - 10$

16. $(13d^6 - 4d^2) + (3d^4 + 2)$
$13d^6 + 3d^4 - 4d^2 + 2$

17. $(7y^3 + 5y^2) - (3y^2 + 4y)$
$7y^3 + 2y^2 - 4y$

18. $(8w^2 - 4w) - (6w^2 + 6w)$
$2w^2 - 10w$

19. $(a^2 - 11) - (-6a^3 + 3a)$
$6a^3 + a^2 - 3a - 11$

20. The measures of the sides of a triangle are shown as polynomials. Write a simplified polynomial to represent the perimeter of the triangle. $4x^3 + 4x^2 + 6x + 8$

$4x^2 + 5$ $6x$ $4x^3 + 3$

155   Holt Algebra 1

7-8 Multiplying Polynomials
Multiply.

21. $4h^3 \cdot 6h^6$
$24h^9$

22. $(x^9 y^5)(-7x^2 y^4)$
$-7x^{11} y^9$

23. $3mn(6m^2 + 4m^3 n)$
$18m^3 n + 12m^4 n^2$

24. $(4w + 3)^2$
$16w^2 + 24w + 9$

25. $(3x^3 + 2y)(5x + y)$
$15x^4 + 3x^3 y + 10xy + 2y^2$

26. $(a^2 + 4)(3a^2 - 4a - 7)$
$3a^4 - 4a^3 + 5a^2 - 16a - 28$

27. Write a simplified polynomial expression for the area of a rectangle whose length is $x + 8$ units and whose width is $x - 5$ units.
$(x^2 + 3x - 40)$ square units

7-9 Special Products of Binomials
Multiply.

28. $(x + 8)^2$
$x^2 + 16x + 64$

29. $(2x + 3)^2$
$4x^2 + 12x + 9$

30. $(3x + 7y)^2$
$9x^2 + 42xy + 49y^2$

31. $(a - 5)^2$
$a^2 - 10a + 25$

32. $(x - y)^2$
$x^2 - 2xy + y^2$

33. $(4x - 3)^2$
$16x^2 - 24x + 9$

34. $(x - 3)(x + 3)$
$x^2 - 9$

35. $(6x - 7)(6x + 7)$
$36x^2 - 49$

36. A swimming pool has a radius of $x - 4$ inches. Write a polynomial that represents the area of the swimming pool. (The formula for the area of a circle is $A = \pi r^2$, where r represents the radius of the circle.) Leave the symbol π in your answer.
$(\pi x^2 - 8\pi x + 16\pi)$ in.^{2}

156   Holt Algebra 1

Holt Algebra 1

8-1 Factors and Greatest Common Factors
Write the prime factorization of each number.

1. 84
$$2^2 \cdot 3 \cdot 7$$

2. 60
$$2^2 \cdot 3 \cdot 5$$

3. 150
$$2 \cdot 3 \cdot 5^2$$

4. 66
$$2 \cdot 3 \cdot 11$$

5. 72
$$2^3 \cdot 3^2$$

6. 156
$$2^2 \cdot 3 \cdot 13$$

Find the GCF of each pair of monomials.

7. $6x^4$ and $9x^2$
$$3x^2$$

8. $25x^3$ and $20x^4$
$$5x^3$$

9. -18 and $27c^5$
$$9$$

10. $5a$ and $7c$
$$1$$

11. Nichole is designing a quilt. She has cut out 60 red squares and 48 green squares. She plans for the quilt to have the same number of colored squares in each row, but, green and red squares will not be in the same row. How many rows will the quilt have if Nichole puts the greatest number of squares in each row? **9 rows**

8-2 Factoring by GCF
Factor each polynomial. Check your answer.

12. $30x^2 + 12x$
$$6x(5x + 2)$$

13. $2a^2 - 10a^3$
$$2a^2(1 - 5a)$$

14. $6x^4 - 15x^3 - 9x^2$
$$3x^2(2x + 1)(x - 3)$$

15. $4x^2 + 12x + 16$
$$4(x^2 + 3x + 4)$$

16. The surface area of a cylinder can be found using the expression $2\pi r^2 + 2\pi rh$, where r represents the radius of the cylinder and h represents the height. Factor this expression. $2\pi r(r + h)$

157
Holt Algebra 1

8-2 Factoring by GCF continued
Factor each polynomial by grouping. Check your answer.

17. $x^3 - 3x^2 + 2x - 6$
$$(x^2 + 2)(x - 3)$$

18. $5x^3 + 10x^2 + x + 2$
$$(5x^2 + 1)(x + 2)$$

19. $2r^3 - 8r^2 - 3r + 12$
$$(2r^2 - 3)(r - 4)$$

20. $3s^3 - 12s^2 - s + 4$
$$(3s^2 - 1)(s - 4)$$

21. $4y^3 + 16y^2 - 2y - 8$
$$(4y^2 - 2)(y + 4)$$

22. $8b^3 + 16b^2 - 2b - 4$
$$(8b^2 - 2)(b + 2)$$

8-3 Factoring $x^2 + bx + c$
Factor each trinomial. Check your answer.

23. $a^2 + 12a + 35$
$$(a + 5)(a + 7)$$

24. $x^2 - 3x - 10$
$$(x - 5)(x + 2)$$

25. $x^2 - 8x + 7$
$$(x - 1)(x - 7)$$

26. $x^2 + 13x - 30$
$$(x + 15)(x - 2)$$

27. $c^2 - 13c + 36$
$$(c - 9)(c - 4)$$

28. $y^2 - 12y + 32$
$$(y - 8)(y - 4)$$

29. Simplify and factor the polynomial $n(n + 7) + 12$. Show that the original polynomial and the factored form describe the same sequence of numbers for $n = 0, 1, 2, 3,$ and 4.
$$n^2 + 7n + 12; (n + 3)(n + 4)$$

8-4 Factoring $ax^2 + bx + c$
Factor each trinomial. Check your answer.

30. $2a^2 + 5a + 2$
$$(2a + 1)(a + 2)$$

31. $6x^2 + 11x + 4$
$$(2x + 1)(3x + 4)$$

32. $3x^2 - x - 10$
$$(3x + 5)(x - 2)$$

33. $4x^2 - 14x + 12$
$$2(2x - 3)(x - 2)$$

34. $6c^2 - 12c - 18$
$$6(c - 3)(c + 1)$$

35. $12y^2 - y - 20$
$$(3y - 4)(4y + 5)$$

36. The area of a rectangle is $(10x^2 + 21x + 9)$ cm^2. The length is $(5x + 3)$ cm. What is the width of the rectangle?
$$(2x + 3) \text{ cm}$$

158
Holt Algebra 1

8-5 Factoring Special Products
Determine whether each trinomial is a perfect square. If so, factor it. If not, explain why.

1. $a^2 + 6a + 9$
$$\text{Yes; } (a + 3)^2$$

2. $16x^2 - 40x + 25$
$$\text{Yes; } (4x - 5)^2$$

3. $w^2 - 12w + 4$
$$\text{No; } 12w \neq 2(w)(2)$$

4. $5y^2 - 14y + 16$
5 is not a perfect square.

5. $x^2 + 4x + 4$
$$\text{Yes; } (x + 2)^2$$

6. $25h^2 - 70h + 49$
$$\text{Yes; } (5h - 7)^2$$

7. An architect is designing rectangular windows with an area of $(x^2 + 22x + 121)$ ft^2. The dimensions of the windows are of the form $ax + b$, where a and b are whole numbers. Find an expression for the perimeter of the windows. Find the perimeter of a window when $x = 3$ ft.
$$4(x + 11); 56 \text{ feet}$$

Determine whether each trinomial is the difference of two squares. If so, factor it. If not, explain why.

8. $r^2 - 144$
$$\text{Yes; } (r - 12)(r + 12)$$

9. $4a^2 - 30$
30 is not a perfect square.

10. $1 - 25a^4$
$$\text{Yes; } (1 - 5a^2)(1 + 5a^2)$$

11. $36k^2 - 9k^6$
$$\text{Yes; } (6k - 3k^3)(6k + 3k^3)$$

12. $49a^2 + 64$
The terms are added.

13. $w^4 - a^2$
$$\text{Yes; } (w^2 - a)(w^2 + a)$$

14. The area of a square is $(49x^2 - 28x + 4)$ in^2.
   a. What is the length of a side of the square? $(7x - 2)$
   b. What is the perimeter of the square? $4(7x - 2)$
   c. What are the length of a side, the perimeter, and the area of the square when $x = 4$ in.? 26 in.; 104 in.; 676 in.^{2}

8-6 Choosing a Factoring Method
Tell whether each expression is completely factored. If not, factor it.

15. $7x^2 + 35x + 7 = 7(x^2 + 5x + 1)$
Yes

16. $16x^3 - 24x^2 = 8x(2x^2 - 3x)$
$$8x^2(2x - 3)$$

159
Holt Algebra 1

8-6 Choosing a Factoring Method continued

17. $4x^5 - 16x = 4x(x^4 - 4)$
$$4x(x^2 - 2)(x^2 + 2)$$

18. $3a^2 - 42a + 147 = 3(a^2 - 14a + 49)$
$$3(a - 7)(a - 7)$$

19. $8y^3 - 8y^2 - 12y + 12 = 4(2y^2 - 3)(y - 1)$
Yes

20. $3y^2 + 17y + 10 = (3y + 2)(y + 5)$
Yes

Factor each polynomial completely. Check your answer.

21. $4x^3 - 24x^2 + 36x$
$$4x(x - 3)^2$$

22. $3x^2y - 12xy^2$
$$3xy(x - 4y)$$

23. $3a^2 + a + 1$
Unfactorable

24. $12x^3 - 3x$
$$3x(2x + 1)(2x - 1)$$

25. $4x^2 + 12x - 112$
$$4(x - 4)(x + 7)$$

26. $x^5 - 16x$
$$x(x - 2)(x + 2)(x^2 + 4)$$

Write an expression for each situation. Then factor your expression.

27. The difference of the square of a pipe's length and 49.
$$\ell^2 - 49 = (\ell + 7)(\ell - 7)$$

28. The square of Catherine's age plus 18 times Catherine's age plus 81.
$$x^2 + 18x + 81 = (x + 9)^2$$

29. Three times the square of a truck's speed minus three times the trucks speed plus 18.
$$3x^2 - 3x + 18 = 3(x - 3)(x + 2)$$

30. Four times the square of cherries on a tree minus 11 times the number of cherries minus 21.
$$4x^2 - 11x - 21; \text{ not factorable}$$

31. Write an expression for the area of the shaded region. Then factor the expression.
$$64x^2 - 36y^2 = 4(4x - 3y)(4x + 3y)$$

160
Holt Algebra 1

234
Holt Algebra 1

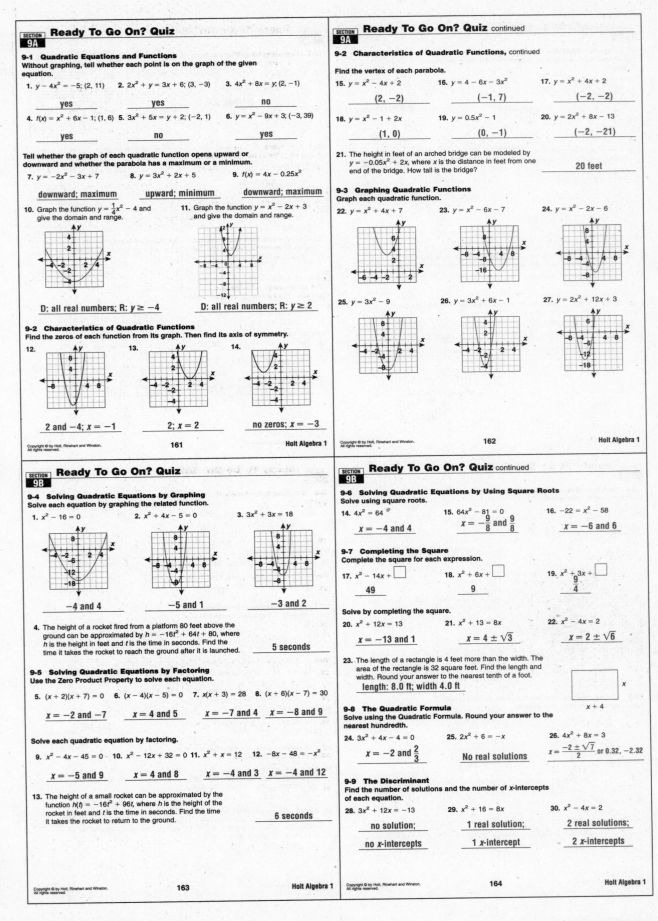

Ready To Go On? Quiz

9A

9-1 Quadratic Equations and Functions

Without graphing, tell whether each point is on the graph of the given equation.

1. $y - 4x^2 = -5$; (2, 11)　　2. $2x^2 + y = 3x + 6$; (3, −3)　　3. $4x^2 + 8x = y$; (2, −1)

　　yes　　　　　　　　yes　　　　　　　　no

4. $f(x) = x^2 + 6x - 1$; (1, 6)　5. $3x^2 + 5x = y + 2$; (−2, 1)　6. $y = x^2 - 9x + 3$; (−3, 39)

　　yes　　　　　　　　no　　　　　　　　yes

Tell whether the graph of each quadratic function opens upward or downward and whether the parabola has a maximum or a minimum.

7. $y = -2x^2 - 3x + 7$　　8. $y = 3x^2 + 2x + 5$　　9. $f(x) = 4x - 0.25x^2$

　downward; maximum　　　upward; minimum　　　downward; maximum

10. Graph the function $y = \frac{1}{4}x^2 - 4$ and give the domain and range.

11. Graph the function $y = x^2 - 2x + 3$ and give the domain and range.

D: all real numbers; R: $y \geq -4$　　　D: all real numbers; R: $y \geq 2$

9-2 Characteristics of Quadratic Functions

Find the zeros of each function from its graph. Then find its axis of symmetry.

12.　　　　　　　　13.　　　　　　　　14.

2 and −4; $x = -1$　　　2; $x = 2$　　　no zeros; $x = -3$

　　　161　　　Holt Algebra 1

Ready To Go On? Quiz continued

9A

9-2 Characteristics of Quadratic Functions, continued

Find the vertex of each parabola.

15. $y = x^2 - 4x + 2$　　16. $y = 4 - 6x - 3x^2$　　17. $y = x^2 + 4x + 2$

　　(2, −2)　　　　　　(−1, 7)　　　　　　(−2, −2)

18. $y = x^2 - 1 + 2x$　　19. $y = 0.5x^2 - 1$　　20. $y = 2x^2 + 8x - 13$

　　(1, 0)　　　　　　(0, −1)　　　　　　(−2, −21)

21. The height in feet of an arched bridge can be modeled by $y = -0.05x^2 + 2x$, where x is the distance in feet from one end of the bridge. How tall is the bridge?

20 feet

9-3 Graphing Quadratic Functions

Graph each quadratic function.

22. $y = x^2 + 4x + 7$　　23. $y = x^2 - 6x - 7$　　24. $y = x^2 - 2x - 6$

25. $y = 3x^2 - 9$　　26. $y = 3x^2 + 6x - 1$　　27. $y = 2x^2 + 12x + 3$

　　　162　　　Holt Algebra 1

Ready To Go On? Quiz

9B

9-4 Solving Quadratic Equations by Graphing

Solve each equation by graphing the related function.

1. $x^2 - 16 = 0$　　2. $x^2 + 4x - 5 = 0$　　3. $3x^2 + 3x = 18$

−4 and 4　　　　　−5 and 1　　　　　−3 and 2

4. The height of a rocket fired from a platform 80 feet above the ground can be approximated by $h = -16t^2 + 64t + 80$, where h is the height in feet and t is the time in seconds. Find the time it takes the rocket to reach the ground after it is launched.

5 seconds

9-5 Solving Quadratic Equations by Factoring

Use the Zero Product Property to solve each equation.

5. $(x + 2)(x + 7) = 0$　6. $(x - 4)(x - 5) = 0$　7. $x(x + 3) = 28$　8. $(x + 6)(x - 7) = 30$

$x = -2$ and -7　$x = 4$ and 5　$x = -7$ and 4　$x = -8$ and 9

Solve each quadratic equation by factoring.

9. $x^2 - 4x - 45 = 0$　10. $x^2 - 12x + 32 = 0$　11. $x^2 + x = 12$　12. $-8x - 48 = -x^2$

$x = -5$ and 9　$x = 4$ and 8　$x = -4$ and 3　$x = -4$ and 12

13. The height of a small rocket can be approximated by the function $h(t) = -16t^2 + 96t$, where h is the height of the rocket in feet and t is the time in seconds. Find the time it takes the rocket to return to the ground.

6 seconds

　　　163　　　Holt Algebra 1

Ready To Go On? Quiz continued

9B

9-6 Solving Quadratic Equations by Using Square Roots

Solve using square roots.

14. $4x^2 = 64$　　15. $64x^2 - 81 = 0$　　16. $-22 = x^2 - 58$

$x = -4$ and 4　　$x = -\frac{9}{8}$ and $\frac{9}{8}$　　$x = -6$ and 6

9-7 Completing the Square

Complete the square for each expression.

17. $x^2 - 14x + \square$　　18. $x^2 + 6x + \square$　　19. $x^2 + \frac{3x}{2} + \square$

　　49　　　　　　　9　　　　　　　$\frac{9}{4}$

Solve by completing the square.

20. $x^2 + 12x = 13$　　21. $x^2 + 13 = 8x$　　22. $x^2 - 4x = 2$

$x = -13$ and 1　　$x = 4 \pm \sqrt{3}$　　$x = 2 \pm \sqrt{6}$

23. The length of a rectangle is 4 feet more than the width. The area of the rectangle is 32 square feet. Find the length and width. Round your answer to the nearest tenth of a foot.

length: 8.0 ft; width 4.0 ft

9-8 The Quadratic Formula

Solve using the Quadratic Formula. Round your answer to the nearest hundredth.

24. $3x^2 + 4x - 4 = 0$　　25. $2x^2 + 6 = -x$　　26. $4x^2 + 8x = 3$

$x = -2$ and $\frac{2}{3}$　　No real solutions　　$x = \frac{-2 \pm \sqrt{7}}{2}$ or 0.32, −2.32

9-9 The Discriminant

Find the number of solutions and the number of x-intercepts of each equation.

28. $3x^2 + 12x = -13$　　29. $x^2 + 16 = 8x$　　30. $x^2 - 4x = 2$

no solution;　　　1 real solution;　　2 real solutions;

no x-intercepts　　1 x-intercept　　2 x-intercepts

　　　164　　　Holt Algebra 1

　　　235　　　Holt Algebra 1

Ready To Go On? Quiz

10-1 Inverse Variation
Tell whether each relationship represents an inverse variation. Explain.

1.
x	2	3	4
y	12	8	6

Yes, the product xy is constant.

2.
x	5	7	9
y	−10	14	18

No, the product xy is not constant.

3. $xy = \frac{1}{2}$ **4.** $y = x + 3$ **5.** $x = \frac{2}{y}$ **6.** $y = 2x$
    Yes   No   Yes   No

7. Write and graph the inverse variation in which $y = 3$ when $x = 3$.

$y = \frac{9}{x}$

8. Write and graph the inverse variation in which $y = -2$ when $x = 3$.

$y = \frac{-6}{x}$

9. The cost of campaign buttons for the student government elections varies inversely to the number of buttons ordered. Fifty buttons cost $0.90 each. How many buttons can be purchased if they cost $0.75 each? __60 buttons__

10-2 Rational Functions
Identify the excluded values and the vertical and horizontal asymptotes for each rational function. Then graph each function.

10. $y = \frac{1}{x}$ excluded value: 0; vertical asymptote: $x = 0$; horizontal asymptote: $y = 0$

11. $y = \frac{2}{x + 1}$ excluded value: −1; vertical asymptote: $x = -1$; horizontal asymptote: $y = 0$

Ready To Go On? Quiz continued

10-2 Rational Functions, continued

12. $y = \frac{5}{x - 2}$ excluded value: 2; vertical asymptote: $x = 2$; horizontal asymptote: $y = 0$

13. $y = \frac{3}{x + 3} + 2$ excluded value: −3; vertical asymptote: $x = -3$; horizontal asymptote: $y = 2$

14. Sara is joining a mail order CD club. She has $60 to spend on CD's. There is a $4 shipping and handling charge. The number of CD's that Sara can buy is given by $y = \frac{60}{x} - 4$, where x represents the cost of each CD in dollars. Describe a reasonable domain and range and graph the function.

D: nonnegative values; R: $y > 0$

10-3 Simplifying Rational Expressions
Find any excluded values of each rational expression.

15. $\frac{2t}{t + 1}$ $t = -1$

16. $\frac{t - 3}{t + 4}$ $t = -4$

17. $\frac{6}{t^2 + 1}$ None

18. $\frac{3}{t^2 - 1}$ $t = \pm 1$

Simplify each rational expression, if possible. Identify any excluded values.

19. $\frac{4n}{12n^3}$ $\frac{1}{3n^2}$; $n \neq 0$

20. $\frac{n^2 + 3n}{6n}$ $\frac{n + 3}{6}$; none

21. $\frac{x - 3}{x^2 + 2x - 15}$ $\frac{1}{x + 5}$; $x \neq -5$

22. $\frac{x^2 + 4x - 12}{x^2 - x - 2}$ $\frac{x + 6}{x + 1}$; $x \neq -1$

23. Suppose the radius of a circle is equal to half the length of the side of a square. Find the ratio of the area of the circle to the area of the square.

$\frac{\pi}{4}$

Ready To Go On? Quiz

10-4 Multiplying and Dividing Rational Expressions
Multiply. Simplify your answer.

1. $\frac{m - 3}{m + 2} \cdot (2m^2 + 4m)$ $2m^2 - 6m$

2. $\frac{3}{x + 3} \cdot (x^2 + 6x + 9)$ $3x + 9$

3. $\frac{12x^4y^3}{x^2y} \cdot \frac{7xy}{3xy^2} \cdot \frac{9x^4}{28x^3y^2}$ $\frac{9x^3}{y}$

4. $\frac{3(a^3 - a)}{a - 1} \cdot \frac{1}{a + 1}$ $3a$

5. $\frac{x^2 + x - 2}{x^2 + 3x - 4} \cdot \frac{x + 3}{x + 4}$ $\frac{x + 3}{x + 4}$

6. $\frac{z^2 - z - 6}{z^2 - 2z - 8} \cdot \frac{z^2 + 7z + 12}{z^2 - 9}$ $\frac{z + 4}{z - 4}$

Divide. Simplify your answer.

7. $4b^5 \div \frac{b^3}{2}$ $8b^2$

8. $\frac{z^2 - 4}{4z^2} \div \frac{z^2 - 3z + 2}{z^2 - z}$ $\frac{z + 2}{4z}$

9. $\frac{x^2 + 2x - 8}{x^2 + x - 6} \div \frac{x + 4}{x - 3}$ $\frac{x - 3}{x + 3}$

10-5 Adding and Subtracting Rational Expressions
Add or subtract. Simplify your answer.

10. $\frac{7}{3x} + \frac{8}{3x}$ $\frac{5}{x}$

11. $\frac{2}{3y} - \frac{6}{3y}$ $\frac{-4}{3y}$

12. $\frac{x^2 + 5x}{x - 6} - \frac{3x + 48}{x - 6}$ $x + 8$

13. $\frac{3m}{5m} + \frac{1}{m^2}$ $\frac{3m^2 + 5}{5m^2}$

14. $\frac{5}{x - 3} - \frac{x - 4}{x^2 - x - 6}$ $\frac{4x + 14}{x^2 - x - 6}$

15. $\frac{5a - 2}{a^2 + a - 20} - \frac{3}{a + 5} + \frac{a}{a - 4}$ $\frac{a + 2}{a - 4}$

Ready To Go On? Quiz continued

10-6 Dividing Polynomials
Divide.

16. $(20n^2 - 10n) \div 5n$ $4n - 2$

17. $(12p^4 + 8p^3 - 24p^2) \div (-4p^2)$ $-3p^2 - 2p + 6$

18. $(x^2 - 8x + 15) \div (x - 3)$ $x - 5$

Divide using long division.

19. $(x^2 - 5x - 36) \div (x + 4)$ $x - 9$

20. $(m^2 + 22m + 121) \div (m + 11)$ $m + 11$

21. $(3y^2 - 7y + 9) \div (y + 1)$ $3y - 10 + \frac{19}{y + 1}$

10-7 Solving Rational Equations
Solve. Identify any extraneous solutions.

22. $\frac{3}{x + 1} = \frac{6}{x}$ $x = -2$

23. $\frac{2}{x^2} = \frac{1}{6x}$ $x = 12$; $x = 0$ is extraneous

24. $\frac{2x}{x + 3} - \frac{x}{x + 7} = \frac{x^2 - 11}{x^2 + 10x + 21}$ $x = -1$

25. $\frac{2}{x + 3} + \frac{1}{x} = \frac{4}{3x}$ $x = \frac{3}{5}$

26. $\frac{4x - 1}{x + 2} = x$ $x = 1$

27. $\frac{2}{x + 3} + \frac{3}{8} = \frac{5}{4x + 12}$ $x = -5$

10-8 Applying Rational Equations
Solve. Check your answer.

28. A greenhouse technician must prepare a solution that is 20% fertilizer. She has 60 milliliters of a solution that is 50% fertilizer. What volume of water must she add to make a solution that is 20% fertilizer?   90 mL

29. You have a lawn-care business. You are looking to add a partner to help you mow lawns. There is a lawn that takes you 30 minutes to mow. The person you are considering to hire can mow it in 45 minutes. How long will it take the two of you to mow the lawn working together?   18 minutes

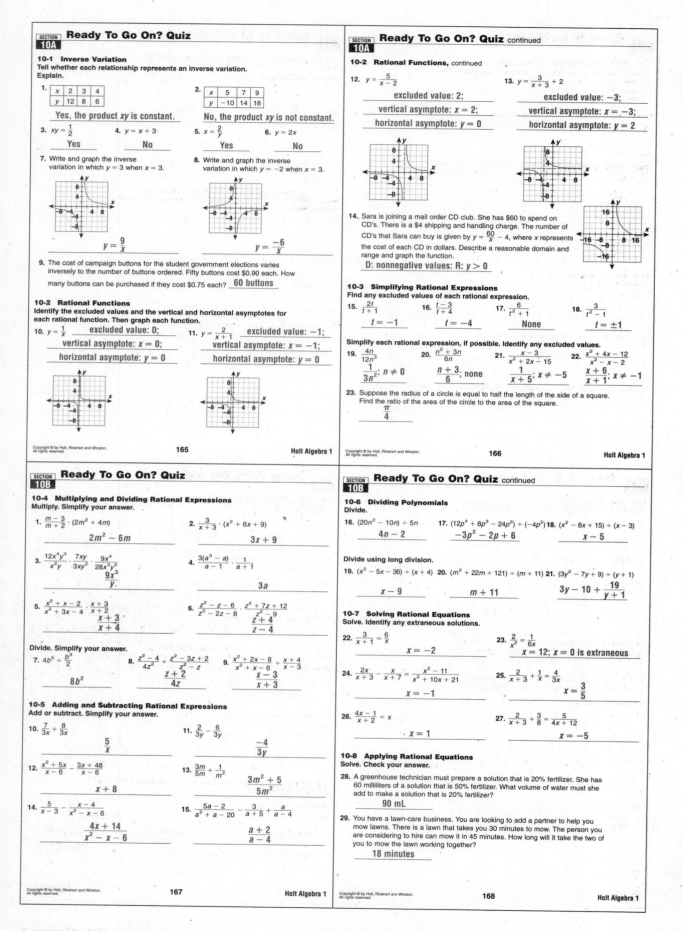

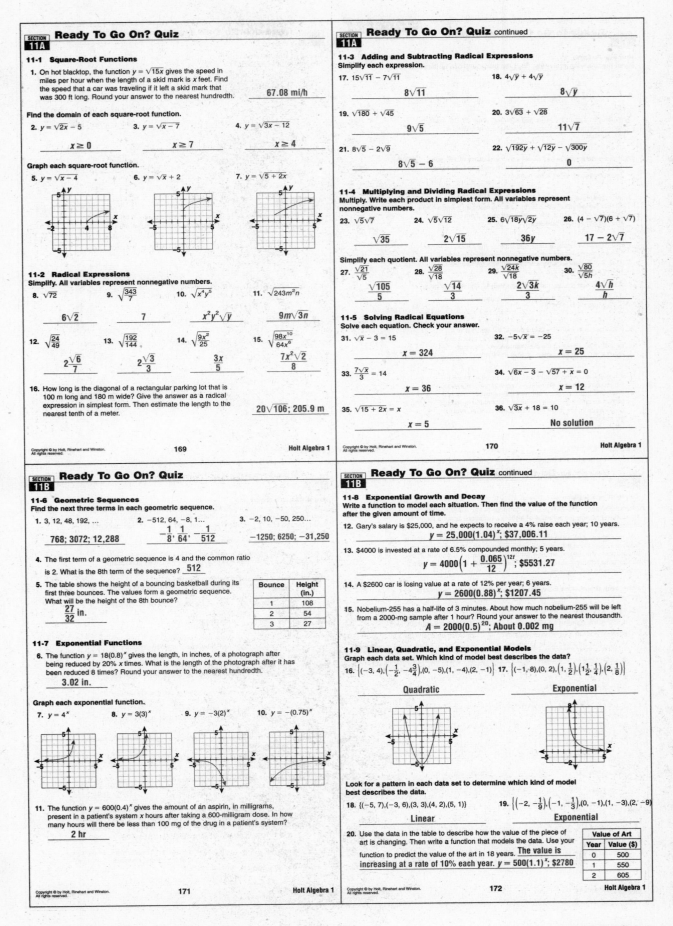

Ready To Go On? Quiz

11-1 Square-Root Functions

1. On hot blacktop, the function $y = \sqrt{15x}$ gives the speed in miles per hour when the length of a skid mark is x feet. Find the speed that a car was traveling if it left a skid mark that was 300 ft long. Round your answer to the nearest hundredth. **67.08 mi/h**

Find the domain of each square-root function.

2. $y = \sqrt{2x} - 5$ $x \geq 0$

3. $y = \sqrt{x - 7}$ $x \geq 7$

4. $y = \sqrt{3x - 12}$ $x \geq 4$

Graph each square-root function.

5. $y = \sqrt{x - 4}$

6. $y = \sqrt{x} + 2$

7. $y = \sqrt{5 + 2x}$

11-2 Radical Expressions
Simplify. All variables represent nonnegative numbers.

8. $\sqrt{72}$ $6\sqrt{2}$

9. $\sqrt{\frac{343}{7}}$ 7

10. $\sqrt{x^4 y^5}$ $x^2 y^2 \sqrt{y}$

11. $\sqrt{243m^2 n}$ $9m\sqrt{3n}$

12. $\sqrt{\frac{24}{49}}$ $\frac{2\sqrt{6}}{7}$

13. $\sqrt{\frac{192}{144}}$ $\frac{2\sqrt{3}}{3}$

14. $\sqrt{\frac{9x^2}{25}}$ $\frac{3x}{5}$

15. $\sqrt{\frac{98x^{10}}{64x^6}}$ $\frac{7x^2 \sqrt{2}}{8}$

16. How long is the diagonal of a rectangular parking lot that is 100 m long and 180 m wide? Give the answer as a radical expression in simplest form. Then estimate the length to the nearest tenth of a meter. $20\sqrt{106}$; 205.9 m

169

Ready To Go On? Quiz continued

11-3 Adding and Subtracting Radical Expressions
Simplify each expression.

17. $15\sqrt{11} - 7\sqrt{11}$ $8\sqrt{11}$

18. $4\sqrt{y} + 4\sqrt{y}$ $8\sqrt{y}$

19. $\sqrt{180} + \sqrt{45}$ $9\sqrt{5}$

20. $3\sqrt{63} + \sqrt{28}$ $11\sqrt{7}$

21. $8\sqrt{5} - 2\sqrt{9}$ $8\sqrt{5} - 6$

22. $\sqrt{192y} + \sqrt{12y} - \sqrt{300y}$ 0

11-4 Multiplying and Dividing Radical Expressions
Multiply. Write each product in simplest form. All variables represent nonnegative numbers.

23. $\sqrt{5}\sqrt{7}$ $\sqrt{35}$

24. $\sqrt{5}\sqrt{12}$ $2\sqrt{15}$

25. $6\sqrt{18y}\sqrt{2y}$ $36y$

26. $(4 - \sqrt{7})(6 + \sqrt{7})$ $17 - 2\sqrt{7}$

Simplify each quotient. All variables represent nonnegative numbers.

27. $\frac{\sqrt{21}}{\sqrt{5}}$ $\frac{\sqrt{105}}{5}$

28. $\frac{\sqrt{28}}{\sqrt{18}}$ $\frac{\sqrt{14}}{3}$

29. $\frac{\sqrt{24k}}{\sqrt{18}}$ $\frac{2\sqrt{3k}}{3}$

30. $\frac{\sqrt{80}}{\sqrt{5h}}$ $\frac{4\sqrt{h}}{h}$

11-5 Solving Radical Equations
Solve each equation. Check your answer.

31. $\sqrt{x} - 3 = 15$ $x = 324$

32. $-5\sqrt{x} = -25$ $x = 25$

33. $\frac{7\sqrt{x}}{3} = 14$ $x = 36$

34. $\sqrt{6x - 3} - \sqrt{57 + x} = 0$ $x = 12$

35. $\sqrt{15 + 2x} = x$ $x = 5$

36. $\sqrt{3x} + 18 = 10$ **No solution**

170

Ready To Go On? Quiz

11-6 Geometric Sequences
Find the next three terms in each geometric sequence.

1. 3, 12, 48, 192, ...   768; 3072; 12,288

2. -512, 64, -8, 1... $\frac{1}{8}, \frac{1}{64}, \frac{1}{512}$

3. -2, 10, -50, 250... -1250; 6250; $-31,250$

4. The first term of a geometric sequence is 4 and the common ratio is 2. What is the 8th term of the sequence? **512**

5. The table shows the height of a bouncing basketball during its first three bounces. The values form a geometric sequence. What will be the height of the 8th bounce? $\frac{27}{32}$ in.

Bounce	Height (in.)
1	108
2	54
3	27

11-7 Exponential Functions

6. The function $y = 18(0.8)^x$ gives the length, in inches, of a photograph after being reduced by 20% x times. What is the length of the photograph after it has been reduced 8 times? Round your answer to the nearest hundredth. **3.02 in.**

Graph each exponential function.

7. $y = 4^x$

8. $y = 3(3)^x$

9. $y = -3(2)^x$

10. $y = -(0.75)^x$

11. The function $y = 600(0.4)^x$ gives the amount of an aspirin, in milligrams, present in a patient's system x hours after taking a 600-milligram dose. In how many hours will there be less than 100 mg of the drug in a patient's system? **2 hr**

171

Ready To Go On? Quiz continued

11-8 Exponential Growth and Decay
Write a function to model each situation. Then find the value of the function after the given amount of time.

12. Gary's salary is $25,000, and he expects to receive a 4% raise each year; 10 years. $y = 25{,}000(1.04)^x$; $37,006.11

13. $4000 is invested at a rate of 6.5% compounded monthly; 5 years. $y = 4000\left(1 + \frac{0.065}{12}\right)^{12t}$; $5531.27

14. A $2600 car is losing value at a rate of 12% per year; 6 years. $y = 2600(0.88)^x$; $1207.45

15. Nobelium-255 has a half-life of 3 minutes. About how much nobelium-255 will be left from a 2000-mg sample after 1 hour? Round your answer to the nearest thousandth. $A = 2000(0.5)^{20}$; About 0.002 mg

11-9 Linear, Quadratic, and Exponential Models
Graph each data set. Which kind of model best describes the data?

16. $\left\{(-3, 4), \left(-\frac{1}{2}, -4\frac{3}{4}\right), (0, -5), (1, -4), (2, -1)\right\}$ **Quadratic**

17. $\left\{(-1, 8), (0, 2), \left(1, \frac{1}{2}\right), \left(1\frac{1}{2}, \frac{1}{4}\right), \left(2, \frac{1}{8}\right)\right\}$ **Exponential**

Look for a pattern in each data set to determine which kind of model best describes the data.

18. $\{(-5, 7), (-3, 6), (3, 3), (4, 2), (5, 1)\}$ **Linear**

19. $\left\{\left(-2, -\frac{1}{9}\right), \left(-1, -\frac{1}{3}\right), (0, -1), (1, -3), (2, -9)\right\}$ **Exponential**

20. Use the data in the table to describe how the value of the piece of art is changing. Then write a function that models the data. Use your function to predict the value of the art in 18 years. **The value is increasing at a rate of 10% each year.** $y = 500(1.1)^x$; $2780

Value of Art	
Year	Value ($)
0	500
1	550
2	605

172

Number Puzzles

Given the following scenarios, fill in the blank with one of these numbers.

6.5	500	−4	1	−75	$\sqrt{17}$	−5	18	$\frac{11}{9}$
$\frac{5}{6}$	$\sqrt{15}$	$\frac{96}{4}$	4.5	$-\sqrt{11}$	0	$\frac{2}{3}$	300	−12

1. When you square my value and subtract it from 23, the result is the square root of 36. I am an irrational number. What is my number? $\sqrt{17}$

2. If you cube my value and divide it by the quotient of 150 and 6, the result is my value. I am not a natural number, but I am a rational number. What is my number? −5

3. When you take my value and multiply it by −8, the result is an integer greater than −220. If you take the result and divide it by the sum of −10 and 2, the result is my value. I am a rational number. What is my number? $\frac{96}{4}$

4. If you take my absolute value and subtract the square of 16, the result is a double-digit number whose prime factorization is $11 \times 2 \times 2$. I am a natural number. What is my number? 300

5. When you add 5 to my value and subtract $1\frac{1}{2}$, the result is twice the square root of 25. I am a terminating decimal. What is my number? 6.5

6. If you take 3 to the value of my power, the result is a non-terminating, non-repeating decimal. If you take 3 and raise it to the power of the absolute value of my value, the result is 81. I am an integer. What is my number? −4

7. When you divide my value by the absolute value of −6, the result is a fraction that when simplified has a numerator that is the first natural number and a denominator that is a perfect square. If you take the square root of the reciprocal of this fraction, the result is 3. I am a real number. What is my number? $\frac{2}{3}$

Holt Algebra 1

Order of Operations

Simplify each expression.

1. $\sqrt{\dfrac{\frac{6 + 16 \cdot 2^3 - 12 + 22}{2(25 - 16) - 14}}{3^3 \div 9 + 3}}$ 1

2. $\dfrac{|-200 - (-450) - 850| \times 2}{2^5 + 2^3} - \left[5(-16 - 4) + \dfrac{18 + 2}{2^2}\right]$ 125

3. $\dfrac{(3^2 + 5 \cdot 4^2 - 12 \cdot 5^2 + 20) + 20(10) + 1}{2 + 3}$ 2

4. $\sqrt{\dfrac{\frac{9 - 6 \cdot 2 - 4 \cdot 6}{-3}}{\frac{2^3 \cdot 2^2 \cdot 2^1}{(\sqrt{169} - 5) \cdot (5 + 3)}}}$ 9

5. $16 \cdot \dfrac{\sqrt{150 - 120 - 45 + 40}}{\sqrt{225} - \left|\frac{150}{-2}\right| + 6 \cdot 10}$ Undefined

6. $\left|\dfrac{\sqrt{4^2 \cdot 4^2 \cdot 4^2} - 120 \cdot \frac{2}{5}}{-2}\right|$ 8

Holt Algebra 1

Diophantine Equations

Diophantus (about 200-284) is known to some as the 'father of algebra'. He studied primarily the solutions of algebraic equations and the theory of numbers.

One type of equation he studied has the form $ax + by = c$ where a, b, and c are all integers and the solutions to the equation (x, y) are also integers. These types of equations are now known as Diophantine Equations. They can be quite difficult to solve and many times the only way to solve them is by guessing and checking.

Solve each Diophantine Equation. Find at least one pair of positive integers for x and y that make the equation true.

1. $3x + 4y = 12$
   a. Solve the equation for y. $y = 3 - \frac{3}{4}x$
   b. What number must x be divisible by? Why? 4; So the result is an integer.
   c. Find at least one solution. (4, 0)

2. $-2x + 3y = -9$
   a. Solve the equation for y. $y = -3 + \frac{2}{3}x$
   b. What number must x be divisible by? Why? 3; So the result is an integer.
   c. Find at least one solution. (6, 1)

3. $x - 2y = 10$ (30, 10)

4. $-4x + y = 15$ (15, 75)

5. $8x - 19y = 100$ (60, 20)

6. $3x + 7y = 35$ (7, 14)

7. $-5x + 11y = 30$ (5, 5)

8. $3x + 4y = 32$ (4, 5)

9. $7x - y = 14$ (3, 7)

10. $-3x + 5y = 9$ (2, 3)

Holt Algebra 1

Proportions in Paint

Thousands of different paint colors are possible because *colorants*, or dyes, are used in different proportions. For example, one type of beige requires 2 parts black, 1 part maroon, and 15 parts deep gold. The ratio describing this situation is shown below.

black:maroon:deep gold = 2:1:15

Suppose 5 ounces of black colorant are used to make the beige. Then how many ounces of maroon and deep gold colorant need to be used?

Step 1 Find the amount of maroon colorant.
$\frac{black}{maroon} \rightarrow \frac{2}{1}$		Write a ratio comparing black to maroon.
$2/1 = 5/x$		Write a proportion. Let x be the ounces of maroon.
$2(x) = 1(5)$		Use cross products.
$2x = 5$		Simplify.
$2x/2 = 5/2$		Divide both sides by 2.
$x = 2.5$		So, 2.5 ounces of maroon colorant are used.

Step 2 Find the amount of deep gold colorant.
$\frac{maroon}{deep\ gold} \rightarrow \frac{1}{15}$		Write a ratio comparing maroon to deep gold.
$1/15 = 2.5/y$		Write a proportion. Let y be the ounces of deep gold.
$1(y) = 15(2.5)$		Use cross products.
$y = 37.5$		So, 37.5 ounces of deep gold colorant are used.

1. An almond color is made by using 4 parts of new green, 3 parts of maroon, and 12 parts of deep gold.
   a) Write a ratio comparing the amounts of new green, maroon, and deep gold. 4:3:12
   b) If 14 ounces of new green colorant are used, how much maroon and deep gold colorants are needed? 10.5 oz maroon, 42 oz deep gold

2. Periwinkle is made by mixing thalo green, thalo blue, and magenta in the ratio 16:20:35. If 15 ounces of thalo blue colorant are used, how much thalo green and magenta colorants need to be used? 12 oz thalo green, 26.25 oz magenta

3. Navy blue is made by using the following colorants: 55 parts black, 14 parts blue, and 50 parts magenta. If 180 grams of magenta colorant are used, how much black and blue colorants are needed? 198 g black, 50.4 g blue

Holt Algebra 1

Holt Algebra 1

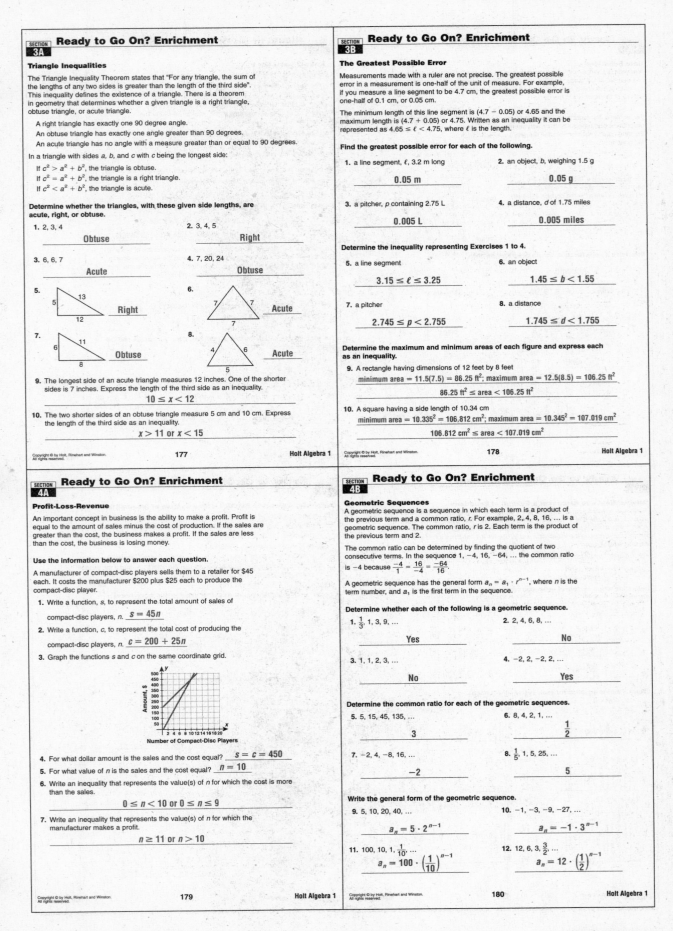

SECTION 3A — Ready to Go On? Enrichment

Triangle Inequalities

The Triangle Inequality Theorem states that "For any triangle, the sum of the lengths of any two sides is greater than the length of the third side". This inequality defines the existence of a triangle. There is a theorem in geometry that determines whether a given triangle is a right triangle, obtuse triangle, or acute triangle.

A right triangle has exactly one 90 degree angle.

An obtuse triangle has exactly one angle greater than 90 degrees.

An acute triangle has no angle with a measure greater than or equal to 90 degrees.

In a triangle with sides a, b, and c with c being the longest side:

If $c^2 > a^2 + b^2$, the triangle is obtuse.
If $c^2 = a^2 + b^2$, the triangle is a right triangle.
If $c^2 < a^2 + b^2$, the triangle is acute.

Determine whether the triangles, with these given side lengths, are acute, right, or obtuse.

1. 2, 3, 4   Obtuse

2. 3, 4, 5   Right

3. 6, 6, 7   Acute

4. 7, 20, 24   Obtuse

5.   Right

6.   Acute

7.   Obtuse

8.   Acute

9. The longest side of an acute triangle measures 12 inches. One of the shorter sides is 7 inches. Express the length of the third side as an inequality.

$$10 \le x < 12$$

10. The two shorter sides of an obtuse triangle measure 5 cm and 10 cm. Express the length of the third side as an inequality.

$$x > 11 \text{ or } x < 15$$

177   Holt Algebra 1

SECTION 3B — Ready to Go On? Enrichment

The Greatest Possible Error

Measurements made with a ruler are not precise. The greatest possible error in a measurement is one-half of the unit of measure. For example, if you measure a line segment to be 4.7 cm, the greatest possible error is one-half of 0.1 cm, or 0.05 cm.

The minimum length of this line segment is (4.7 − 0.05) or 4.65 and the maximum length is (4.7 + 0.05) or 4.75. Written as an inequality it can be represented as $4.65 \le \ell < 4.75$, where ℓ is the length.

Find the greatest possible error for each of the following.

1. a line segment, ℓ, 3.2 m long   0.05 m

2. an object, b, weighing 1.5 g   0.05 g

3. a pitcher, p containing 2.75 L   0.005 L

4. a distance, d of 1.75 miles   0.005 miles

Determine the inequality representing Exercises 1 to 4.

5. a line segment $3.15 \le \ell \le 3.25$

6. an object $1.45 \le b < 1.55$

7. a pitcher $2.745 \le p < 2.755$

8. a distance $1.745 \le d < 1.755$

Determine the maximum and minimum areas of each figure and express each as an inequality.

9. A rectangle having dimensions of 12 feet by 8 feet

minimum area = 11.5(7.5) = 86.25 ft²; maximum area = 12.5(8.5) = 106.25 ft²

$$86.25 \text{ ft}^2 \le \text{area} < 106.25 \text{ ft}^2$$

10. A square having a side length of 10.34 cm

minimum area = 10.335² = 106.812 cm²; maximum area = 10.345² = 107.019 cm²

$$106.812 \text{ cm}^2 \le \text{area} < 107.019 \text{ cm}^2$$

178   Holt Algebra 1

SECTION 4A — Ready to Go On? Enrichment

Profit-Loss-Revenue

An important concept in business is the ability to make a profit. Profit is equal to the amount of sales minus the cost of production. If the sales are greater than the cost, the business makes a profit. If the sales are less than the cost, the business is losing money.

Use the information below to answer each question.

A manufacturer of compact-disc players sells them to a retailer for $45 each. It costs the manufacturer $200 plus $25 each to produce the compact-disc player.

1. Write a function, s, to represent the total amount of sales of compact-disc players, n. $s = 45n$

2. Write a function, c, to represent the total cost of producing the compact-disc players, n. $c = 200 + 25n$

3. Graph the functions s and c on the same coordinate grid.

4. For what dollar amount is the sales and the cost equal? $s = c = 450$

5. For what value of n is the sales and the cost equal? $n = 10$

6. Write an inequality that represents the value(s) of n for which the cost is more than the sales.

$$0 \le n < 10 \text{ or } 0 \le n \le 9$$

7. Write an inequality that represents the value(s) of n for which the manufacturer makes a profit.

$$n \ge 11 \text{ or } n > 10$$

179   Holt Algebra 1

SECTION 4B — Ready to Go On? Enrichment

Geometric Sequences

A geometric sequence is a sequence in which each term is a product of the previous term and a common ratio, r. For example, 2, 4, 8, 16, … is a geometric sequence. The common ratio, r is 2. Each term is the product of the previous term and 2.

The common ratio can be determined by finding the quotient of two consecutive terms. In the sequence 1, −4, 16, −64, … the common ratio is −4 because $\frac{-4}{1} = \frac{16}{-4} = \frac{-64}{16}$.

A geometric sequence has the general form $a_n = a_1 \cdot r^{n-1}$, where n is the term number, and a_1 is the first term in the sequence.

Determine whether each of the following is a geometric sequence.

1. $\frac{1}{3}$, 1, 3, 9, …   Yes

2. 2, 4, 6, 8, …   No

3. 1, 1, 2, 3, …   No

4. −2, 2, −2, 2, …   Yes

Determine the common ratio for each of the geometric sequences.

5. 5, 15, 45, 135, …   3

6. 8, 4, 2, 1, … $\frac{1}{2}$

7. −2, 4, −8, 16, …   −2

8. $\frac{1}{5}$, 1, 5, 25, …   5

Write the general form of the geometric sequence.

9. 5, 10, 20, 40, … $a_n = 5 \cdot 2^{n-1}$

10. −1, −3, −9, −27, … $a_n = -1 \cdot 3^{n-1}$

11. 100, 10, 1, $\frac{1}{10}$, … $a_n = 100 \cdot \left(\frac{1}{10}\right)^{n-1}$

12. 12, 6, 3, $\frac{3}{2}$, … $a_n = 12 \cdot \left(\frac{1}{2}\right)^{n-1}$

180   Holt Algebra 1

Holt Algebra 1

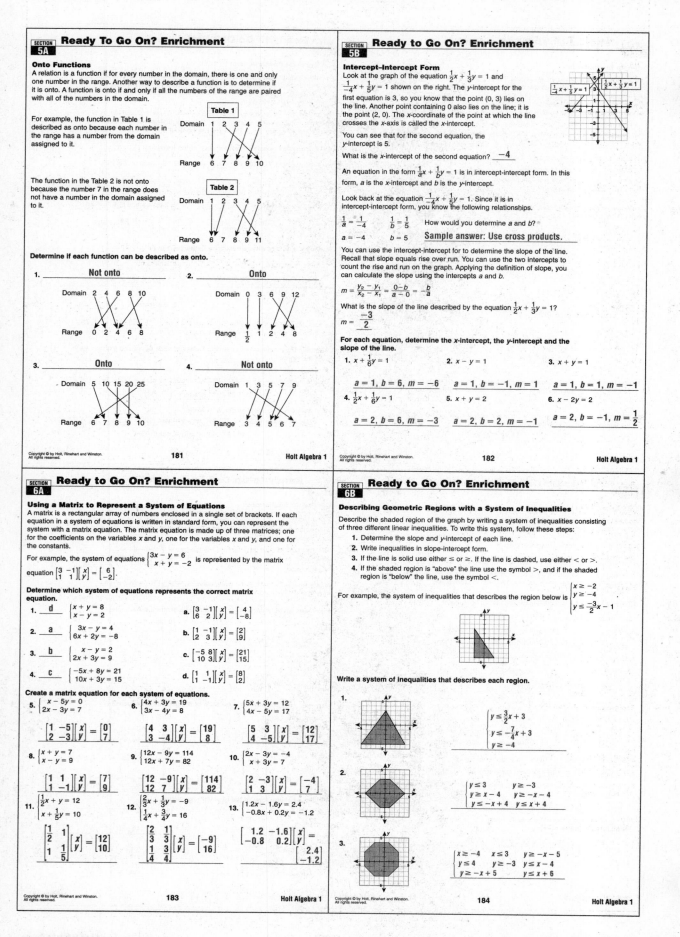

Ready To Go On? Enrichment

Onto Functions

A relation is a function if for every number in the domain, there is one and only one number in the range. Another way to describe a function is to determine if it is onto. A function is onto if and only if all the numbers of the range are paired with all of the numbers in the domain.

For example, the function in Table 1 is described as onto because each number in the range has a number from the domain assigned to it.

Table 1

Domain 1 2 3 4 5

Range 6 7 8 9 10

The function in the Table 2 is not onto because the number 7 in the range does not have a number in the domain assigned to it.

Table 2

Domain 1 2 3 4 5

Range 6 7 8 9 11

Determine if each function can be described as onto.

1. **Not onto**

Domain 2 4 6 8 10

Range 0 2 4 6 8

2. **Onto**

Domain 0 3 6 9 12

Range $\frac{1}{2}$ 1 2 4 8

3. **Onto**

Domain 5 10 15 20 25

Range 6 7 8 9 10

4. **Not onto**

Domain 1 3 5 7 9

Range 3 4 5 6 7

Holt Algebra 1

Ready to Go On? Enrichment

Intercept–Intercept Form

Look at the graph of the equation $\frac{1}{2}x + \frac{1}{3}y = 1$ and $\frac{1}{-4}x + \frac{1}{5}y = 1$ shown on the right. The y-intercept for the first equation is 3, so you know that the point (0, 3) lies on the line. Another point containing 0 also lies on the line; it is the point (2, 0). The x-coordinate of the point at which the line crosses the x-axis is called the x-intercept.

You can see that for the second equation, the y-intercept is 5.

What is the x-intercept of the second equation? **−4**

An equation in the form $\frac{1}{a}x + \frac{1}{b}y = 1$ is in intercept-intercept form. In this form, a is the x-intercept and b is the y-intercept.

Look back at the equation $\frac{1}{-4}x + \frac{1}{5}y = 1$. Since it is in intercept-intercept form, you know the following relationships.

$\frac{1}{a} = \frac{1}{-4}$ $\frac{1}{b} = \frac{1}{5}$ How would you determine a and b?

$a = -4$ $b = 5$ **Sample answer: Use cross products.**

You can use the intercept-intercept for to determine the slope of the line. Recall that slope equals rise over run. You can use the two intercepts to count the rise and run on the graph. Applying the definition of slope, you can calculate the slope using the intercepts a and b.

$m = \frac{y_2 - y_1}{x_2 - x_1} = \frac{0-b}{a-0} = -\frac{b}{a}$

What is the slope of the line described by the equation $\frac{1}{2}x + \frac{1}{3}y = 1$?

$m = \frac{-3}{2}$

For each equation, determine the x-intercept, the y-intercept and the slope of the line.

1. $x + \frac{1}{6}y = 1$ 2. $x - y = 1$ 3. $x + y = 1$

$a = 1, b = 6, m = -6$ $a = 1, b = -1, m = 1$ $a = 1, b = 1, m = -1$

4. $\frac{1}{2}x + \frac{1}{6}y = 1$ 5. $x + y = 2$ 6. $x - 2y = 2$

$a = 2, b = 6, m = -3$ $a = 2, b = 2, m = -1$ $a = 2, b = -1, m = \frac{1}{2}$

Holt Algebra 1

Ready to Go On? Enrichment

Using a Matrix to Represent a System of Equations

A matrix is a rectangular array of numbers enclosed in a single set of brackets. If each equation in a system of equations is written in standard form, you can represent the system with a matrix equation. The matrix equation is made up of three matrices; one for the coefficients on the variables x and y, one for the variables x and y, and one for the constants.

For example, the system of equations $\begin{cases} 3x - y = 6 \\ x + y = -2 \end{cases}$ is represented by the matrix equation $\begin{bmatrix} 3 & -1 \\ 1 & 1 \end{bmatrix}\begin{bmatrix} x \\ y \end{bmatrix} = \begin{bmatrix} 6 \\ -2 \end{bmatrix}$.

Determine which system of equations represents the correct matrix equation.

1. **d** $\begin{cases} x + y = 8 \\ x - y = 2 \end{cases}$ a. $\begin{bmatrix} 3 & -1 \\ 6 & 2 \end{bmatrix}\begin{bmatrix} x \\ y \end{bmatrix} = \begin{bmatrix} 4 \\ -8 \end{bmatrix}$

2. **a** $\begin{cases} 3x - y = 4 \\ 6x + 2y = -8 \end{cases}$ b. $\begin{bmatrix} 1 & -1 \\ 2 & 3 \end{bmatrix}\begin{bmatrix} x \\ y \end{bmatrix} = \begin{bmatrix} 2 \\ 9 \end{bmatrix}$

3. **b** $\begin{cases} x - y = 2 \\ 2x + 3y = 9 \end{cases}$ c. $\begin{bmatrix} -5 & 8 \\ 10 & 3 \end{bmatrix}\begin{bmatrix} x \\ y \end{bmatrix} = \begin{bmatrix} 21 \\ 15 \end{bmatrix}$

4. **c** $\begin{cases} -5x + 8y = 21 \\ 10x + 3y = 15 \end{cases}$ d. $\begin{bmatrix} 1 & 1 \\ 1 & -1 \end{bmatrix}\begin{bmatrix} x \\ y \end{bmatrix} = \begin{bmatrix} 8 \\ 2 \end{bmatrix}$

Create a matrix equation for each system of equations.

5. $\begin{cases} x - 5y = 0 \\ 2x - 3y = 7 \end{cases}$ 6. $\begin{cases} 4x + 3y = 19 \\ 3x - 4y = 8 \end{cases}$ 7. $\begin{cases} 5x + 3y = 12 \\ 4x - 5y = 17 \end{cases}$

$\begin{bmatrix} 1 & -5 \\ 2 & -3 \end{bmatrix}\begin{bmatrix} x \\ y \end{bmatrix} = \begin{bmatrix} 0 \\ 7 \end{bmatrix}$ $\begin{bmatrix} 4 & 3 \\ 3 & -4 \end{bmatrix}\begin{bmatrix} x \\ y \end{bmatrix} = \begin{bmatrix} 19 \\ 8 \end{bmatrix}$ $\begin{bmatrix} 5 & 3 \\ 4 & -5 \end{bmatrix}\begin{bmatrix} x \\ y \end{bmatrix} = \begin{bmatrix} 12 \\ 17 \end{bmatrix}$

8. $\begin{cases} x + y = 7 \\ x - y = 9 \end{cases}$ 9. $\begin{cases} 12x - 9y = 114 \\ 12x + 7y = 82 \end{cases}$ 10. $\begin{cases} 2x - 3y = -4 \\ x + 3y = 7 \end{cases}$

$\begin{bmatrix} 1 & 1 \\ 1 & -1 \end{bmatrix}\begin{bmatrix} x \\ y \end{bmatrix} = \begin{bmatrix} 7 \\ 9 \end{bmatrix}$ $\begin{bmatrix} 12 & -9 \\ 12 & 7 \end{bmatrix}\begin{bmatrix} x \\ y \end{bmatrix} = \begin{bmatrix} 114 \\ 82 \end{bmatrix}$ $\begin{bmatrix} 2 & -3 \\ 1 & 3 \end{bmatrix}\begin{bmatrix} x \\ y \end{bmatrix} = \begin{bmatrix} -4 \\ 7 \end{bmatrix}$

11. $\begin{cases} \frac{1}{2}x + y = 12 \\ x + \frac{1}{5}y = 10 \end{cases}$ 12. $\begin{cases} \frac{2}{3}x + \frac{1}{3}y = -9 \\ \frac{1}{4}x + \frac{3}{4}y = 16 \end{cases}$ 13. $\begin{cases} 1.2x - 1.6y = 2.4 \\ -0.8x + 0.2y = -1.2 \end{cases}$

$\begin{bmatrix} \frac{1}{2} & 1 \\ 1 & \frac{1}{5} \end{bmatrix}\begin{bmatrix} x \\ y \end{bmatrix} = \begin{bmatrix} 12 \\ 10 \end{bmatrix}$ $\begin{bmatrix} \frac{2}{3} & \frac{1}{3} \\ \frac{1}{4} & \frac{3}{4} \end{bmatrix}\begin{bmatrix} x \\ y \end{bmatrix} = \begin{bmatrix} -9 \\ 16 \end{bmatrix}$ $\begin{bmatrix} 1.2 & -1.6 \\ -0.8 & 0.2 \end{bmatrix}\begin{bmatrix} x \\ y \end{bmatrix} = \begin{bmatrix} 2.4 \\ -1.2 \end{bmatrix}$

Holt Algebra 1

Ready to Go On? Enrichment

Describing Geometric Regions with a System of Inequalities

Describe the shaded region of the graph by writing a system of inequalities consisting of three different linear inequalities. To write this system, follow these steps:

1. Determine the slope and y-intercept of each line.
2. Write inequalities in slope-intercept form.
3. If the line is solid use either ≤ or ≥. If the line is dashed, use either < or >.
4. If the shaded region is "above" the line use the symbol >, and if the shaded region is "below" the line, use the symbol <.

For example, the system of inequalities that describes the region below is $\begin{cases} x \geq -2 \\ y \geq -4 \\ y \leq \frac{-3}{2}x - 1 \end{cases}$

Write a system of inequalities that describes each region.

1.

$\begin{cases} y \leq \frac{3}{2}x + 3 \\ y \leq \frac{-7}{4}x + 3 \\ y \geq -4 \end{cases}$

2.

$\begin{cases} y \leq 3 & y \geq -3 \\ y \geq x - 4 & y \geq -x - 4 \\ y \leq -x + 4 & y \leq x + 4 \end{cases}$

3.

$\begin{cases} x \geq -4 & x \leq 3 & y \geq -x - 5 \\ y \leq 4 & y \geq -3 & y \leq x - 4 \\ y \geq -x + 5 & & y \leq x + 6 \end{cases}$

Holt Algebra 1

Holt Algebra 1

Ready To Go On? Enrichment

Digits

Using the digits 1, 2, 3 and 4 and addition, subtraction, multiplication, division, parentheses, and exponents, write an expression equivalent to the numbers 1 to 20.

- You must use all four digits in each expression.
- You may use any of the operations but each symbol may be used only once in each expression.

An example has been done for you. There may be more than one correct expression for a given number. **Sample answers given**

$1 = 3 \cdot 2 - (4 + 1)$

$2 = \dfrac{3 \cdot \frac{2}{1} - 4}{}$

$3 = \underline{4 - 3 + 2 \cdot 1}$

$4 = \dfrac{(3 - 2) \cdot \frac{4}{1}}{}$

$5 = \underline{3 \cdot 1 + 4 - 2}$

$6 = 3^1 \cdot (4 - 2)$

$7 = \underline{4 + 3 \cdot 1^2}$

$8 = \underline{(4 - 2) \cdot (3 + 1)}$

$9 = \underline{(4 + 1 - 2) \cdot 3}$

$10 = \dfrac{4 \cdot 3 - \frac{2}{1}}{}$

$11 = \underline{2^3 + (4 - 1)}$

$12 = \underline{2^3 + (4 \cdot 1)}$

$13 = \underline{2^4 - (3 \cdot 1)}$

$14 = \dfrac{(4 + 3) \cdot \frac{2}{1}}{}$

$15 = \underline{(4 + 2 - 1) \cdot 3}$

$16 = \underline{(3 + 2 - 1) \cdot 4}$

$17 = \underline{(4 + 2) \cdot 3 - 1}$

$18 = \underline{2^4 + (3 - 1)}$

$19 = \underline{2^4 + (3 \cdot 1)}$

$20 = \dfrac{(3 + 2) \cdot \frac{4}{1}}{}$

Ready to Go On? Enrichment

Pascal's Triangle

Pascal's Triangle is a geometric arrangement of numbers. These numbers represent the binomial coefficients. That is, they represent the coefficients of the terms of the expansion of $(x + y)^n$. The first seven rows of Pascal's Triangle look like this.

Row 0							1						
Row 1						1		1					
Row 2					1		2		1				
Row 3				1		3		3		1			
Row 4			1		4		6		4		1		
Row 5		1		5		10		10		5		1	
Row 6	1		6		15		20		15		6		1

Notice that each number is the sum of the two numbers above it.

For example what two numbers were added to get 10 in the 5th row? __4 and 6__

What are the numbers for the 7th row? __1, 7, 21, 35, 35, 21, 7, 1__

As an example, find $(x + y)^3$.

Look at row 3, what are the coefficients of the expansion? __1, 3, 3, 1__

The first term of the expansion starts with the highest power of x, namely x^3, and the lowest power of y, namely $y^0 = 1$. The power of x increases by 1 for each successive term and the power of y increases by 1 for each successive term.

$(x + y)^3 = \underline{1 \cdot x^3 \cdot y^0} + \underline{3 \cdot x^2 \cdot y^1} + \underline{3 \cdot x^1 \cdot y^2} + \underline{1 \cdot x^0 \cdot y^3}$

$ = x^3 + 3x^2y + 3xy^2 + y^3$

Expand each of the following polynomials.

1. $(x + y)^4$
$x^4 + 4x^3y + 6x^2y^2 + 4xy^3 + y^4$

2. $(x + 1)^5$
$x^5 + 5x^4 + 10x^3 + 10x^2 + 5x + 1$

3. $(x + 3)^4$
$x^4 + 12x^3 + 54x^2 + 108x + 81$

4. $(x + 2)^3$
$x^3 + 6x^2 + 12x + 8$

5. $(x + 1)^9$
$x^9 + 9x^8 + 36x^7 + 84x^6 + 126x^5 + 126x^4 + 84x^3 + 36x^2 + 9x + 1$

6. $(x + 2y)^5$
$x^5 + 10x^4y + 40x^3y^3 + 80x^2y^3 + 80xy^4 + 32y^5$

Ready To Go On? Enrichment

Sum and Differences of Cubes

While it is possible to factor the sum and differences of two squares, it is also possible to factor the sum and differences of two cubes.

The sum of two cubes can be factored in the following way:

$$a^3 + b^3 = (a + b)(a^2 - ab + b^2)$$

The differences of two cubes can be factored in the following way:

$$a^3 - b^3 = (a - b)(a^2 + ab + b^2)$$

Factor each of the following.

1. $r^3 - s^3$
$(r - s)(r^2 + rs + s^2)$

2. $x^3 + y^3$
$(x + y)(x^2 - xy + y^2)$

3. $x^3 + 8$
$(x + 2)(x^2 - 2x + 4)$

4. $n^3 - 64$
$(n - 4)(n^2 + 4n + 16)$

5. $8y^3 + 27$
$(2y + 3)(4y^2 - 6y + 9)$

6. $pq^3 - 64p$
$p(q - 4)(q^2 + 4q + 16)$

Express each of the following as the sum or difference of two cubes.

7. $(m - 1)(m^2 + m + 1)$
$m^3 - 1$

8. $(2 + 3t)(4 - 6t + 9t^2)$
$8 + 27t^3$

9. $(b - 64)(b^2 + 4b + 16)$
$b^3 - 4^3$

10. $(x + 7)(x^2 - 7x + 49)$
$x^3 + 7^3$

11. $(2y - 1)(4y^2 + 2y + 1)$
$8y^3 - 1$

12. $(3 + 2t)(9 - 6t + 4t^2)$
$27 + 8t^3$

13. $(s + 10)(s^2 - 10s + 100)$
$s^3 + 1000$

14. $2(x - 4)(x^2 + 4x + 16)$
$2x^3 - 128$

Ready To Go On? Enrichment

Fourth Degree Trinomials

Sometimes it is possible to write a trinomial of the fourth degree, $a^4 + a^2b^2 + b^4$, as a difference of two squares and then factor.

Example: Factor $4a^4 - 21a^2b^2 + 9b^4$.

Step I Find the square roots of the first and last terms.

$\sqrt{4a^4} = 2a^2 \qquad \sqrt{9b^4} = 3b^2$

Step II Find twice the product of the square roots from the terms in Step 1.

$2(2a^2)(3b^2) = 12a^2b^2$

Step III Split the middle term of the trinomial into two parts. One part is either the answer from the Step II or its opposite. The other part should be the opposite of a perfect square.

$-21a^2b^2 = -12a^2b^2 - 9a^2b^2$

Step IV Rewrite the trinomial as the difference of two squares and then factor.

$4a^4 - 21a^2b^2 + 9b^4 = (4a^4 - 12a^2b^2 + 9b^4) - 9a^2b^2$
$= (2a^2 - 3b^2)^2 - 9a^2b^2$
$= [(2a^2 - 3b^2) - 3ab][(2a^2 - 3b^2) - 3ab]$
$= (2a^2 + 3ab - 3b^2)(2a^2 - 3ab - 3b^2)$

Factor each trinomial.

1. $16d^4 + 7d^2 + 1$
$(4d^2 - d + 1)(4d^2 + d + 1)$

2. $p^4 + p^2 + 1$
$(p^2 + p + 1)(p^2 - p + 1)$

3. $4x^4 - 13x^2 + 1$
$(2x^2 + 3x - 1)(2x^2 - 3x - 1)$

4. $4x^4 - 9x^2y^2 + 16y^4$
$(2x^2 - 5xy + 4y^2)(2x^2 + 5xy + 4y^2)$

5. $9r^4 + 26r^2s^2 + 25s^4$
$(3r^2 + 2rs + 5s^2)(3r^2 - 2rs + 5s^2)$

6. $4a^4 - 5a^2c^2 + 25c^4$
$(2a^2 - 5ac + 5c^2)(2a^2 + 5ac + 5c^2)$

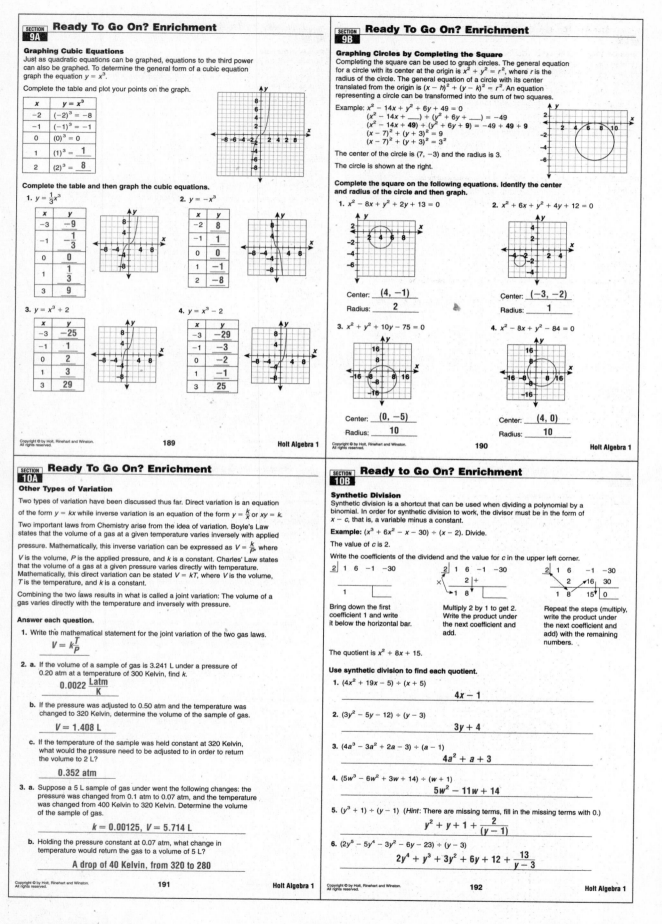

Ready To Go On? Enrichment
SECTION 9A

Graphing Cubic Equations

Just as quadratic equations can be graphed, equations to the third power can also be graphed. To determine the general form of a cubic equation graph the equation $y = x^3$.

Complete the table and plot your points on the graph.

x	$y = x^3$
-2	$(-2)^3 = -8$
-1	$(-1)^3 = -1$
0	$(0)^3 = 0$
1	$(1)^3 = 1$
2	$(2)^3 = 8$

Complete the table and then graph the cubic equations.

1. $y = \frac{1}{3}x^3$

x	y
-3	-9
-1	$-\frac{1}{3}$
0	0
1	$\frac{1}{3}$
3	9

2. $y = -x^3$

x	y
-2	8
-1	1
0	0
1	-1
2	-8

3. $y = x^3 + 2$

x	y
-3	-25
-1	1
0	2
1	3
3	29

4. $y = x^3 - 2$

x	y
-3	-29
-1	-3
0	-2
1	-1
3	25

189   Holt Algebra 1

Ready To Go On? Enrichment
SECTION 9B

Graphing Circles by Completing the Square

Completing the square can be used to graph circles. The general equation for a circle with its center at the origin is $x^2 + y^2 = r^2$, where r is the radius of the circle. The general equation of a circle with its center translated from the origin is $(x - h)^2 + (y - k)^2 = r^2$. An equation representing a circle can be transformed into the sum of two squares.

Example: $x^2 - 14x + y^2 + 6y + 49 = 0$
$(x^2 - 14x + \underline{\quad}) + (y^2 + 6y + \underline{\quad}) = -49$
$(x^2 - 14x + 49) + (y^2 + 6y + 9) = -49 + 49 + 9$
$(x - 7)^2 + (y + 3)^2 = 9$
$(x - 7)^2 + (y + 3)^2 = 3^2$

The center of the circle is $(7, -3)$ and the radius is 3.

The circle is shown at the right.

Complete the square on the following equations. Identify the center and radius of the circle and then graph.

1. $x^2 - 8x + y^2 + 2y + 13 = 0$

Center: $(4, -1)$

Radius: 2

2. $x^2 + 6x + y^2 + 4y + 12 = 0$

Center: $(-3, -2)$

Radius: 1

3. $x^2 + y^2 + 10y - 75 = 0$

Center: $(0, -5)$

Radius: 10

4. $x^2 - 8x + y^2 - 84 = 0$

Center: $(4, 0)$

Radius: 10

190   Holt Algebra 1

Ready To Go On? Enrichment
SECTION 10A

Other Types of Variation

Two types of variation have been discussed thus far. Direct variation is an equation of the form $y = kx$ while inverse variation is an equation of the form $y = \frac{k}{x}$ or $xy = k$.

Two important laws from Chemistry arise from the idea of variation. Boyle's Law states that the volume of a gas at a given temperature varies inversely with applied pressure. Mathematically, this inverse variation can be expressed as $V = \frac{k}{P}$, where V is the volume, P is the applied pressure, and k is a constant. Charles' Law states that the volume of a gas at a given pressure varies directly with temperature. Mathematically, this direct variation can be stated $V = kT$, where V is the volume, T is the temperature, and k is a constant.

Combining the two laws results in what is called a joint variation: The volume of a gas varies directly with the temperature and inversely with pressure.

Answer each question.

1. Write the mathematical statement for the joint variation of the two gas laws.

$V = k\frac{T}{P}$

2. a. If the volume of a sample of gas is 3.241 L under a pressure of 0.20 atm at a temperature of 300 Kelvin, find k.

$0.0022 \frac{L\,atm}{K}$

b. If the pressure was adjusted to 0.50 atm and the temperature was changed to 320 Kelvin, determine the volume of the sample of gas.

$V = 1.408$ L

c. If the temperature of the sample was held constant at 320 Kelvin, what would the pressure need to be adjusted to in order to return the volume to 2 L?

0.352 atm

3. a. Suppose a 5 L sample of gas under went the following changes: the pressure was changed from 0.1 atm to 0.07 atm, and the temperature was changed from 400 Kelvin to 320 Kelvin. Determine the volume of the sample of gas.

$k = 0.00125$, $V = 5.714$ L

b. Holding the pressure constant at 0.07 atm, what change in temperature would return the gas to a volume of 5 L?

A drop of 40 Kelvin, from 320 to 280

191   Holt Algebra 1

Ready to Go On? Enrichment
SECTION 10B

Synthetic Division

Synthetic division is a shortcut that can be used when dividing a polynomial by a binomial. In order for synthetic division to work, the divisor must be in the form of $x - c$, that is, a variable minus a constant.

Example: $(x^3 + 6x^2 - x - 30) \div (x - 2)$. Divide.

The value of c is 2.

Write the coefficients of the dividend and the value for c in the upper left corner.

Bring down the first coefficient 1 and write it below the horizontal bar.

Multiply 2 by 1 to get 2. Write the product under the next coefficient and add.

Repeat the steps (multiply, write the product under the next coefficient and add) with the remaining numbers.

The quotient is $x^2 + 8x + 15$.

Use synthetic division to find each quotient.

1. $(4x^2 + 19x - 5) \div (x + 5)$

$4x - 1$

2. $(3y^2 - 5y - 12) \div (y - 3)$

$3y + 4$

3. $(4a^3 - 3a^2 + 2a - 3) \div (a - 1)$

$4a^2 + a + 3$

4. $(5w^3 - 6w^2 + 3w + 14) \div (w + 1)$

$5w^2 - 11w + 14$

5. $(y^3 + 1) \div (y - 1)$ (*Hint:* There are missing terms, fill in the missing terms with 0.)

$y^2 + y + 1 + \frac{2}{(y - 1)}$

6. $(2y^5 - 5y^4 - 3y^2 - 6y - 23) \div (y - 3)$

$2y^4 + y^3 + 3y^2 + 6y + 12 + \frac{13}{y - 3}$

192   Holt Algebra 1

242   Holt Algebra 1

Ready To Go On? Enrichment

Derive the Distance Formula from the Pythagorean Theorem

The Pythagorean Theorem, $a^2 + b^2 = c^2$, can be used to find the length of the hypotenuse of a right triangle given the length of the two legs. The figure below shows that a right triangle can be created between any two points.

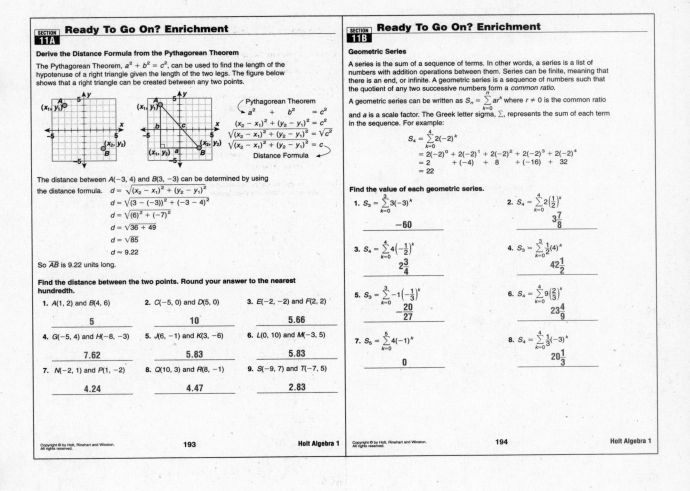

Pythagorean Theorem
$$a^2 + b^2 = c^2$$
$$(x_2 - x_1)^2 + (y_2 - y_1)^2 = c^2$$
$$\sqrt{(x_2 - x_1)^2 + (y_2 - y_1)^2} = \sqrt{c^2}$$
$$\sqrt{(x_2 - x_1)^2 + (y_2 - y_1)^2} = c$$
Distance Formula

The distance between $A(-3, 4)$ and $B(3, -3)$ can be determined by using
the distance formula.

$$d = \sqrt{(x_2 - x_1)^2 + (y_2 - y_1)^2}$$
$$d = \sqrt{(3 - (-3))^2 + (-3 - 4)^2}$$
$$d = \sqrt{(6)^2 + (-7)^2}$$
$$d = \sqrt{36 + 49}$$
$$d = \sqrt{85}$$
$$d \approx 9.22$$

So $\overline{AB}$ is 9.22 units long.

Find the distance between the two points. Round your answer to the nearest hundredth.

1. $A(1, 2)$ and $B(4, 6)$

_____5_____

2. $C(-5, 0)$ and $D(5, 0)$

_____10_____

3. $E(-2, -2)$ and $F(2, 2)$

_____5.66_____

4. $G(-5, 4)$ and $H(-8, -3)$

_____7.62_____

5. $J(6, -1)$ and $K(3, -6)$

_____5.83_____

6. $L(0, 10)$ and $M(-3, 5)$

_____5.83_____

7. $N(-2, 1)$ and $P(1, -2)$

_____4.24_____

8. $Q(10, 3)$ and $R(8, -1)$

_____4.47_____

9. $S(-9, 7)$ and $T(-7, 5)$

_____2.83_____

Holt Algebra 1

Ready To Go On? Enrichment

Geometric Series

A series is the sum of a sequence of terms. In other words, a series is a list of numbers with addition operations between them. Series can be finite, meaning that there is an end, or infinite. A geometric series is a sequence of numbers such that the quotient of any two successive numbers form a *common ratio*.

A geometric series can be written as $S_n = \sum_{k=0}^{n} ar^k$ where $r \neq 0$ is the common ratio and a is a scale factor. The Greek letter sigma, Σ, represents the sum of each term in the sequence. For example:

$$S_4 = \sum_{k=0}^{4} 2(-2)^k$$
$$= 2(-2)^0 + 2(-2)^1 + 2(-2)^2 + 2(-2)^3 + 2(-2)^4$$
$$= 2 \quad + (-4) \quad + 8 \quad + (-16) \quad + 32$$
$$= 22$$

Find the value of each geometric series.

1. $S_3 = \sum_{k=0}^{3} 3(-3)^k$

_____-60_____

2. $S_4 = \sum_{k=0}^{4} 2\left(\frac{1}{2}\right)^k$

_____$3\frac{7}{8}$_____

3. $S_4 = \sum_{k=0}^{4} 4\left(-\frac{1}{2}\right)^k$

_____$2\frac{3}{4}$_____

4. $S_3 = \sum_{k=0}^{3} \frac{1}{2}(4)^k$

_____$42\frac{1}{2}$_____

5. $S_3 = \sum_{k=0}^{3} -1\left(-\frac{1}{3}\right)^k$

_____$\frac{20}{27}$_____

6. $S_4 = \sum_{k=0}^{4} 9\left(\frac{2}{3}\right)^k$

_____$23\frac{4}{9}$_____

7. $S_5 = \sum_{k=0}^{5} 4(-1)^k$

_____0_____

8. $S_4 = \sum_{k=0}^{4} \frac{1}{3}(-3)^k$

_____$20\frac{1}{3}$_____

Holt Algebra 1

Holt Algebra 1